Elementary Algebra

THIRD EDITION

Donald S. Russell

Ventura College
Ventura, California

Allyn and Bacon, Inc.

Boston

LIBRARY OF CONGRESS CATALOG CARD NUMBER: 68–24446

PRINTED IN THE UNITED STATES OF AMERICA.

THIRD PRINTING . . . SEPTEMBER, 1970

Preface

Elementary Algebra was originally designed as a text for college students who had no previous training in algebra as well as for others who felt the need for an intensive review of the basic fundamentals of algebra. The first revision, though somewhat more rigorous, was developed for the same students. This second revision, which is characterized by the addition of a minimum amount of increased rigor, is again designed for the same students.

Numerous changes have been made in the general format of the text. Two chapters included in the previous editions, "Signed Numbers" and "Parentheses and Other Symbols Used for Grouping," have been removed and their content incorporated in other chapters. The concept of set theory has been expanded to include its application to more algebraic processes. Considerably more emphasis has been placed on inequalities in an additional chapter.

The drill exercises have been, in most cases, divided into two groups. For a minimum course only those problems found in the A group may suffice. In such cases the B group will provide additional challenge for the more enterprising students who find insufficient motivation in group A. For a more intensive course both groups of problems may be used.

Throughout the book terms are defined as they are introduced. The theory is presented in a simple style to assist the student in his understanding of algebra. Following the development of each topic, illustrative examples are presented to aid the student in the application of theory to practical problems. Considerable care has been taken to develop each example in a manner that will give the student full comprehension of what has been done as well as the reasons for each step in the solution of the problem.

The chapter directed toward changing the subject of formulas has been retained. The emphasis on this unit of study is designed to assist the student with his study of physics and chemistry.

All students, even the superior ones, find that the conversion of statements into algebraic language is difficult. In an attempt to help students in this phase of the course, the author has retained, from the very beginning of the text, exercises for training in this respect.

The Review Tests used in the previous editions have been retained and may be used either as additional drill exercises or strictly as tests and examinations.

Answers to the odd-numbered problems are included in the text. Answers to the even-numbered problems are available from the publishers.

Those faculty members who are using or who have used the text and who submitted suggestions for the revision were extremely helpful to the author as he developed this revision. For this he is most grateful. The author is also indebted to his colleagues for their inspiration and numerous suggestions in the preparation of the manuscript for this revision. To the editorial staff of Allyn and Bacon, Inc. is extended appreciation for the efforts they have made in making this publication a reality.

D. S. R.

Contents

vi

1

The Number System

1. SETS

In our culture the use of the word *set* is very familiar. Common usage of the word includes the following: a set of dishes, a set of silverware, a set of tools, a set of blocks, and a set of twins. Each of these sets consists of a certain number of things. Every set, then, consists of objects or things that make up that set. These objects are known as the *members* or *elements* of the set.

In order to facilitate our discussion of sets as applied to mathematics, we start with the discussion of natural numbers.

> *Natural numbers* are those numbers we use for counting objects.

Thus the numbers 1, 2, 3, 4, . . . (the three dots mean "and so on indefinitely") are the natural numbers. By the use of Latin prefixes we may extend the natural numbers infinitely such that there is no end to those numbers. The three dots may also be used to abbreviate our work even though the set of numbers being considered does not extend indefinitely. We must always start with at least three numbers to establish the pattern. Thus 1, 2, 3, . . . , 20 means all natural numbers up to and including 20.

In the study of mathematics the use of sets is a meaningful approach to certain developmental processes. Simple illustrations of sets as applied to mathematics include the following: the set of all even numbers greater than 4 and less than 10, the set of all natural numbers less than 30 that are exactly divisible by 3, or the set of all odd one-digit natural numbers. In all of these sets there should be no confusion as to the specific members or elements of the sets. In mathematics it is most important that the set be so stated that there is no question as to the elements that make up the set.

A *set*, then, is a well-defined collection of objects or things.

To test how well-defined a set is, one should be able to select an object or number and, without any question whatever, decide whether or not that object or thing is a member of the set under consideration. An example of a well-defined set is "the set of all one-digit natural numbers." On the other hand, "the set of five one-digit numbers that are most easily written" might not include the same members for several individuals concerned. This would not be a well-defined collection of numbers.

A set may consist of no members, a definite number of members, or an indefinite number of members. The set of all one-digit natural numbers greater than 10 is an example of a set with no members since there are no such numbers. This is called an *empty set* or the *null set*, and is designated by the symbol "$\emptyset$." The set of all one-digit natural numbers is a definite set that includes the numbers 1, 2, 3, 4, 5, 6, 7, 8, 9. Such a set is called a *finite set*. If we were asked to write all the fractions greater than zero and less than 1, the task could never be accomplished since there are an infinite number of numbers that could be placed in both the numerator and denominator. The only requirement for such fractions, of course, would be that the number in the numerator be smaller than the one found in the denominator. A set that has an infinite number of members is called an *infinite set*. A set can be indicated by a sentence that describes the set in such a way that it tells exactly what the elements are. Such a description could be: The set of all natural numbers less than 8. A capital italic letter is usually used to name a set. Thus the above set might be stated as: A is the set of natural numbers less than 8. Most sets are stated by listing the elements and enclosing them within braces. In this form the above set would be written: $A = \{1, 2, 3, 4, 5, 6, 7\}$. This may also be written: $A = \{1, 2, 3, \ldots, 7\}$.

Two sets are equal *if and only if* each member of the first set is a member of the second set and each member of the second set is a member of the first set. Thus if $A = \{5, 7, 9\}$ and $B = \{9, 5, 7\}$, then $A = B$. One set may be included in another set even though the sets are not equal. Suppose $M = \{2, 4, 6, 8\}$ and $N = \{1, 2, 3, 4, 5, 6, 7, 8\}$. Thus set M is included in set N but $M \neq N$ ($\neq$ means "not equal to") because the two sets do not meet the above definition of equal sets.

If a is a member of set A, we denote this by the symbolism $a \in A$ (read: "a is an element of A"), and if b is not an element of set A, it is written $b \notin A$ (read: "b is not an element of A"). As an illustration of the above, if we let $A = \{a, c, d\}$, then $a \in A$ and $b \notin A$.

If we have a collection of objects or things from which smaller sets can be obtained, the entire set is called the *universal set* or the *universe* and is denoted by U. Sets selected from the universal set are called *subsets* of the universe and are indicated by the symbol "$\subseteq$." An example of the universal set might be the set of natural numbers. Subsets from U could include the following: the set of all even natural numbers, the set of all numbers greater than 6 and less than 15, and the set of all natural two-digit odd numbers. The null set and the set itself are subsets of the set.

As we proceed with the study of algebra, we shall be making extensive use of the word *variable*.

A *variable* is a symbol used to denote any element of a set having more than one element.

The symbol "$\{x \in U \mid \quad \}$" is called the *set builder*. The x in this case is the variable with which we are concerned at a given time; it can include only one or more of the elements found in U, or if the solution to the given problem does not include any of those elements, we would indicate this by the use of the symbol "$\emptyset$." Any letter, of course, may be used for the variable. The vertical line following the variable is read: "such that." In the blank space following the vertical line shown in the set builder above, we place the condition imposed upon the variable in a particular problem. Thus if $U = \{1, 2, 3, 4, 5, 6\}$ and $A = \{x \in U \mid x$ is an even number$\}$, then those elements from U that satisfy the condition imposed on x would be the set $\{2, 4, 6\}$, which is known as the *solution set* of the given problem.

The *solution set*, then, is the set that contains all the elements from U that satisfy the condition placed upon the variable.

To denote that two things are not equal, we use the symbol "$\neq$." If we know that two things are not equal, this fact may not indicate which of the two is the greater. If a and b are two numbers that are unequal, then either $a > b$ (read: "a is greater than b") or $a < b$ (read: "a is less than b"). The expression $A = \{x \in U \mid x < 4\}$ means that the set A is made up of all the members of U which are less than 4. Thus if $U =$

$\{1, 2, 3, \ldots, 9\}$, the solution set of A above would be $A = \{1, 2, 3\}$. For the same set U, the expression $B = \{x \in U \mid 3 < x < 6\}$ means that the set B consists of the members 4 and 5, and thus the solution set is $B = \{4, 5\}$.

Often, in order to simplify the format, the set builder is written as $\{x \mid \quad \}$. In such cases it must be kept in mind that the solution set contains only such elements as are found in U, or if none of those elements are included, the $\emptyset$ is used.

Example 1. If $X = \{1, 2, 3\}$, list the subsets of X.

a. $\emptyset \subseteq X$, since every set contains the subset $\emptyset$.
b. $\{1, 2, 3\} \subseteq X$, since every set is a subset of itself.
c. $\{1\} \subseteq X$, since 1 is a member of X.
d. $\{2\} \subseteq X$, since 2 is a member of X.
e. $\{3\} \subseteq X$, since 3 is a member of X.
f. $\{1, 2\} \subseteq X$, since 1 and 2 are members of X.
g. $\{1, 3\} \subseteq X$, since 1 and 3 are members of X.
h. $\{2, 3\} \subseteq X$, since 2 and 3 are members of X.

We could show our answer in this manner: The subsets of X are $\emptyset, X, \{1\}, \{2\}, \{3\}, \{1, 2\}, \{1, 3\}, \{2, 3\}$.

Example 2. If $U = \{1, 2, 3, \ldots, 9\}$, find the solution set for $\{x \mid x$ is divisible by 3$\}$.

$$\{x \mid x \text{ is divisible by } 3\} = \{3, 6, 9\}$$

Example 3. If $U = \{2, 4, 6, \ldots, 20\}$, find the solution set for $\{x \mid 4 < x < 16\}$.

$$\{x \mid 4 < x < 16\} = \{6, 8, 10, 12, 14\}$$

2. THE RELATIONS BETWEEN SETS

When we are considering any *relation* between two given sets, we refer to the fact that the sets have elements in common or do not have elements in common.

Disjoint sets are two sets that have no elements in common.

To illustrate the relation between sets, we sometimes use Venn diagrams as shown in Figures 1, 2, 3, and 4. The rectangle, R, may be used to represent the set of natural numbers.

If $A = \{2, 4, 6, 8\}$ and $B = \{1, 3, 5, 7\}$, these two sets are represented by circles A and B in Figure 1, in which all elements in set A are in circle A and all elements in set B are in circle B. It is evident by inspection that A and B have no elements in common and each is entirely independent of the other circle.

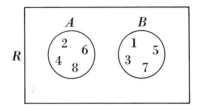

Figure 1

If $A = \{1, 2, 3, \ldots, 9\}$ and $B = \{x \mid x \text{ is a one-digit natural number}\}$, then $A = B$. This relationship is shown in Figure 2. Considering sets **A**

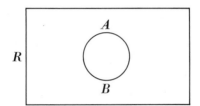

Figure 2

and B as shown in Figure 2, answer the following questions:

a. How many elements are there in set A?
b. How many elements are there in set B?
c. Name any elements in set A that are not in set B.
d. What elements are common to both set A and set B?

If $A = \{1, 2, 3, 4, 5\}$ and $B = \{x \mid x \text{ is an odd natural number less than } 10\}$, then sets A and B are represented in Figure 3. It can be observed that certain elements in set B are also in set A.

Observing sets A and B as shown in Figure 3, answer the following questions:

a. How many elements are there in set A?
b. How many elements are there in set B?

c. What elements are found in set A but not in set B?
d. What elements are found in set B but not in set A?
e. What elements are common to sets A and B?

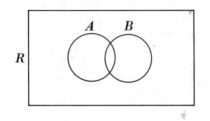

Figure 3

Figure 3 illustrates the *intersection* of two sets.

> If A and B are two given sets, those elements that are common to *both* A and B are called the *intersection* of A and B.

The symbol "$\cap$" is used to denote the intersection of two sets. Thus $A \cap B$ is read: "the intersection of A and B" or "A intersection B." If $A = \{1, 2, 3, 4, 5\}$ and $B = \{x \mid x$ is an odd natural number less than 10$\}$, then $A \cap B = \{1, 3, 5\}$.

The intersection of sets A and B with the use of the set builder is shown as follows: $A \cap B = \{x \mid x \in A$ and $x \in B\}$.

More than two sets may intersect. If $A = \{1, 2, 3\}$, $B = \{2, 3, 4\}$, and $C = \{3, 4, 5\}$, then $A \cap B \cap C = \{3\}$. This problem could be illustrated by a Venn diagram as shown in Figure 4.

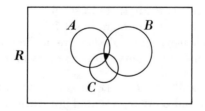

Figure 4

If $A = \{1, 2, 3, 4\}$ and $B = \{3, 4, 5, 6\}$ and if we combine the elements in set A with the elements in set B to form a new set C, then $C = \{1, 2, 3, 4, 5, 6\}$. This set C is known as the *union* of A and B.

The *union* of two sets A and B is a set composed of the elements in set A or set B or both.

This definition infers that any member of the union of the two sets A and B is a member of A, a member of B, or a member of both A and B.

The symbol "$\cup$" is used to denote the union of two sets. Thus if $A = \{4, 5, 6\}$ and $B = \{5, 6, 7\}$, then $A \cup B = \{4, 5, 6, 7\}$. All of the shaded area in Figure 5 indicates the union of sets A and B.

As with the intersection of sets, we may have the union of more than two sets. The union of sets A, B, and C is denoted by $A \cup B \cup C$.

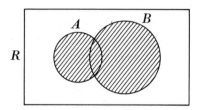

Figure 5

Figure 6 shows that set B is a subset of set A.

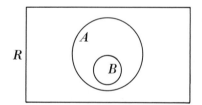

Figure 6

Example 1. If $A = \{a, b, c, d\}$ and $B = \{b, c, d, e, f\}$, find $A \cap B$ and $A \cup B$.

$$A \cap B = \{b, c, d\}$$
$$A \cup B = \{a, b, c, d, e, f\}$$

Example 2. If $A = \{5, 7, 9\}$ and $B = \{2, 3\}$, find $A \cap B$ and $A \cup B$.

$$A \cap B = \varnothing$$
$$A \cup B = \{2, 3, 5, 7, 9\}$$

A

Write the set, listing the members, of each set described below:

1. The set of all natural numbers greater than 12 and less than 20
2. The set of all natural numbers
3. The set of one-digit odd natural numbers
4. The set of all natural numbers less than 100 that are perfect squares
5. The set of all natural numbers less than 50 that are exactly divisible by 9
6. The set of all months of the year that have exactly 31 days in them
7. The set of all natural numbers greater than 5 and less than 6
8. The set of all natural numbers greater than 8 and less than 40 that are exactly divisible by 6
9. The set of all even natural numbers
10. The set of all odd numbers that divide 15 exactly

Describe each of the following sets:

11. {13, 17, 19}
12. {22, 24, 26, 28}
13. {1, 4, 9}
14. {Alaska, Hawaii}
15. {6, 16, 26, 36}
16. {Tuesday, Thursday}
17. {7, 14, 21, 28}
18. {4, 8, 12, . . .}
19. {1, 3, 5, . . .}
20. {2, 3, 5, 7}

B

If $U = \{1, 2, 3, \ldots, 15\}$, list the members of each of the following sets:

1. $\{x \in U \mid x < 5\}$
2. $\{x \in U \mid x > 5\}$
3. $\{x \in U \mid x < 1\}$
4. $\{x \in U \mid x \text{ is an odd number}\}$
5. $\{x \in U \mid x \text{ is an even number}\}$
6. $\{x \in U \mid x \text{ is a fraction}\}$
7. $\{x \in U \mid 3 < x < 9\}$
8. $\{x \in U \mid 15 < x\}$
9. $\{x \in U \mid 6 < x < 12\}$
10. $\{x \in U \mid 8 < x < 10\}$
11. List the subsets of A if $A = \{0, 1, 2\}$.
12. List the subsets of B if $B = \{a, b, c, d\}$.
13. If $A = \{0, 1, 2, 3\}$ and $B = \{4, 5, 6\}$, find $A \cap B$ and $A \cup B$.
14. If $A = \{3, 4, 5, 6\}$ and $B = \{4, 5, 6, 7\}$, show, by the use of Venn diagrams, $A \cap B$ and $A \cup B$.
15. If $A = \{3, 4, 5\}$ and $B = \{7, 8, 9\}$, show, by the use of Venn diagrams, $A \cap B$ and $A \cup B$.

3. THE ORIGIN OF OUR NUMBER SYSTEM

The number system which we use today is one that developed gradually over a period of many hundreds of years. In the earliest civilizations man found little use for mathematics—quite possibly only for the counting of objects. The use of pebbles or sticks or the fingers on his hand may have served as adequate symbols for representing those objects that were counted. Numbers are merely ideas in the minds of individuals. But when it becomes necessary to record those ideas, symbols are needed to represent the ideas we have in mind or wish to express. Any symbol used to represent a number is called a *numeral*. There are many ways in which we can represent a number. *A numeral may be thought of as any symbol used to represent a number.* For example, we use "5" to represent the number five. We could very well use the following symbols to represent the same number: "$4 + 1$"; "$8 - 3$"; "$10/2$." The Romans used the symbol "V" to represent the number five.

As civilization progressed, certain types of calculations and solutions became extremely complex. To simplify both the operations and the understanding of those complex situations, man found it necessary to formulate a systematic and logical approach to the study of mathematics. This branch of study, though quite simple at the beginning, has developed over the centuries since its inception into an intricate and complex system.

Algebra is one branch of that complex system and, in general, consists of a logical structure of mathematics designed to lead the student to proficiency in problem-solving through the use of variables to represent numbers. As previously stated, a *variable*—usually a letter—is a symbol used to denote any element of a set having more than one element.

The letters used for numbers may represent value, size, or quantity, and the same letter will indicate a different number in each situation in which it is used. The fact that a letter is not a definite or constant value provides us with a system whereby we can derive results that are general. We can then use that system or principle in specific numerical cases in which the letter or letters are used.

4. ZERO

In an earlier discussion we defined *natural numbers* as those numbers used for counting $(1, 2, 3, \ldots)$. For a time, as man began to think in terms of numbers, the one digit numerals 1 through 9 provided ample representation of numbers. The most simple system of mathematics in our culture makes use of base 10, in which we have unit's place, ten's place, hundred's place, and so on. In order to symbolize the number ten, we use the numeral 1 in ten's place. To avoid confusion, it was necessary to invent a symbol— one that has no value—to indicate unit's place when the 1 was placed in ten's place. The zero, in all probability, was introduced as a symbol indicating no value and was placed with the 1 to form the numeral 10, signifying 1 ten and no units. Likewise, we understand the numeral 105 to mean 1 hundred, no ten's, and 5 units. Thus zero is used as a *placeholder* when no value exists in that place. Also, when set notation is used, the 0 represents the number of elements in the empty set.

5. THE NUMBER LINE

The numbers we use can be represented graphically by use of what we call the *number line*. In Figure 7 we represent zero and the natural numbers by

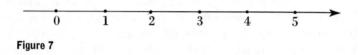

Figure 7

designating the starting position with zero. Then to the right of zero we locate the natural numbers, each equally spaced one from the other in numerical order, the space in each case being equal to the distance from zero to 1. The arrow at the right end of the number line indicates that the line continues indefinitely in that direction. Our choice of a line is optional, but the horizontal line is usually used both for convenience and consistency.

6. THE REAL NUMBERS

With the introduction of trade and business transactions between individuals and, later, between groups of individuals formed into business organizations, it became necessary to have numerals to represent parts of things which were traded. This led to the introduction of common fractions as we use them today. These fractions can also be located on the number line as shown in Figure 8.

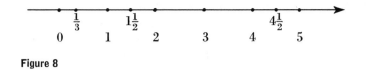

Figure 8

With the development of scientific investigation and the endeavors involved with it, there arose the need for a new type of number. If, in business transactions, profits were represented by the use of natural numbers, how could losses be represented? Again, if natural numbers represented distance above sea level, how could distances below sea level be represented?

We might think of a given distance below sea level as the *opposite* of an equal distance above sea level. In a similar manner, every number located on the number line to the right of zero has an opposite on that number line to the left of zero. Each number and its opposite are equally spaced from zero—one to the right of zero and one to the left of zero. Thus the opposite of 3 is a point three units to the left of zero and is denoted by -3, which we call a negative 3. Likewise, the negative of -3 is the opposite of -3, located three units to the right of zero. This, of course, is 3. Certain numbers and their negatives are shown in Figure 9.

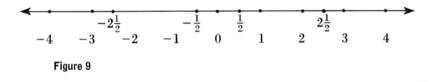

Figure 9

Any number is known as the *additive inverse* of its opposite. Thus 3 is the additive inverse of -3. Likewise, -3 is the additive inverse of 3. Hence, the sum of any number and its additive inverse is equal to zero.

The opposite of zero is assumed to be zero. Care must be taken when working with letters representing numbers. Assume that we have the number represented by $-m$. We do not know whether the m is a positive number, a negative number, or zero. To evaluate $-m$ we must know whether the replacement for m is positive or negative.

If 3 is used as a replacement for m, then $-m = -3$.
If -3 is used as a replacement for m, then $-m = -(-3)$
$= 3$.
If 0 is used as a replacement for m, then $-m = 0$.

Positive and negative numbers are called *signed numbers* and are associated with direction. Both positive and negative numbers extend infinitely far in their respective direction, as indicated on the number line in Figure 9.

Temperature readings on a thermometer, as shown in Figure 10, can be associated with positive and negative numbers, those above zero being positive and those below zero representing negative readings. The thermometer represents the number line in a vertical rather than horizontal position.

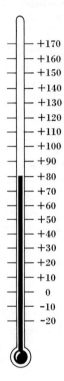

Figure 10

Business transactions involving profit might be thought of as positive numbers and those involving losses as negative numbers.

·Time can be thought of in terms of positive and negative numbers. Three years from the present time would represent a positive value and be denoted by 3; three years in the past would be denoted by −3.

If money deposited in a bank account represents positive amounts, then withdrawals would represent negative amounts. Any balance in one's account is a positive value. Should the bank honor a check that is $10 greater than the balance in one's account, the account would be overdrawn by $10 and the balance would be represented by −$10.

Altitudes are usually measured in terms of feet above or below sea level. If distances above sea level are represented by positive numbers, then those below sea level would be represented by negative numbers.

All of the natural numbers and their negatives along with zero are called *integers*.

> A *rational number* is any number that can be expressed in the form a/b $(b \neq 0)$, in which case a and b are integers. More simply, a *rational number* is sometimes defined as any number that can be expressed as the ratio of two integers.

An *irrational number* is any number that cannot be expressed as the ratio of two integers. Examples of irrational numbers are $\sqrt{2}$, $\sqrt[3]{4}$, and π.

An endless number of additional points may be located on the number line represented in Figure 9. Between any two integers there could be located an infinite number of points. All such points between zero and 1 would represent a proper fraction or a decimal fraction, the value of each being positive and less than 1.

The above-described numbers constitute what we call the *real number system*, which consists of all the integers, rational numbers, and irrational numbers. Any real number can be located on the number line and, conversely, every point on the number line represents a real number.

7. PROPERTIES OF REAL NUMBERS

When working with real numbers, we make use of certain basic assumptions. These basic assumptions are sometimes called *axioms* and at other times are called *postulates* or *laws*. In this discussion we shall refer to them as *laws*. When stating these laws, it will be necessary, at times, to make use of parentheses for grouping numbers. When such grouping symbols are used, it is understood that the part enclosed within them represents one quantity. At a later time in this text we shall discuss more extensively the use of grouping symbols.

1. The law of closure. *If a and b are any real numbers, there exists a unique (one and only one) real number called the sum of a and b. The sum of a and b is indicated by $a + b$.*

The law of closure, then, states that the system of real numbers is closed under addition or the sum of two real numbers is a real number. If we were restricting ourselves to a set of natural numbers from 1 to 15, the set would not be closed under addition because, for example, the sum of 9 and 8 would not be included in the given set of numbers.

If a and b are any real numbers, there is a unique real number called the difference between a and b. That difference is indicated as a − b.

If a and b are any real numbers, there exists a unique real number called their product (the answer obtained when multiplying together two or more numbers). That product is indicated by ab.

If a and b are any real numbers and a is divided by b, there exists a unique number called their quotient. That quotient is indicated by a/b. (This holds true for all real numbers except that *b* cannot be zero. In our number system division by zero is never permitted. This will be explained later in our discussion.)

2. The laws for addition.   *If a and b are any real numbers, then*

$$a + b = b + a$$

This is the *commutative law for addition* and means that the *addends* (the numbers to be added) may be taken in any order. Thus $3 + 4 = 4 + 3 = 7$. This law holds true for any number of addends.

If a, b and c are any real numbers, then

$$a + (b + c) = (a + b) + c$$

This is the *associative law for addition* and states that the addends may be grouped or associated together in any order. Thus

$$3 + (4 + 7) = (3 + 4) + 7$$
$$3 + 11 = 7 + 7$$
$$14 = 14$$

3. The laws for multiplication.   *If a, b, and c are any real numbers, then*

$$a \cdot b = b \cdot a \qquad \text{(The raised dot between two numbers indicates multiplication)}$$

This is the *commutative law for multiplication* and means that the factors (the numbers to be multiplied together) may be placed in any order. Thus $2 \cdot 5 = 5 \cdot 2 = 10$.

If a, b, and c are any real numbers, then

$$a(bc) = (ab)c$$

This is the *associative law for multiplication* and states that factors to be multiplied together may be grouped or associated together in any manner. Thus

$$3(2 \cdot 4) = (3 \cdot 2)4$$
$$3(8) = (6)4$$
$$24 = 24$$

4. The distributive law for multiplication with respect to addition. *If a, b, and c are any real numbers, then*

$$a(b + c) = ab + ac$$

The distributive law for multiplication with respect to addition means that the factor a is distributed over all the addends included within the parentheses. Thus

$$3(5 + 2) = 3 \cdot 5 + 3 \cdot 2$$
$$= 15 + 6$$
$$= 21$$

This problem may be solved by first finding the sum of the addends within the parentheses and then multiplying that sum by 3. Thus $3(5 + 2) = 3(7) = 21$.

5. *There exists a real number 1 such that $a \cdot 1 = a$ for all real numbers.* The 1 in this law is called the *multiplicative identity*.

6. *If a is any real number, there exists a unique number 0 such that $a + 0 = a$.* The number that may be added to a to obtain a sum which is equal to a is known as the *additive identity*. Thus the additive identity is 0.

If $a = b$, we have a statement of equality. A statement that two things are equal is called an *equation*. That part of the statement to the left of the equality symbol ($=$) is called the *left member of the equation*, and that part to the right of the symbol is called the *right member of the equation*. The equality symbol intersected by an oblique line ($\neq$) means that the parts of the statement are not equal. Thus $a \neq b$ is read: "a is not equal to b." Such a symbol gives no clue to the relative values of a and b—it states only that they are unequal. The symbol "$<$" means "less than" and the symbol "$\leq$" means "less than or equal to." Thus in the expression $a < b$ we say that "a is less than b." The expression $a > b$ means "a is greater than b" and $a \geq b$ means "a is greater than or equal to b."

7. The law of trichotomy. *If a and b are any real numbers, then either $a = b$, $a > b$, or $a < b$.*

8. The reflexive property of relationships. *If a is any real number, then a = a.*

9. The symmetric property of relationships. *If a = b, then b = a.*

10. The transitive property of relationships. *If a = b and b = c, then a = c.* This law states that quantities that are equal to the same or equal quantities are equal to each other.

The *reflexive*, *symmetric*, and *transitive* properties are often called the *equivalence* relationships.

11. *Given: a, b, x, and y are real numbers. If a = b and x = y, then a + x = b + y.* This law states that if equals are added to equals, then the sums are equal.

12. *Given: a, b, x, and y are real numbers. If a = b and x = y, then ax = by.* This law states that if equals are multiplied by equals, then the products are equal.

EXERCISE 2

If all of the letters used in the problems below are real numbers, state which of the foregoing laws are used to make the statements true.

A

1. $m + n = n + m$

2. $m + (n + p) = (m + n) + p$

3. $mn + mp = m(n + p)$

4. $m(np) = n(mp)$

5. $m + n$ is a real number

6. mn is a real number

7. $(mn)p = m(np)$

8. $mn = nm$

9. If $3m = 6$, then $m = 2$

10. If $m = n$ and $r = t$, then $mr = nt$

B

1. If $\frac{1}{3}x = 6 + 0$, then $x = 18$

2. $x + y + z = y + z + x$

3. $a(b + c + d) = ab + ad + ac$

4. If $x + y = c + d$, then $d + c = y + x$

5. If $2 = a$ and $3 = b$, then $6 = ab$ and $ab = 6$

8. RELATIONS BETWEEN THREE SETS

In an earlier discussion we considered, for the most part, relations between two sets. If three sets are considered, the possibilities of relationships between the three sets becomes somewhat more complicated. There is the possibility, of course, that all three are disjoint sets. If so, it is quite evident that they have no elements in common.

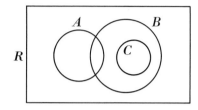

Figure 11

Consider Figure 11. In the first place we observe that set C is a subset of set B but is disjoint with respect to set A. Furthermore, since set A and set B are overlapping, they have an intersection. The fact that set C is a subset of set B indicates there is an intersection of sets C and B. What is the intersection of sets C and B? ($C \cap B$).

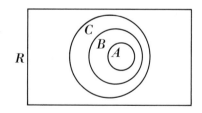

Figure 12

Consider Figure 12 and the relationships between sets A, B, and C. We observe that set A is a subset of set B and of set C. Likewise, set B is a subset of C. What is the intersection of sets B and C? Of sets A and C? Of sets A and B? Of sets A, B, and C? The intersection of sets A, B, and C is a binary operation—a *binary operation* because we must have two numbers or two sets with which to perform an operation. When we are working with three sets, we work with two of them to find the intersection of the two sets and use the set obtained from those two as a new set with which to intersect with the remaining set. Thus we may group sets A, B, and C

to find their intersection in the following manner: $A \cap (B \cap C)$ or $(A \cap B) \cap C$. In the former case we would find the intersection of sets B and C and use that solution as a new set to intersect with set A. In the latter case we would find the intersection of sets A and B and use that solution as a set to intersect with set C.

Example 1. If $A = \{1, 2, 3\}$, $B = \{2, 3, 4\}$, and $C = \{3, 4, 5\}$, find $A \cap B \cap C$.

$$
\begin{aligned}
A \cap B \cap C &= (A \cap B) \cap C \\
&= \{2, 3\} \cap \{3, 4, 5\} \\
&= \{3\}
\end{aligned}
$$

or

$$
\begin{aligned}
A \cap B \cap C &= A \cap (B \cap C) \\
&= \{1, 2, 3\} \cap \{3, 4\} \\
&= \{3\}
\end{aligned}
$$

The union of three sets is found in a similar manner. Thus the union of sets A, B, and C would be set up as: $A \cup (B \cup C)$ or $(A \cup B) \cup C$.

Example 2. If $A = \{4, 5\}$, $B = \{5, 6, 7\}$, and $C = \{7, 8\}$, find $A \cup B \cup C$.

$$
\begin{aligned}
A \cup B \cup C &= A \cup (B \cup C) \\
&= \{4, 5\} \cup \{5, 6, 7, 8\} \\
&= \{4, 5, 6, 7, 8\}
\end{aligned}
$$

or

$$
\begin{aligned}
A \cup B \cup C &= (A \cup B) \cup C \\
&= \{4, 5, 6, 7\} \cup \{7, 8\} \\
&= \{4, 5, 6, 7, 8\}
\end{aligned}
$$

It should be observed in Example 2 that any element is not repeated in the union of sets. Examples 1 and 2 illustrate the associative law as it applies to the intersection and union of sets.

Both union and intersection of sets may be used in the same problem, though the associative law does not apply in this case. This fact is shown in Example 3.

Example 3. If $A = \{1, 2, 3\}$, $B = \{3, 4, 5\}$, and $C = \{4, 5, 6, 7\}$, find $A \cup (B \cap C)$.

$$
\begin{aligned}
A \cup (B \cap C) &= \{1, 2, 3\} \cup \{4, 5\} \\
&= \{1, 2, 3, 4, 5\}
\end{aligned}
$$

It can be observed in the following problem that if we reassociate or regroup the parts of Example 3, we do not obtain the same solution set.

Thus if both the intersection and union operations are included in the same problem, we must indicate the order of operations by the use of parentheses in that problem, as was done in the original form of Example 3.

$$(A \cup B) \cap C = \{1, 2, 3, 4, 5\} \cap \{4, 5, 6, 7\}$$
$$= \{4, 5\}$$

Both addition and multiplication are binary operations since we perform the operations with two numbers at a time. Thus $3 + 4 + 5 = (3 + 4) + 5 = 7 + 5 = 12$ or $3 + (4 + 5) = 3 + 9 = 12$. In a similar manner, the product of 3, 4, and 5 could be set up as $3(4 \cdot 5) = 3 \cdot 20 = 60$ or $(3 \cdot 4)5 = 12 \cdot 5 = 60$.

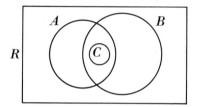

Figure 13

Consider Figure 13. What can you say concerning the intersection of sets A and B? Of sets C and B? Of sets C and A? Of sets A, B, and C?

EXERCISE 3

A

If $A = \{1, 2, 3, 4\}$, $B = \{3, 4, 5, 6\}$, and $C = \{5, 6, 7, 8\}$, find the following:

1. $A \cap B$
2. $A \cup B$
3. $A \cap C$
4. $A \cup C$
5. $B \cap C$
6. $B \cup C$
7. $A \cap (B \cap C)$
8. $A \cup (B \cup C)$
9. $(A \cap B) \cap C$
10. $(A \cup B) \cup C$

B

If $A = \{-2, -1, 0\}$, $B = \{-1, 0, 1\}$, $C = \{0, 1, 2\}$, and $D = \{1, 2, 3\}$, find the following:

1. $A \cap (B \cap C)$ 2. $A \cup (B \cup C)$ 3. $(A \cap B) \cap D$
4. $(A \cup B) \cup D$ 5. $(A \cap B) \cap (C \cap D)$ 6. $(A \cup B) \cup (C \cup D)$
7. $A \cup (B \cap C)$ 8. $A \cup (B \cap D)$ 9. $(A \cap B) \cup (C \cap D)$
10. $(A \cup B) \cap (C \cup D)$

9. DEFINITIONS AND MEANINGS

Many words and expressions used in arithmetic are similarly used in algebra.

The parts of an algebraic expression that are separated from one another by the signs $+$ and $-$ are called *terms*. If no sign appears with a term, that term is understood to be positive. The following are examples of single terms: -3, 34, $-3x$, and ab.

In some expressions two or more terms may be used. Examples of this are: $x + y$, $a - 3$, $3b + 2c$, and $x^2 - y + z$.

The result obtained when two or more expressions are added is called the *sum* of those expressions.

$$
\begin{array}{r} 12 \\ +5 \\ \hline 17 \end{array} \text{ (sum)}
\qquad
\begin{array}{r} 16 \\ 8 \\ +11 \\ \hline 35 \end{array} \text{ (sum)}
$$

The result of subtracting one number from another number is called the *difference* or *remainder*.

$$
\begin{array}{r} 14 \\ -8 \\ \hline 6 \end{array} \text{ (difference)}
\qquad
\begin{array}{r} 9 \\ -5 \\ \hline 4 \end{array} \text{ (difference)}
$$

A *product* is the result of multiplying two or more numbers together. In arithmetic the "$\times$" was used to denote multiplication. In algebra, because x is used so often as an unknown quantity, other symbols are used to indicate multiplication in order to avoid confusion in the use of the x. A raised dot placed between two expressions indicates the process of multiplication. Another method of showing that multiplication is implied is to place the expressions to be multiplied together within parentheses— side by side and with no sign between them.

$$
\begin{aligned}
3 \cdot 4 &= 12 \\
(3)(4) &= 12 \\
a \cdot b &= ab \\
(a)(b) &= ab
\end{aligned}
$$

If a and b are any numbers (except $b \neq 0$), the quotient $a \div b$ or a/b represents some number x such that $bx = a$. In other words, the *quotient* is the number obtained by dividing one number by another number.

$$\frac{a}{b} = x \qquad (x \text{ is the quotient if } b \neq 0)$$

$$\frac{12}{3} = 4 \qquad (4 \text{ is the quotient})$$

$$\frac{x}{y} \qquad \begin{array}{l}\text{(This expression indicates a quotient but its} \\ \text{numerical value cannot be determined unless} \\ \text{the values of } x \text{ and } y \text{ are known and } y \neq 0)\end{array}$$

A natural number a is said to be even if it can be expressed as $2b$, where b is a natural number. Thus an *even number* is a natural number that is exactly divisible by 2.

A natural number a is said to be an *odd number* if it can be expressed as $2b - 1$, where b is a natural number. Thus an *odd number* is a natural number that is not even.

The *factors* of a product are any two or more numbers which when multiplied together result in a given product. Thus 6 and 4 are factors of 24 and a, b, and c are factors of abc. The algebraic expression $5xy + 4z$ has two terms, $5xy$ and $4z$. The first term consists of three factors, namely 5, x, and y, and the second term contains the two factors 4 and z.

A natural number is said to be *prime* if it is greater than 1 and has no positive integral factors except itself and 1. (The number 1 is often called *unity*.) Such numbers as 7, 19, and 41 are prime numbers.

The *prime factors* of a product are those factors that are prime numbers. The factors of 24 as stated above are not prime factors because neither 6 nor 4 is a prime number. The prime factors of 24 are 2, 2, 2, and 3.

The expression $a + 3$ means that 3 is added to the number represented by a. The expression $a - 3$ means that 3 is subtracted from the number represented by a. The expression $a - 3$ is equivalent to $a + (-3)$, as will be shown in a subsequent discussion.

The expression $2x$ means that the number represented by x is multiplied by 2.

The expression $2x - 4$ means that the number represented by x is multiplied by 2 and from that product 4 is subtracted.

The expression $3x + 2y$ means that the number represented by x is multiplied by 3 and to that product is added the result of multiplying by 2 the number represented by y.

The expression x^2 means that the number represented by x is used as a factor two times ($x \cdot x = x^2$). This is usually referred to as *squaring* the number represented by x.

The expression a^3, referred to as *a cubed*, means that the number represented by a is used as a factor three times ($a^3 = a \cdot a \cdot a$).

The expression $\dfrac{2x + 3}{4}$ means that 3 is added to twice the number represented by x and that sum is divided by 4.

The expression $3(a + b)$ means that the sum of a and b is multiplied by 3.

Every algebraic expression, regardless of how complicated it may seem, represents a number and is governed by all the laws and rules that apply to any number in our system of numbers.

EXERCISE 4

A

Write one or more sentences stating what is meant by each of the following expressions:

1. $m + n$
2. $a - b$
3. $a + b - c$
4. $2a + 1$
5. $3b + a$
6. $\dfrac{3b}{2}$
7. x^2
8. b^3
9. $x^2 - 1$
10. $\dfrac{3x}{5}$
11. $\dfrac{x - y}{3}$
12. $5a$

Write an algebraic expression representing each of the following statements:

13. The sum of four times a and 5.
14. The sum of three times x and twice y.
15. The remainder when x is subtracted from m.
16. The difference when 3 is subtracted from four times the number represented by c.
17. Three times the sum of x and y.
18. Twice the sum of three times the number represented by a and four times the number represented by b.
19. The product of π and d.
20. The product of four times the number represented by m and the number represented by n.
21. One-half the sum of x, y, and z.
22. The result of dividing by 3 the remainder when 7 is subtracted from x.
23. One-fourth the product of $3x$ and y.
24. Three times the sum of x, y, and z.
25. Three times the number represented by x subtracted from two times the number represented by a.

B

Write one or more sentences stating what is meant by each of the following expressions:

1. $3x^2$
2. $3m + 1$
3. $x^2 + y^2$
4. $x^2 - y^3$
5. $\dfrac{x^3 + 3}{2}$
6. $2(m - n)$
7. $\dfrac{3(x + y)}{4}$
8. $x(x + y)$

Write an algebraic expression representing each of the following statements:

9. The quotient obtained when four times the number represented by d is divided by 5.
10. Twice the square of the number represented by s.
11. The result when x is cubed and then divided by 2.
12. The product of a squared and b cubed.
13. The result when x is cubed and then subtracted from 6.
14. The sum of m and n multiplied by 4.
15. Two-thirds of the product of a and b.

10. SUBSTITUTION IN THE ALGEBRAIC EXPRESSION

In a great many algebraic problems it is necessary to substitute the given values for the variables in the expression. This process is known as *evaluating* the algebraic expression. To evaluate an expression in which all of the variables are given or can be determined, we substitute those values in the expression, observing the arithmetical operations indicated.

Example 1. Find the value of $a + 2b$ when $a = 2$ and $b = 3$.
$$a + 2b = 2 + 2(3) = 2 + 6 = 8$$

Example 2. Find the value of $3a - 5b$ when $a = 4$ and $b = 2$.
$$3a - 5b = (3)(4) - (5)(2) = 12 - 10 = 2$$

EXERCISE 5

A

If $x = 2$, $y = 1$, and $z = 3$, find the value of each of the following expressions:

1. $3x - z$	2. xy	3. xyz
4. $\dfrac{x + y}{3}$	5. $x + y - z$	6. $3x + 2z$
7. $x^2 - y$	8. $x^2 + y^2$	9. $z^2 - x^2$
10. $2x^2 - y$	11. $x - y^2$	12. x^2y^2
13. $\dfrac{x + y + z}{3}$	14. $\dfrac{x^2z}{3}$	15. $\dfrac{x^2 - y^2}{3}$
16. $3y^2 - z$	17. $x^2 - y^2 + z$	18. $\dfrac{2z^2}{6}$
19. $6z - 4y$	20. $3xyz$	21. $3y^2$
22. $z(x - y)$	23. $z^2(x - y)$	24. $\dfrac{y^2}{3}$
25. $2x^2 - 3y^2$	26. $2x(x - y)$	27. yz
28. $z - y - x$	29. $y(z - x)$	30. $4x^2z$

B

If $x = \frac{1}{2}$, $y = 2$, and $z = 1$, find the value of each of the following expressions:

1. $2x - y + 2z^2$	2. $4xz$	3. $2y - 4x - z$
4. $2x(y - z)$	5. $\dfrac{2x}{3z - y}$	6. $\dfrac{4x - y}{z}$
7. $x + \frac{1}{2}y + z$	8. $\dfrac{2y - 3z}{4x}$	9. $3z^2 - 4x$
10. $x + y + \frac{1}{2}z$		

EXERCISE 6

A

Describe each of the following sets:

1. $\{3, 6, 9, \ldots\}$	2. $\{7, 8, 9\}$	3. $\{2, 3, 5, 7\}$
4. $\{12, 14, 16, \ldots\}$	5. $\{25, 36, 49\}$	6. $\{5, 10, 15, \ldots\}$

24   THE NUMBER SYSTEM

If $A = \{1, 2, 3\}$, $B = \{3, 4, 5\}$, and $C = \{5, 6, 7\}$, find each of the following:

7. $A \cap B$

8. $B \cap C$

9. $A \cup C$

10. $A \cup (B \cap C)$

Write a statement to indicate what each of the following algebraic expressions means:

11. $4 - m$

12. $z^2 - 1$

13. $\frac{2}{3}x^2$

14. $x^2 - \frac{a^2}{4}$

15. $\frac{m + 3n}{2}$

Evaluate each of the following if $a = 1$, $b = 1$, and $c = 3$:

16. $c - b$

17. $2c + a$

18. $c^2 + b^2$

19. $2b^2$

20. $c^2 - a^2$

B

If $A = \{-3, -1, 1\}$, $B = \{-2, 0, 2\}$, and $C = \{3, 4, 5\}$, find each of the following:

1. $A \cap (B \cap C)$

2. $(A \cap C) \cap B$

3. $(A \cup B) \cup C$

4. $A \cup (B \cap C)$

5. $(A \cap B) \cup C$

6. $(A \cap C) \cap B$

Evaluate each of the following if $a = 1$, $b = 2$, and $c = 3$:

7. $\frac{3c - a}{2}$

8. $3(a^2 + b^2)$

9. $\frac{2a + c}{5}$

10. $\frac{1}{3}(c^2 + b^2 + 2a)$

REVIEW TEST 1

On a sheet of paper write the numbers 1 through 15 to correspond to the following numbered statements. Select, from the right-hand column below, the answer that correctly matches each statement and write its letter after the appropriate number.

1. When 6 is added to a certain number, the result is 18.

2. When a certain number is multiplied by 2 and increased by 8, the result is 24.

3. Two-thirds of a certain number is 30.

4. If 6 is added to three times a certain number, the result is 18.

a. $d - 3 = 4$
b. $2a - 8 = 24$
c. $3x + 6 = 18$
d. $\frac{2}{3}(a + b) = 24$
e. $8 - 2a = 24$
f. $p = b - a$
g. $d = 140$
h. $n + 6 = 18$

5. If 8 is diminished by twice a certain number, the result is 24.

6. Three numbers are selected. The first one added to twice the second one equals the third number.

7. A man spent 3 dollars and had 4 dollars left.

8. If the side of a square is increased by 3, the perimeter is 24.

9. Three times a certain number diminished by two times another number is equal to 30.

10. The distance an automobile travels if it averages 40 miles per hour for $3\frac{1}{2}$ hours.

11. What was the profit made if a merchant bought an article for a cents and sold it for b cents?

12. Two-thirds of a number is 30.

13. The distance an automobile travels if it averages 60 miles per hour for 2 hours and 15 minutes.

14. Twice a certain number diminished by 8 is equal to 24.

15. A man spent 4 dollars and had 3 dollars left.

i. $3a - 2b = 30$
j. $2b + a = c$
k. $2a + 8 = 24$
l. $d - 4 = 3$
m. $\frac{2}{3}b = 30$
n. $d = 135$
o. $4(s + 3) = 24$

REVIEW TEST 2

On a sheet of paper write the numbers 1 through 10. Select, from the right-hand column below, the answer that correctly matches each statement in the left-hand column and write its letter after the appropriate number.

1. The set of one-digit prime numbers.

2. The set of natural numbers whose squares are greater than 25 and less than 100.

3. The set of odd numbers greater than 50 and less than 60.

4. The set of all one-digit odd numbers.

5. The set of all numbers that are one more than a one-digit prime number.

6. The set of prime numbers greater than or equal to 51 and less than 60.

7. The set of one-digit prime numbers that are perfect squares.

8. The set of all natural numbers greater than or equal to $3\frac{1}{2}$ and less than $3\frac{2}{3}$.

a. $\{3, 4, 6, 8\}$
b. $\{6, 7, 8, 9\}$
c. $\varnothing$
d. $\{1, 4, 9\}$
e. $\{2, 3, 5, 7\}$
f. $\{1, 3, 5, \ldots\}$
g. $\{3, 5, 7\}$
h. $\{3, 4, 5, 6\}$
i. $\{51, 53, 55, 57, 59\}$
j. $\{1, 3, 5, 7\}$
k. $\{53, 59\}$
l. $\{4, 9\}$
m. $\{36, 49, 64, 81\}$
n. $\{1, 3, 5, 7, 9\}$
o. $\{53, 57, 59\}$

9. The set of all one-digit perfect squares.

10. The set of all even prime numbers greater than 8.

REVIEW TEST 3

On a sheet of paper write the numbers 1 through 10. Select, from the right-hand column below, the answer that correctly matches each statement in the left-hand column and write its letter after the appropriate number, if $A = \{2, 4, 6\}$, $B = \{1, 3, 5\}$, and $C = \{5, 6\}$.

1. $A \cup C$

2. $A \cup B$

3. $B \cap C$

4. $C \cup B$

5. $A \cap C$

6. $A \cap B$

7. $A \cap A$

8. $B \cup (A \cap C)$

9. $(B \cap C) \cup A$

10. $(B \cup A) \cup C$

a. $\{1, 3, 5, 6\}$
b. $\{1, 2, 4, 5, 6\}$
c. $\{2, 4, 5, 6\}$
d. $\{5\}$
e. $\{2, 4, 6\}$
f. $\{1, 2, 3, 4, 5\}$
g. $\{6\}$
h. $\varnothing$
i. $\{5, 6\}$
j. $\{2, 3, 4, 5, 6\}$
k. $\{2\}$
l. $\{4, 6\}$
m. $\{1, 2, 3, 4, 5, 6\}$

REVIEW TEST 4

Evaluate each of the following if $x = 3$, $y = 1$, and $z = 2$:

1. $3xz$

2. $\frac{1}{2}(x - y)$

3. $\frac{2}{3}(x + y + z)$

4. $3x - 4y$

5. $z^2 - y$

6. $x^2y^2 - z^2$

7. $\dfrac{y^2 + x - z}{2}$

8. $x(z - y)$

9. $8 - z^2$

10. $\dfrac{x + z}{y}$

11. $2z^2 - 6$

12. $6 - 2y^2$

13. πy

14. $\pi(y + z)$

15. $\pi(x - y^2)$

2

Addition and Subtraction
of Signed Numbers

11. ADDITION OF SIGNED NUMBERS

The signed numbers and fractions are our own inventions and it will be
our responsibility to define their meanings, especially as to how they are
used in the basic operations.

As we consider the addition of signed numbers, let us refer once more
to the number line. If, in Figure 14, we select a number to the right of

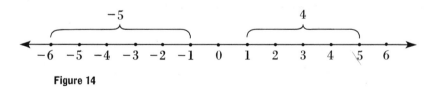

Figure 14

zero, we have a positive number. Moving to the right may be thought of
as adding a positive number whose value is equal to the number of units
moved. In Figure 14 if we start with the number 1 and add 4 units to
that 1, we arrive at the point on the number line represented by the
number 5. Thus $1 + 4 = 5$.

When moving to the left on the number line, we may think of this
directional movement as adding a negative number to a given number.

If, in Figure 14, we wish to add a -5 to -1, we would start at -1 and move to the left 5 units to the point representing -6. Thus $(-1) + (-5)$ $= -6$.

In the two examples above we confined our operations to either the positive region or the negative region. In each case we added the numbers involved and affixed the sign that was common to the addends. There remains only the case in which we cross over the point on the number line represented by zero.

In Figure 15 we present two illustrations of the addition of two numbers whose signs differ.

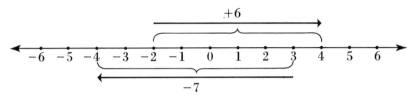

Figure 15

If we wish to add $+6$ to -2, we start at -2 and move 6 units to the right, which places us at $+4$. Thus $(-2) + (+6) = +4$.

Then if we wish to add -7 to $+3$, we move 7 units to the left of $+3$, which places us at -4. Hence $(+3) + (-7) = -4$.

It can be observed from these examples in which we added two numbers with unlike signs that we found the difference of the unsigned numbers and prefixed to that difference the sign of the larger addend.

The following specific examples illustrate the addition of signed numbers and may help to clarify the process of the addition of such numbers.

If you deposit $10 in the bank on Monday and $15 later in the week, how much did you deposit in the two transactions? Deposits represent positive numbers.

$$+\$10$$
$$+\$15$$
$$\overline{+\$25}$$

If you withdrew $10 on Wednesday and $15 on Friday, what was the sum or total of your withdrawals in the two transactions? Remember that withdrawals represent negative numbers.

$$-\$10$$
$$-\$15$$
$$\overline{-\$25}$$

In the two problems above addition was used. In the first case the unsigned values were added and the sign of the sum was the same as the signs (called the *common* sign) of the two addends.

If you went to the bank twice this week, depositing $12 the first time and withdrawing $7 the second time, how did the two transactions affect your bank balance?

$$
\begin{aligned}
&+\$12 \\
&-\$\ 7 \\
\hline
&+\$\ 5
\end{aligned}
$$

This means that during the week your balance increased by $5.

During another week you made two trips to the bank, the first time withdrawing $15 and the second time depositing $6. How did those two transactions affect your bank balance?

$$
\begin{aligned}
&-\$15 \\
&+\$\ 6 \\
\hline
&-\$\ 9
\end{aligned}
$$

This means, of course, that during the week your bank balance decreased by $9.

We are now ready to define the addition of signed numbers.

Definition 1. If a and b are any positive numbers, then

$$
\begin{aligned}
(a) + (b) &= +(a + b) \\
(-a) + (-b) &= -(a + b) \\
(a) + (-b) &= (-b) + (a) \\
&= +(a - b) \qquad \text{(if } a > b) \\
&= -(b - a) \qquad \text{(if } b > a) \\
&= 0 \qquad\qquad\ \text{(if } a = b) \\
(a) + 0 = 0 + (a) &= a \\
(-a) + 0 = 0 + (-a) &= -a
\end{aligned}
$$

To add more than two signed numbers, we may take them in the order given, add two of them, and to their sum add the next number, and so on. This, as previously stated, is a binary operation. Thus

$$
\begin{aligned}
(8) + (-2) + (-5) + (4) &= (6) + (-5) + (4) \\
&= 1 + 4 \\
&= 5
\end{aligned}
$$

The same numbers may be added by using the commutative law for addition and placing in succession the positive numbers and then the negative numbers. We first add together the positive numbers and then the negative numbers. Finally we add those two sums. Thus

$$(8) + (-2) + (-5) + (4) = (8) + (4) + (-2) + (-5)$$
$$= [(8) + (4)] + [(-2) + (-5)]$$
$$= [+(8 + 4)] + [-(2 + 5)]$$
$$= 12 + (-7)$$
$$= 5$$

12. SUBTRACTION OF SIGNED NUMBERS

In our discussion of negative numbers the minus sign was attached to the number and meant that it was located to the left of zero on the number line. We can extend the concept of negative numbers if we keep in mind that the negative of any number has the same magnitude as the number itself but with the other sign attached to it. Also, the negative of any number is on the opposite side of zero on the number line. If a is a positive number, its negative is $-a$. The negative of that $-a$ then is written $-(-a)$, which is a positive a. We often refer to two numbers of the same magnitude as *opposites* of each other. Thus $-a$ is the opposite of a and a is the opposite of $-a$. Hence the opposite of a positive number is a negative number and the opposite of a negative number is a positive number.

Another use of the minus sign is made throughout the study of algebra. That is when it is used to connect two numbers $(a - b)$ in a manner similar to that when a and b were added $(a + b)$. The expression $a - b$ means that b is subtracted from a. Subtraction is defined as follows:

Definition 2. If a and b are any directed numbers, $a - b$ shall represent another directed number m such that $b + m = a$.

Thus m is some number which, when added to b, makes it equal to a. In other words, we are defining subtraction in terms of addition.

If $b + m = a$, then $m = a - b$. Here we have added $-b$ to each member of the equation.

It was shown previously that $a = a$. This holds true for any algebraic expression. Therefore

$b + [a + (-b)] = b + [a + (-b)]$	(Reflexive relationship)
$= [a + (-b)] + b$	(Commutative law for addition)
$= a + [(-b) + b]$	(Associative law for addition)
$= a + [b + (-b)]$	(Commutative law for addition)
$= a + [0]$	(Additive inverse)
$= a$	(Definition of addition)

Thus we have shown that $b + [a + (-b)] = a$. It was shown above that $b + m = a$. Hence $m = a + (-b)$. Since $m = a - b$, we have, by substitution,

$$a - b = a + (-b)$$

From the discussion above, then, we observe that any subtraction problem becomes an addition problem (adding the negative of that part to the number) and its solution follows the general procedure for the addition of signed numbers.

In every subtraction problem the number that is to be subtracted from another number is called the *subtrahend*. The number from which the subtrahend is to be subtracted is known as the *minuend*. The result (or answer) is called the *remainder* (or *difference*).

Example 1. Subtract 13 from 17.

$$(17) - (13) = (17) + (-13)$$
$$= 4$$

Example 2. Subtract -7 from 5.

$$(5) - (-7) = (5) + (+7)$$
$$= 12$$

Example 3. From -15 subtract -9.

$$(-15) - (-9) = (-15) + (+9)$$
$$= -6$$

Observe carefully the statement in a problem involving subtraction. In Examples 1 and 2 above the subtrahend is stated before the minuend, whereas in Example 3 the minuend is stated first.

13. ADDITION AND SUBTRACTION OF LITERAL TERMS

A *literal term* is an algebraic term that includes one or more letters that are factors in that term.

In the algebraic expression $4m^2$, the 4 is said to be the *coefficient* of m^2. A number or letter, or a combination of both, may be used as a coefficient. In the expression $3xy^2$, the 3 is the coefficient of xy^2, $3x$ is the coefficient of y^2, and $3y^2$ is the coefficient of x. If no numerical coefficient is shown, it is understood that it is 1. Thus the numerical coefficient of x^2 is 1. In the expression $5(x - y)$, 5 is the coefficient of $(x - y)$.

In the expression x^2, the 2 is called the *exponent* of x and indicates how many times the letter x is used as a factor. Thus $x^2 = x \cdot x$ and $x^4 = x \cdot x \cdot x \cdot x$. If no exponent is shown, it is understood to be 1.

For purposes of simplifying the work in algebra, if either a coefficient or an exponent is 1, it is omitted.

The expression $5xy^2$ means that 5, x, y, and y are all multiplied together. Thus the 5, x, y, and y are all factors of the expression. All such numbers are called *numerical factors* and the letters are known as *literal factors*.

Terms were defined in Chapter 1 as the parts of an algebraic expression that are separated one from the other by the signs $+$ and $-$.

> *Similar terms* are terms that are exactly alike except for the numerical coefficient. The expressions $3x$ and $6x$ are similar terms, as are $3x^2$ and $6x^2$. But $2x^2$ and $5x^3$ are not similar terms since the exponents of the literal factors are not alike.
>
> A *monomial* is an algebraic expression consisting of one term. Examples of monomials are: $4x$, $18y^2$, $10xy$, $-7x$, and $15xyz^3$.
>
> A *binomial* is an algebraic expression consisting of two terms. Examples of binomials are: $x - y$, $3x + 4$, $x^2 + y^2$, $2xyz + 3am$, and $xy^2 + 3ab$.
>
> A *trinomial* is an algebraic expression consisting of three terms. Examples of trinomials are: $a + b + c$, $x - 2y + 3$, $x^2 - y^2 + z^2$, and $3m + 2n - 1$.
>
> A *multinomial* is an algebraic expression consisting of two or more terms. Examples of multinomials are: $x + y$, $2a + 1$, $a - b - c$, $3 - 4m$, and $ab - 3c + 4x - y^2$.

Again, it must be kept in mind that every algebraic expression, whether it be a monomial, a binomial, a trinomial, or any other expression, always represents a number and must follow the laws that we have developed for our number system.

Only similar terms may be combined into a single term in both addition and subtraction.

Certain of the laws presented in Chapter 1 are used in the process of addition and subtraction. To illustrate this, consider the following problem: $2x^2 + 5x^2 - 3x^2$. Here

$$2x^2 + 5x^2 - 3x^2 = x^2(2 + 5 - 3) \tag{1}$$

by the law of symmetry becomes

$$x^2(2 + 5 - 3) = 2x^2 + 5x^2 - 3x^2 \tag{2}$$

and (2) above is a true statement by use of the distributive law of multi-plication with respect to addition. Then (2) becomes

$$x^2(4) = 2x^2 + 5x^2 - 3x^2 \tag{3}$$

by combining the numerical terms in the parentheses in (2). Then, from the commutative law for multiplication, $x^2(4) = 4x^2$. Thus (3) may be written

$$4x^2 = 2x^2 + 5x^2 - 3x^2 \tag{4}$$

Again from the law of symmetry, (4) becomes

$$2x^2 + 5x^2 - 3x^2 = 4x^2 \tag{5}$$

It can readily be observed in (5) that in the addition of similar mo-nomial terms we find the algebraic sum of the numerical coefficients and attach to that sum the literal factor that is common to each of the addends.

If we have more than one term in each of the numbers to be added or subtracted, each similar term is combined as in the above example. Consider the following problem:

$$(2x + 4y + 3z) + (x + 3y + 2z) + (3x - 2y - 4z)$$

We may group the similar terms by use of the associative and commuta-tive laws for addition to obtain

$$(2x + x + 3x) + (4y + 3y - 2y) + (3z + 2z - 4z)$$

and this becomes

$$(2 + 1 + 3)x + (4 + 3 - 2)y + (3 + 2 - 4)z$$

Then by obtaining the algebraic sum of the numerical coefficients of the variables we have

$$6x + 5y + z$$

This same problem may be solved by arranging the similar terms in columns and adding each column independently of the other columns:

$$
\begin{aligned}
2x + 4y + 3z \\
x + 3y + 2z \\
\underline{3x - 2y - 4z} \\
6x + 5y + \ \ z
\end{aligned}
$$

We previously defined subtraction in terms of addition when we stated that $a - b = a + (-b)$. In a similar manner we define the subtraction of larger units as follows: If we wish to subtract $(a + b)$ from $(2a + 3b)$, the $(a + b)$, of course, is the subtrahend, and the negative of $(a + b)$ is $(-a - b)$ or $-(a + b)$. Thus

$$(2a + 3b) - (a + b) = (2a + 3b) + (-a - b)$$

and, again, by use of the associative and commutative laws for addition, this becomes

$$(2a - a) + (3b - b)$$

which may be written as
$$(2a) + (-a) + (3b) + (-b)$$
Then by adding the similar terms we have
$$(2 - 1)a + (3 - 1)b$$
Finally, this becomes the solution to the problem, which is
$$a + 2b$$
This problem may also be set up in columns and solved in the same manner as the addition problem. We shall first show this as a subtraction problem and then as the resulting addition problem obtained by stating the negative of the subtrahend.

Subtraction	Addition
$(2a) + (3b)$	$(2a) + (3b)$
$(a) + (b)$	$(-a) + (-b)$
	$a + \quad 2b$

Example 1. Subtract $3xy$ from $5xy$.
$$\begin{aligned} (5xy) - (3xy) &= (5xy) + (-3xy) \\ &= (5 - 3)xy \\ &= 2xy \end{aligned}$$

Example 2. From $-9mn$ subtract $4mn$.
$$\begin{aligned} (-9mn) - (4mn) &= (-9mn) + (-4mn) \\ &= (-9 - 4)mn \\ &= [(-9) + (-4)]mn \\ &= -13mn \end{aligned}$$

Example 3. Subtract $3a^2 + b$ from $-4a^2 + 3b$.
$$\begin{aligned} (-4a^2 + 3b) - (3a^2 + b) &= (-4a^2 + 3b) + (-3a^2 - b) \\ &= (-4a^2 - 3a^2) + (3b - b) \\ &= [(-4) + (-3)]a^2 + [(3) + (-1)]b \\ &= -7a^2 + 2b \end{aligned}$$

Example 4. From $3m^2 - 7n + 3p$ subtract $m^2 - 3n + 4p$.
$$\begin{aligned} (3m^2 - 7n + 3p) &- (m^2 - 3n + 4p) \\ &= (3m^2 - 7n + 3p) + (-m^2 + 3n - 4p) \\ &= (3m^2 - m^2) + (-7n + 3n) + (3p - 4p) \\ &= (3 - 1)m^2 + (-7 + 3)n + (3 - 4)p \\ &= [(3) + (-1)]m^2 + [(-7) + (3)]n + [(3) + (-4)]p \\ &= [2]m^2 + [-4]n + [-1]p \\ &= 2m^2 - 4n - p \end{aligned}$$

A

Add:

1. $(+3) + (+7) + (-2) + (-5)$
2. $(+5) + (-6) + (-3) + (+8)$
3. $(-4) + (-3) + (+7) + (-6)$
4. $(-9) + (-7) + (-2) + (+8)$
5. $(+12) + (+4) + (-10) + (-5)$
6. $(-10) + (+14) + (+2) + (+7)$
7. $(-12) + (-10) + (+7) + (+10)$
8. $(4y^3) + (7y^3) + (-6y^3)$
9. $(-2s) + (-8s) + (-9s)$
10. $(-4mnp) + (-7mnp) + (-8mnp) + (9mnp)$
11. $(x^2 - y) + (3x^2 + 4y)$
12. $(-4m^3 - 3n^2) + (-3m^3 - 7n^2)$
13. $(4c^2 + 2d) + (3c^2 + 5d) + (-7c^2 + 3d) + (4c^2 - 9d)$
14. $(2a - 3b + 4c) + (5a + 6b - 3c) + (-3a + b - c)$
15. $(4x^2 - 3y^2 + 7z^2) + (-8x^2 + 5y^2) + (-2y^2 - 4z^2)$
16. $(7ax - c) + (5ax - 3c) + (-3ax + 5c) + (-6ax - c)$
17. $(-4b^2 + 2d) + (7b^2 + 3d) + (2b^2 + d) + (-3b^2 - 4d)$
18. $(5a + 3b - 4c) + (-2a + 6b - 7c) + (8a + 5b) + (-3c + 4b - 6a)$
19. $(2a^2b^2c - 2de + 3ab^2) + (-a^2b^2c - 2ab^2 + 6de) + (5ab^2 - 7de + 3a^2b^2c)$
20. $(a + b + c + d + e) + (2a + 7e + 3b) + (3b - 2c + 6d + 3e) +$
    $(7a - 3e - 3c + 2b - 8d)$

Subtract:

21. $(+6) - (+4)$ 22. $(+10) - (-2)$
23. $(-14) - (-11)$ 24. $(-28) - (+6)$
25. $(6xy) - (3xy)$ 26. $(-12ab^2c) - (-6ab^2c)$
27. Subtract $2a - b$ from $3a + b$.
28. Subtract $5xy^2 + 7z$ from $3xy^2 - 3z$.
29. From $a - b + c$ subtract $a + b - c$.
30. From $a^2 - 3b + c^2$ subtract $-a^2 - 5b - 3c^2$.

B

Add:

1. $(4x^2y - 2xy^2 - 3z^2) + (3x^2y + xy^2) + (3z^2)$
2. $(m^2 + p^2) + (2n^2) + (-m^2 - n^2 - 3p^2)$
3. $(2a^2 - 3b + 2c^2 + d^2) + (5a^2 - b - c^2 + d^2)$

4. $(2a + b - c - d) + (4a - b + c - d) + (5a + 3b - 4c + 5d)$
5. $(4c^2d - 3d^2c + 2x - 3y) + (5c^2d + 4x) + (4d^2c + 8y)$

Subtract:

6. $(-3rst) - (17rst)$ 7. $(3x^2y) - (9x^2y)$
8. $(-13mn) - (6mn)$ 9. $(17x^2a) - (-8x^2a)$
10. $(3m^2 - 4n + x) - (5m^2 - 7n + 8y)$
11. $(4d^2 - 7e + 8f - 7) - (8d^2 - 3f - 7)$

Subtract the sum of the first two trinomials from the third trinomial:

12. $7a - 4b + c, 3a + 2b - 5c, 4a + 3b + 2c$
13. $4d - 3e + f, 2d + e - 3f, 7d - 4e + 5f$
14. $3x + y - z, -2x + 3y - 7z, 4x + y - z$

From the sum of the first two trinomials subtract the third trinomial:

15. $m + n + p, 8m - 3n + 4p, 3m - n - p$
16. $m^2 + n^2 - 1, 3m^2 + 4n^2 + 5, 2m^2 - n^2 + 6$
17. $a^2b^2 - c + d, 4a^2b^2 + 3c - 5d, 7a^2b^2 - 4c + d$

Subtract the sum of the first two trinomials from the sum of the last two trinomials:

18. $3x + y - 5z, 7x - 3y + z, 11x + 3y - 5z, -3x - 4y + z$
19. $a^2 + b^2 - c^2, 4a^2 - 2b^2 + 3c^2, 7a^2 - b^2 + 3c^2, 2a^2 + 5b^2 + 2c^2$

From the sum of the first two trinomials subtract the sum of the last two trinomials:

20. $4w + 8m - 2n, 7w - 3m + 5n, 3w - m - n, 2w + 3m - 2n$
21. $3r - 5s + 4t, 2r - 5s - 4t, -r + s + t, 3r - s + 3t$

14. GROUPING SYMBOLS

In certain of the previous discussions we made use of parentheses and brackets to group parts of algebraic expressions. At this time it is important that we discuss more extensively the use of such grouping symbols.

A great many times in the study of mathematics an algebraic expression becomes large and complex. When this occurs, there is a possibility that the expression and how it is to be treated will become confusing. One or more parts of the problem may have to be dealt with independently of the other parts. Certain terms or factors of the expression may constitute a part that must be treated as a single unit. It becomes necessary to think of those parts as a unit. In order to avoid confusion or to clarify the use of certain parts of the expression, several different symbols are used. At times it is both convenient and useful to insert more than one set of those symbols in the same problem.

The following three types of symbols may be found in mathematics, science, and technical books: *parentheses*, $(a + b)$; *brackets*, $[a + b]$; and *braces*, $\{a + b\}$. All three forms may be used in the same manner and all three forms mean that the sum of a and b is to be treated as a unit. If we were asked to subtract the sum of x and y from a, the problem could be written with any of the three symbols.

With parentheses: $\quad a - (x + y)$
With brackets: $\quad\quad a - [x + y]$
With braces: $\quad\quad\, a - \{x + y\}$

The negative sign in each of the above examples is a sign of operation, which means that the sum of x and y is to be subtracted from a. The coefficient of x is positive, as are those of a and y.

When using the unit $(m - n)$ in an algebraic computation, it is understood to be *one* of those units. In removing the parentheses, we would, of course, make use of the distributive law and distribute the coefficient of the group (understood to be 1 when none is shown) over the addends within the parentheses.

Example 1. Remove the parentheses in the following expression: $m - (c - d)$.

$$m - (c - d) = m + (-c + d)$$
$$= m - c + d$$

Example 2. Remove the brackets in the following expression: $c + [x - 2y]$.

$$c + [x - 2y] = c + x - 2y$$

Example 3. Remove the braces in the following expression: $2d + c + \{-x + y\}$.

$$2d + c + \{-x + y\} = 2d + c - x + y$$

If, after all grouping symbols have been removed, there are two or more similar terms, they must be combined.

Example 4. Simplify $3a - (b - a) + 2b + (3a - b)$.

$$3a - (b - a) + 2b + (3a - b) = 3a + (a - b) + 2b + (3a - b)$$
$$= 3a + a - b + 2b + 3a - b$$
$$= 3a + a + 3a + 2b - b - b$$
$$= (3 + 1 + 3)a + (2 - 1 - 1)b$$
$$= (7)a + (0)b$$
$$= 7a$$

Example 5. Simplify $-(3x - y) + 5x - (x + 2y)$.
$$\begin{aligned}
-(3x - y) + 5x - (x + 2y) &= 5x - (3x - y) - (x + 2y) \\
&= 5x + (-3x + y) + (-x - 2y) \\
&= 5x - 3x + y + (-x) + (-2y) \\
&= (5 - 3 - 1)x + (1 - 2)y \\
&= (1)x + (-1)y \\
&= x - y
\end{aligned}$$

When more than one set of symbols is used in the same problem, that is, one set within another, errors are easily made. To avoid making such errors, we remove the innermost set first. If, after removing that innermost set, there still remains one set within another, then remove that innermost one and finally remove the last set.

Example 6. Simplify $2a - [a + (b - c) + 2b]$.
$$\begin{aligned}
2a - [a + (b - c) + 2b] &= 2a - [a + b - c + 2b] \\
&= 2a + [-a - b + c - 2b] \\
&= 2a + (-a) + (-b) + c + (-2b) \\
&= a - 3b + c
\end{aligned}$$

Example 7. Simplify $4x - \{y - [x - (y + z) + 2y] - 3x\} + z$.
$$\begin{aligned}
4x - \{y - [x - (y + z) + 2y] - 3x\} + z \\
= 4x - \{y - [x + (-y - z) + 2y] - 3x\} + z \\
= 4x - \{y - [x - y - z + 2y] - 3x\} + z \\
= 4x - \{y + [-x + y + z - 2y] - 3x\} + z \\
= 4x - \{y - x + y + z - 2y - 3x\} + z \\
= 4x + \{-y + x - y - z + 2y + 3x\} + z \\
= 4x - y + x - y - z + 2y + 3x + z \\
= (4 + 1 + 3)x + (-1 - 1 + 2)y + (-1 + 1)z \\
= (8)x + (0)y + (0)z \\
= 8x
\end{aligned}$$

Example 8. Simplify $m + [m - (3m - n) + (2m + 3n)] - n$.
$$\begin{aligned}
m + [m - (3m - n) + (2m + 3n)] - n \\
= m + [m + (n - 3m) + (2m + 3n)] - n \\
= m + [m + n - 3m + 2m + 3n] - n \\
= m + m + n - 3m + 2m + 3n - n \\
= (1 + 1 - 3 + 2)m + (1 + 3 - 1)n \\
= (1)m + (3)n \\
= m + 3n
\end{aligned}$$

A

Simplify:

1. $m + (n - 2) - 4n + (2m + 3)$ 2. $2c + d - (c - 5d + 6) + 3$
3. $x - [2y + 3x] - y + 4x$ 4. $5 - \{r - 3s\} + 4s - 3 + 2r$
5. $2x + (y + 3) - x + 2y$ 6. $a + 6 + [4a - 2] - 3a$
7. $p - [3q - p] + 3 + [p - q] + 5$ 8. $2y - 3z - (3y - z) + y$
9. $[5x - 3y] - [4x + 5y] - x$ 10. $y + 3 - \{2y - 6\} + \{4y - 2\}$
11. $z - (x - y) - (z - 4x + y)$ 12. $3m - (2n - 4) - m - (n - 5)$
13. $-[w - 5] - 3 - [-4w + 1]$ 14. $b - a + (4b + 2a) - (a - b)$
15. $x - y - \{2z + y\} - 5y$ 16. $7 - (a - b) - 4 + (3a - 2b)$
17. $(x + 3y) - 2y - (x - y) + 2x$
18. $3m - [n + m] - 2n + [4m + 6n]$
19. $4p - \{-q + (p - 3q) + 4q\} - p$
20. $s + 3t - [3t - s + (t - 3s) + t]$

B

Simplify:

1. $y - [3 + 2y - \{y - 3 + x\} - 3x]$
2. $-(z - 3y - [3x - z - 2y] + 3z + 2y) - x$
3. $d - \{c + 3d - (d + 3) - 4 + (-3d - 5)\} + 4d$
4. $7b + \{6 - (c + 4 - [3c + 6] - 2c) + 1\}$
5. $r + [3r - s - \{3s - r\} - 4r] + 5s$
6. $(m - 3) - [n + 6 - (2m - 5n + 10)] + 2$
7. $b - 3a + \{3b - a - (b - a) + 2b - a\}$
8. $3 + 6c - (c - 4 + [5c - 1]) - 3$
9. $m - n - [m - n - (m - n) - (m - n)]$
10. $-[3x - (y + 3x - \{2y + x\}) - 2]$

15. ADDING AND SUBTRACTING LARGER UNITS

Sometimes an expression such as $(x + y)$ is considered a unit. The coefficient of that unit is 1. The coefficient of the expression $5(a - b)$ is 5, and of the expression $-7(m + n)$ is -7. When adding or subtracting such expressions, the coefficients are added or subtracted, as the problem may indicate, and the unit affixed.

Example 1. Add $4(x - y)$ and $3(x - y)$.

$$\begin{array}{r} 4(x - y) \\ 3(x - y) \\ \hline 7(x - y) \end{array}$$

Example 2. Add $7(a + b)$, $-4(a + b)$, and $2(a + b)$.

$$\begin{array}{r} 7(a + b) \\ -4(a + b) \\ 2(a + b) \\ \hline 5(a + b) \end{array}$$

Example 3. Subtract $-3(m + n)$ from $-5(m + n)$.

$$\begin{array}{r} -5(m + n) \\ -3(m + n) \\ \hline -2(m + n) \end{array}$$

Example 4. From $7(x + y + z)$ subtract $-2(x + y + z)$.

$$\begin{array}{r} 7(x + y + z) \\ -2(x + y + z) \\ \hline 9(x + y + z) \end{array}$$

EXERCISE 9

Add:

1. $\begin{array}{r} -3(c + d) \\ 4(c + d) \\ \hline \end{array}$
   2. $\begin{array}{r} 6(s + t) \\ -3(s + t) \\ \hline \end{array}$
   3. $\begin{array}{r} 4(w - v) \\ 2(w - v) \\ \hline \end{array}$

4. $\begin{array}{r} -3(x + 2y) \\ -5(x + 2y) \\ \hline \end{array}$
   5. $\begin{array}{r} (x + 3) \\ -4(x + 3) \\ \hline \end{array}$
   6. $\begin{array}{r} 4(a - b) \\ (a - b) \\ \hline \end{array}$

7. $\begin{array}{r} 3(x + y + z) \\ 2(x + y + z) \\ \hline \end{array}$
   8. $\begin{array}{r} -(a - b + c) \\ -2(a - b + c) \\ \hline \end{array}$
   9. $\begin{array}{r} -7(m + n - p) \\ 3(m + n - p) \\ \hline \end{array}$

10. $\begin{array}{r} -2(m - 3n + p) \\ -5(m - 3n + p) \\ 8(m - 3n + p) \\ \hline \end{array}$
    11. $\begin{array}{r} 4(3 - 7y + z) \\ 5(3 - 7y + z) \\ -6(3 - 7y + z) \\ \hline \end{array}$
    12. $\begin{array}{r} 5(c + 3d - e) \\ -3(c + 3d - e) \\ -2(c + 3d - e) \\ \hline \end{array}$

13. $\begin{array}{r} 2(x - y) \\ -5(x - y) \\ -7(x - y) \\ 3(x - y) \\ \hline \end{array}$
    14. $\begin{array}{r} 5(c - 3d) \\ (c - 3d) \\ 2(c - 3d) \\ -4(c - 3d) \\ \hline \end{array}$
    15. $\begin{array}{r} 5(m + n - p) \\ -3(m + n - p) \\ -2(m + n - p) \\ (m + n - p) \\ \hline \end{array}$

Subtract:

16. $7(d - c)$
 $-4(d - c)$

17. $-2(x - y)$
 $-5(x - y)$

18. $8(x + 3)$
 $-2(x + 3)$

19. $5(3 - a)$
 $2(3 - a)$

20. $-6(x + m)$
 $3(x + m)$

21. $5(d + b)$
 $-2(d + b)$

22. $3(x - y - z)$
 $-2(x - y - z)$

23. $5(a + b - 2)$
 $7(a + b - 2)$

24. $-5(m - a - x)$
 $-2(m - a - x)$

25. Subtract $4(x - 3y)$ from $9(x - 3y)$.
26. Subtract $-7(a + 2b)$ from $-8(a + 2b)$.
27. From $3(x - y - z)$ subtract $9(x - y - z)$.
28. From $12(m - 3 + n)$ subtract $-3(m - 3 + n)$.
29. Add $7(a + b - c)$, $-2(a + b - c)$, and $4(a + b - c)$.
30. Add $-3(x + y + z - 1)$, $2(x + y + z - 1)$, and $(x + y + z - 1)$.
31. Add $7(3x - 7y + 2z)$, $-4(3x - 7y + 2z)$, and $-3(3x - 7y + 2z)$.
32. Subtract $4(a + b - 3c)$ from $-7(a + b - 3c)$.
33. From $-7(a + b + c + d)$ subtract $-5(a + b + c + d)$.
34. Add $-4(p + q + r)$, $-5(p + q + r)$, $-3(p + q + r)$, and $7(p + q + r)$.
35. From $8(h + a + x + 3)$ subtract $-(h + a + x + 3)$.

16. NUMERICAL VALUES OF ALGEBRAIC EXPRESSIONS

Many problems in algebra require that, if the value of a literal factor or expression is known or can be determined, the value be substituted in the expression to find its numerical value.

Example 1. If $x = 3$ and $y = 2$, find the value of $5x - 2y$.

$$5x - 2y = 5(3) - 2(2)$$
$$= 15 - 4$$
$$= 11$$

Example 2. If $a = 2$ and $b = 3$, find the value of $3a^2 + 2b^2$.

$$3a^2 + 2b^2 = 3(2)^2 + 2(3)^2$$
$$= 3(4) + 2(9)$$
$$= 12 + 18$$
$$= 30$$

Example 3. If $m = -1$ and $n = 5$, find the value of $3m^2 - 2n$.

$$3m^2 - 2n = 3(-1)^2 - 2(5)$$
$$= 3(1) - 2(5)$$
$$= 3 - 10$$
$$= -7$$

Example 4. If $c = -4$ and $d = -2$, find the value of $3(c + d)$.

$$3(c + d) = 3(-4 + [-2])$$
$$= 3(-6)$$
$$= -18$$

Example 5. If $a = 3$, $b = 2$, and $c = -3$, find the value of $b^2(a^2 + c^2)$.

$$b^2(a^2 + c^2) = 2^2[3^2 + (-3)^2]$$
$$= 4(9 + 9)$$
$$= 4(18)$$
$$= 72$$

EXERCISE 10

If $a = 4$, $b = 1$, and $c = 2$, find the value of the following:

1. $a - b$
2. $b + a$
3. $c - a$
4. $2c + b$
5. $c^2 - b^2$
6. $3a^2 - 1$
7. $b^2 + c^2 - a^2$
8. $2c^2 - 4b^2$
9. $c^2 - b + 2$

If $s = 2$, $t = -2$, and $u = 3$, find the value of the following:

10. $2(s - u)$
11. $5(s + t)$
12. $7(s^2 + u^2)$
13. $5t^2 + 3$
14. $s^2u^2 + s$
15. $t + s$
16. $s + t + u$
17. $-u^2 + t$
18. $s^2 - t^2 + u^2$

If $x = -1$, $y = 2$, and $z = 3$, find the value of the following:

19. $3y^2 - 4$
20. $y^2 + x^2$
21. $4z^2 - 6x^2$
22. $-6x - y^2$
23. $4(x^2 - z)$
24. $y(z^2 + 1)$
25. $x(z - y^2)$
26. $x^2(z - 1)$
27. $yz(x - z)$
28. $z^2(1 + x)$
29. $2y^2(1 + z)$
30. $x^2y^2(z - y)$

EXERCISE 11

Add:

1. $(3a - 4) + (-5a + 1)$
2. $(7x - 3y) + (-4x + 5y)$
3. $(3m^2 - 5) + (-8m^2 + 6)$
4. $(4m^2 - n) + (-3m^2 + 4n) + (2m^2 - 2n)$
5. $(2c^2d + b) + (-3c^2d - 2b) + (c^2d + 3b)$

6. $(y + 3z) + (3y - 2z) + (-5y - 2z)$
7. $(x^2 + 2y^2 - z^2) + (3x^2 - 4z^2) + (-3y^2 + 2z^2)$
8. $(2a^2 - 3b^2 + 3c^2) + (2b^2 - 2c^2) + (-4a^2 + 5c^2)$
9. $(8m + 2n - 3p) + (-4m + 3p) + (m + 5n)$

Subtract:

10. $(7x) - (3x)$
11. $(4a^2) - (-3a^2)$
12. $(3b) - (-b)$
13. $(4y - 3z) - (3y + 8z)$
14. $(2a^2 + b^2) - (a^2 - 3b^2)$
15. $(z^2 - 5y^2) - (-3z^2 + y^2)$
16. $(3c - 5) - (c + 4)$
17. $(m^2 - 3n^2) - (4m^2 - 2n^2)$
18. $(4s - 3t) - (-2s - 5t)$
19. $(3a + 2b - 6c) - (a - 2b + 3c)$
20. $(c^2 - d^2 + 1) - (2c^2 - 4d^2 - 3)$
21. $(9 - 3t + 2s) - (-4 - 2t - s)$
22. Add $3x - y$, $7x + 3y$, and $-2x - 5y$.
23. Add $x^2 - 2y^2 + 3z^2$, $-2x^2 - y^2 + z^2$, and $3x^2 - 2y^2 - 6z^2$.
24. Add $4a - 3b + c$, $-3a + 2b - 6c$, and $-2a - b - c$.
25. Subtract $7a + b - c$ from $-7a - 3b + 6c$.
26. Subtract $c^2 - d^2$ from $a^2 - c^2 - 3d^2$.
27. From $ab + 5$ subtract $3ab - c + 6$.
28. From $x^2 - 2y^2 + z$ subtract $-x^2 + 3y^2 - 5z$.
29. Add $7(a - b)$, $-3(a - b)$, $4(a - b)$, and $-6(a - b)$.
30. Add $-3(x - y + z)$, $-2(x - y + z)$, $4(x - y + z)$, and $(x - y + z)$.
31. Subtract $4(m - n + p)$ from $6(m - n + p)$.
32. From $5(r + s + t)$ subtract $-2(r + s + t)$.
33. From the sum of $a + b$ and $3a - 2b$ subtract the sum of $5a - 3b$ and $-4a + 2b$.
34. Subtract the sum of $x - y$, $3x - y$, and $4x + 3y$ from $8x - 2y$.
35. Subtract $9m + 3n$ from the sum of $4m + 2n$ and $8m - 3n$.

Evaluate the following if $x = 3$, $y = -2$, and $z = 4$:

36. $3x^2$
37. $4x + y$
38. $z - x^2$
39. $y - z$
40. $2z^2 - x$
41. $x^2 + z^2$
42. $4x^2 - 3$
43. $z^2 - 2y$
44. $x^2z - z^2$
45. $4(z - x)$
46. $3(x^2 - 2)$
47. $5(2y - x^2)$
48. $2y - (x - z)$
49. $z(x^2 - z)$
50. $z^2 - x^2 - 2y$

REVIEW TEST 5

Write the numbers 1 to 15 on a sheet of paper and after each number write the word *positive* or *negative* to complete the following statements correctly:

1. If $4a$ and $2a$ are added, the sign of the sum is _____.
2. When $-x^2$ is added to $-3x^2$, the sign of the sum is _____.

3. If $3x^2$ is added to $7x^2$, the sign of the sum is _____.

4. If $3(a - c)$ and $-2(a - c)$ are added, the sign of the coefficient of $(a - c)$ is _____.

5. When $-4x$ is subtracted from $6x$, the sign of the difference is _____.

6. If from $2x^2$ we subtract $7x^2$, the sign of the difference is _____.

7. If $-3ab^2$ is subtracted from $-7ab^2$, the sign of the difference is _____.

8. If $8(x - z)$ is subtracted from $7(x - z)$, the coefficient of the expression $(x - z)$ is a _____ number.

9. If $-3(m + 2n)$ is subtracted from $-2(m + 2n)$, the sign of the difference is _____.

10. If from $9(c - 3d)$ we subtract $3(c - 3d)$, the sign of the coefficient of the expression $(c - 3d)$ is _____.

11. If $a = 1$ in the expression $2a^2$, the answer is a _____ number.

12. If $x = 2$ in the expression $3x - 5$, the answer is a _____ number.

13. If $x = -2$ and $y = 1$ in the expression $x^2 - y$, the answer is a _____ number.

14. If $m = 3$ and $n = 4$ in the expression $m^2 - n^2$, the sign of the answer is _____.

15. If $d = 2$ in the expression $7 - d^2$, the answer is a _____ number.

REVIEW TEST 6

On a sheet of paper write the numbers 1 to 20 to correspond to the statements below. After each number place the letter from the right-hand column that matches the expression in the left-hand column. Some of the answers in the right-hand column do not match any statement in the left-hand column. No letter is to be repeated.

1. The sum of the square of x and y.

2. Three times the sum of m and n.

3. Three times the sum of 1 and m.

4. The difference between y and z if z is greater than y.

5. The sum of $4x^2$ and $-3x^2$.

6. The difference if $-2y$ is subtracted from t.

7. The difference between y and z if y is greater than z.

8. The sum of 8 and a negative $2r$.

9. The difference when $3x^2$ is subtracted from x^2.

a. $\frac{1}{2}(4m - 2p)$
b. $z - y$
c. $2t$
d. $6(x - a)$
e. $8 + 2r$
f. $4(2d - c)$
g. $x^2 + y$
h. $-(1 - x)$
i. $y - z$
j. $-8(s - 4)$
k. $4(c - 2d)$
l. $-8t^2$
m. $t - 2y$
n. $3(m + 1)$
o. $4a - a^3$

10. One-half the sum of $4m$ and $-2p$.

11. Four times the difference between c and $2d$ if d is larger than c.

12. The sum of $r + s + t$ and $-r + s - t$.

13. Five times the square of t subtracted from negative three times the square of t.

14. Two times the cube of m.

15. The difference if $-2t$ is subtracted from $4t$.

16. Four times the difference between c and $2d$ if c is greater than $2d$.

17. The sum of $5(x - a)$ and $-(x - a)$.

18. The difference when $3(1 - x)$ is subtracted from $-4(1 - x)$.

19. Four times the quantity $(s - 4)$ subtracted from negative four times the quantity $(s - 4)$.

20. The cube of a number subtracted from four times the number.

p. $2m^3$
q. $8 - 2r$
r. zero
s. $3(m + n)$
t. $4(x - a)$
u. $-2x^2$
v. $-7(1 - x)$
w. x^2
x. $2s$
y. $6t$
z. $t + 2y$

3

Multiplication and Division

17. MULTIPLICATION AND DIVISION OF SIGNED NUMBERS

Multiplication in algebra, as in arithmetic, implies that a product is to be obtained by taking one of the numbers times the other number. In arithmetic only positive numbers are used but in algebra both positive and negative numbers are used. The number that is to be multiplied by another number is known as the *multiplicand*. The number that the multiplicand is to be multiplied by is called the *multiplier*. These two numbers, the multiplicand and the multiplier, are often referred to as *factors* to be multiplied together. The result, or answer, obtained by multiplying two factors together is the *product* of the two factors.

Multiplication is frequently defined as repeated addition. We know that $3 \cdot 4 = 12$. As repeated addition we may consider this to mean that 4 is used as an addend three times or that 3 is used as an addend four times. Thus

$$3 \cdot 4 = 4 + 4 + 4$$
$$= 12$$

or

$$3 \cdot 4 = 3 + 3 + 3 + 3$$
$$= 12$$

We shall assume that to multiply $(4)(-3)$ by the use of repeated addition means using the -3 as an addend four times. Thus

47

$$(4)(-3) = (-3) + (-3) + (-3) + (-3)$$
$$= -12$$

We *cannot* use the same reasoning to say that $(-3)(4)$ means to use 4 as an addend negative three times. However, by use of the commutative law, $(-3)(4) = (4)(-3)$, and the problem reverts to the previous one.

In a similar manner, $4 \cdot 0 = 0 + 0 + 0 + 0 = 0$ and $0 \cdot 4 = 4 \cdot 0$ by the commutative law. In Chapter 1 we defined the *additive identity* as 0 such that for any real number a, $a + 0 = a$. We may now state the two properties of zero.

For any real number a, $a + 0 = a$ and $a \cdot 0 = 0$.

There remains the case of multiplying together two negative numbers. Before continuing with that concept, let us consider the following sequence of products:

-3	-3	-3	-3	-3	-3
4	3	2	1	0	-1
-12	-9	-6	-3	0	?

Using the example $(-3)(-4)$, the laws of closure, commutativity, and associativity would apply should we define the product to be 12 or -12. The distributive law, as shown in the following example, requires that the product be positive. Consider the example $(-3)[4 + (-4)]$ $= (-3)(0)$. If we apply the distributive law, we get

$$(-3)[4 + (-4)] = (-3)(0)$$
$$(-3)(4) + (-3)(-4) = 0$$

From the previous discussion, $(-3)(4) = -12$, and the above equation becomes

$$-12 + (-3)(-4) = 0$$

and in order for the left member of the equation to equal zero, $(-3)(-4)$ must be equal to a positive 12. This example leads us to believe that the product of two negative numbers is positive.

To ensure that the above reasoning holds true for all real numbers, let us assume that a and b are any positive real numbers. Then

1. $b + (-b) = b + (-b)$ 1. The reflexive relationship from Law 8 (p. 16).

2. $b + (-b) = 0$ 2. The sum of any number and its negative is 0.

3. $a[b + (-b)] = a \cdot 0$ 3. Law 12: If equals are multiplied by equals, the products are equal.

4. $a[b + (-b)] = 0$ 4. The product of any number and zero is 0.

5. $ab + a(-b) = 0$	5. Law 4: The distributive law for multiplication with respect to addition.

From step 5 above we know, from the law of closure for multiplication, that ab (the product of two positive numbers) is a positive number. We have shown in step 5 that the sum of two numbers is equal to zero. For that part to the left of the equals sign to be equal to zero, the product of $a(-b)$ must be the negative number $-ab$. Thus the product of a positive number and a negative number is a negative number.

Again, to ensure that the product of two negative numbers is a positive number for all real numbers, we use the following proof. If a and b are any positive real numbers, then

1. $b + (-b) = b + (-b)$	1. The reflexive relationship from Law 8.
2. $b + (-b) = 0$	2. The sum of any number and its negative is zero.
3. $-a[b + (-b)] = -a \cdot 0$	3. Law 12: If equals are multiplied by equals, the products are equal.
4. $-a[b + (-b)] = 0$	4. The product of any number and zero is 0.
5. $-a(b) + (-a)(-b) = 0$	5. Law 4: The distributive law for multiplication with respect to addition.

In the first proof it was shown that the product of a positive number and a negative number is a negative number. Thus, from Step 5 above, $-a(b) = -ab$.

In order for the expression to the left of the equals sign in step 5 to be equal to zero, the product of $(-a)(-b)$ must be a positive number since the sum of any number and its negative is equal to zero. Thus $(-a)(-b) = +ab$. At the onset we assumed that a and b were positive real numbers. Now it is evident that the product of any two negative numbers is a positive number.

From the above discussion, then, we may state that *the product of any two numbers with like signs is a positive number, and the product of any two numbers with unlike signs is a negative number.*

In general, then, if a and b are signed numbers,

$$(+a)(+b) = +(ab)$$
$$(-a)(-b) = +(ab)$$
$$(+a)(-b) = (-b)(+a) = -(ab)$$
$$(+a)(0) = (0)(+a) = 0$$
$$(-a)(0) = (0)(-a) = 0$$

Example 1. What is the product of 3 and 5?

$$
\begin{array}{ll}
3 & \text{(multiplicand)} \\
\underline{5} & \text{(multiplier)} \\
15 & \text{(product)}
\end{array}
$$

Example 2. What is the product of -3 and -5?

$$
\begin{array}{l}
-3 \\
\underline{-5} \\
15
\end{array}
$$

Example 3. What is the product of -3 and 5?

$$
\begin{array}{l}
-3 \\
\underline{5} \\
-15
\end{array}
$$

Example 4. What is the product of 3 and -5?

$$
\begin{array}{l}
3 \\
\underline{-5} \\
-15
\end{array}
$$

Example 5. What is the value of $(-a)(b)$ if $a = -2$ and $b = -3$?

$$
\begin{aligned}
(-a)(b) &= [-(-2)](-3) \\
&= (2)(-3) \qquad [\text{because } (-a)(b) = -ab] \\
&= -6
\end{aligned}
$$

Example 6. What is the value of $(-a)(-b)$ if $a = -1$ and $b = -2$?

$$
\begin{aligned}
(-a)(-b) &= [-(-1)][-(-2)] \\
&= (1)(2) \\
&= 2
\end{aligned}
$$

Example 7. What is the value of $-(-a)(-b)$ if $a = -3$ and $b = -4$?

$$
\begin{aligned}
-(-a)(-b) &= -[-(a)][-(b)] \\
&= -[-(-3)][-(-4)] \\
&= -[3][4] \\
&= -[12] \\
&= -12
\end{aligned}
$$

In the process of division the number that is being divided is called the *dividend.* The number that is being divided into the dividend is known as the *divisor,* and the result, or answer, is called the *quotient.*

Division may be thought of as the inverse of multiplication. By this we mean that one of two factors that produce a product can be divided into that product and the quotient will be the other factor.

The multiplication problem

$$\begin{array}{r} 8 \\ 3 \\ \hline 24 \end{array}$$

might be phrased: "What is the product when 8 is multiplied by 3?" Considering the same values in a division problem

$$\frac{24}{8} = 3$$

we might say: "If 24 is divided by 8, the quotient is 3." Thinking of this as a multiplication, we might ask: "What number multiplied by 8 results in a product of 24?" Likewise,

$$\frac{24}{-8} = -3$$

since the product obtained by multiplying -8 by -3 is 24. Furthermore,

$$\frac{-24}{8} = -3$$

since the product obtained by multiplying 8 by -3 is -24.

In general, then, if a, b, and x are any real numbers and

$$\frac{a}{b} = x \qquad (b \neq 0)$$

then $x \cdot b = a$. If a and b are positive numbers, then x must be positive since $(b)(x) = a$. If both a and b are positive, then

$$\frac{-a}{-b} = x$$

and x is positive because $(x)(-b) = -a$. In a similar manner, if a and b are positive, then

$$\frac{-a}{b} = -x$$

because $(-x)(b) = -a$, and

$$\frac{a}{-b} = -x$$

because $(-x)(-b) = a$.

We may state, then, that *if both the dividend and the divisor have like signs, the quotient will be a positive number, and if their signs are unlike, the quotient will be a negative number.*

Example 8. What is the quotient when 12 is divided by 3?

$$\frac{12}{3} = 4$$

Example 9. If -12 is divided by -3, what is the quotient?

$$\frac{-12}{-3} = 4$$

Example 10. Divide -12 by 3.

$$\frac{-12}{3} = -4$$

Example 11. Divide 12 by -3.

$$\frac{12}{-3} = -4$$

EXERCISE 12

Multiply:

1. $+7$
   $+3$

2. $+8$
   -4

3. -6
   -5

4. $+11$
   $-\ 9$

5. -12
   $+\ 3$

6. -13
   $-\ 4$

7. $+14$
   $-\ 4$

8. -15
   $-\ 6$

9. $+8$
   $+7$

10. -6
    $+9$

11. $+\ 9$
    -11

12. $+16$
    $+\ 3$

13. -23
    $-\ 4$

14. $-\ 6$
    $+14$

15. $+19$
    $+\ 6$

16. $+18$
    $-\ 8$

17. $+27$
    $+\ 5$

18. -23
    $+\ 8$

19. $+35$
    $-\ 3$

20. -36
    $-\ 8$

Divide:

21. $\dfrac{-6}{+3}$

22. $\dfrac{+12}{-6}$

23. $\dfrac{-18}{-3}$

24. $\dfrac{-24}{+3}$

25. $\dfrac{+14}{+7}$

26. $\dfrac{+28}{-7}$

27. $\dfrac{-32}{-8}$

28. $\dfrac{-36}{+9}$

29. $\dfrac{+35}{-5}$

30. $\dfrac{-48}{-12}$

31. $\dfrac{+39}{-3}$

32. $\dfrac{+56}{+14}$

33. $+60$	34. -96	35. -72	36. $+80$
$\underline{-15}$	$\underline{-16}$	$\underline{+24}$	$\underline{+16}$
37. $+76$	38. -108	39. $+112$	40. -121
$\underline{-19}$	$\underline{-3}$	$\underline{-7}$	$\underline{+11}$

18. MULTIPLICATION AND DIVISION OF MONOMIALS

In a previous discussion it was stated that x^2 means that x is used as a factor two times. Likewise, x^4 means that x is used as a factor four times. Thus, if we multiply x^2 by x^4, we would have

$$\begin{aligned} x^2 \cdot x^4 &= (x \cdot x)(x \cdot x \cdot x \cdot x) \\ &= x \cdot x \cdot x \cdot x \cdot x \cdot x \\ &= x^6 \end{aligned}$$

Hence, when literal factors of the same letter or identical numerical factors are multiplied, the exponents are added. The above example might be written

$$\begin{aligned} x^2 \cdot x^4 &= x^{2+4} \\ &= x^6 \end{aligned}$$

Also,

$$\begin{aligned} 3^2 \cdot 3^3 &= 3^{2+3} \\ &= 3^5 \end{aligned}$$

In the first example x is called the *base*, as is the 3 in the second example. If no exponent is shown, it is assumed to be 1. The addition of exponents should be done mentally.

In a later chapter we shall discuss exponents much more extensively. However, our first basic law concerning exponents is as follows:

Law 1. *If a is any real number and both m and n are positive integers, then*

$$a^m \cdot a^n = a^{m+n}$$

To multiply two or more monomials, we make use of the commutative law for multiplication. Consider the following problem: Multiply $2x^2yz$ by $6xz^2$.

$$\begin{aligned} (2x^2yz)(6xz^2) &= 2 \cdot x^2 \cdot y \cdot z \cdot 6 \cdot x \cdot z^2 \\ &= 2 \cdot 6 \cdot x^2 \cdot x \cdot y \cdot z \cdot z^2 \\ &= 12x^3yz^3 \end{aligned}$$

The application of the commutative law can be done mentally and the following instructions followed. To multiply two or more monomials, first multiply the numerical coefficients of the monomials to obtain the numerical coefficient of the product. To determine each literal factor of the product, add the exponents of similar letters and use that power of the letter as a literal factor in the product. If a certain letter appears in only one of the factors, it will appear as a factor in the product in the same form as it was given in the original factor. Since each monomial represents a number, our laws that apply to signed numbers must be followed to determine if the product is a positive number or a negative number.

Example 1. Multiply m^3 by m^2.

$$m^3 \cdot m^2 = m^5$$

Example 2. Multiply $2b$ by $3b^3$.

$$2b \cdot 3b^3 = 6b^4$$

Example 3. Multiply $-5a$ by $3a^4$.

$$-5a \cdot 3a^4 = -15a^5$$

Example 4. Multiply $-4n^2$ by $-2n^5$.

$$-4n^2 \cdot -2n^5 = 8n^7$$

Example 5. Multiply $-3ab^2$ by a^2b.

$$-3ab^2 \cdot a^2b = -3a^3b^3$$

Example 6. Multiply $-4r^2a$ by $-3ra^2$.

$$-4r^2a \cdot -3ra^2 = 12r^3a^3$$

Division by zero is never permitted. Consider the following: If

$$\frac{x}{0} = \text{some number}$$

then that number times zero would equal x. This, of course, is not true because any number times zero is 0. Thus we cannot divide by zero. The value of any fraction whose denominator is zero or equal to zero is said to be *undefined*.

There is the case of $0/0$, called an *indeterminate form*, which one encounters in a considerably more advanced course in mathematics. In this discussion we shall not be concerned with the indeterminate form.

If zero is our dividend and the divisor is any real number except zero, the quotient is 0. Observe the following in which x and y are any real numbers except $x \neq 0$. If

$$\frac{0}{x} = y$$

then $y \cdot x = 0$.

In order for $y \cdot x$ to equal zero, either y or x must be zero. We previously stated that $x \neq 0$, and hence $y = 0$. Then zero divided by any real number except zero gives us a quotient of zero.

In arithmetic a fraction is simplified by dividing both the numerator and denominator by the same value.

Example 7. Simplify the fraction $\frac{12}{3}$.

$$\frac{12}{3} = \frac{4}{1}$$
$$= 4$$

This simplification is accomplished by dividing both the numerator and denominator by 3. By use of the commutative law for multiplication and the fact that any number divided by itself is equal to 1, we could solve the same problem as follows (observe that the numerator is factored; when possible, factor both the numerator and denominator):

$$\frac{12}{3} = \frac{(4)(3)}{3}$$
$$= \frac{(3)(4)}{3}$$
$$= \frac{3}{3} \cdot 4$$
$$= 1 \cdot 4$$
$$= 4$$

The same principle applies to algebraic expressions. Hence if we wish to divide x^4 by x^2, we have

$$\frac{x^4}{x^2} = \frac{x \cdot x \cdot x \cdot x}{x \cdot x}$$
$$= \frac{x}{x} \cdot \frac{x}{x} \cdot x \cdot x$$
$$= 1 \cdot 1 \cdot x \cdot x$$
$$= x^2$$

Since division is the inverse of multiplication, the exponent of a letter in the quotient is the difference of the exponents of a given letter found in the dividend and divisor.

The above problem could have been written

$$\frac{x^4}{x^2} = x^{4-2}$$
$$= x^2$$

Consider the following problem:

$$\frac{x^2}{x^4} = \frac{\overset{1}{x} \cdot \overset{1}{x}}{x \cdot x \cdot x \cdot x}$$

$$= \frac{1}{x^2}$$

This problem could very well have been written

$$\frac{x^2}{x^4} = \frac{1}{x^{4-2}}$$

$$= \frac{1}{x^2}$$

These two examples lead to the second of the laws of exponents with which we shall be concerned in this chapter.

Law 2. *If a is any real number and both m and n are positive integers, then*

$$\frac{a^m}{a^n} = a^{m-n} \qquad (if\ m > n\ and\ a \neq 0)$$

$$\frac{a^m}{a^n} = \frac{1}{a^{n-m}} \qquad (if\ n > m\ and\ a \neq 0)$$

Example 8. Divide $9x^5$ by $3x^2$.

$$\frac{9x^5}{3x^2} = 3x^3$$

Example 9. Divide $-12c^3d^4$ by $-3cd$.

$$\frac{-12c^3d^4}{-3cd} = 4c^2d^3$$

Example 10. Divide $-10x^2y^5$ by $-5x^4y^2$.

$$\frac{-10x^2y^5}{-5x^4y^2} = \frac{2y^3}{x^2}$$

Example 11. Divide $3ab^4$ by $12a^3b$.

$$\frac{3ab^4}{12a^3b} = \frac{b^3}{4a^2}$$

EXERCISE 13

A

Multiply:

1. $x^2 \cdot x^3$
2. $x \cdot x^4$
3. $a^5 \cdot a^2$
4. $b \cdot b^3$
5. $d^6 \cdot d^3$
6. $m \cdot m^5$
7. $r^2 \cdot r^5$
8. $y^8 \cdot y^3$
9. $3^2 \cdot 3^3$
10. $2^4 \cdot 2$
11. $4^2 \cdot 4^3$
12. $7^3 \cdot 7^5$
13. $b \cdot b \cdot b$
14. $z^2 \cdot z \cdot z$
15. $w^2 \cdot w^2 \cdot w$
16. $b^4 \cdot b^3$
17. $-x \cdot x^2$
18. $a^2 \cdot -a^3$
19. $5m \cdot m$
20. $-3y \cdot y^5$
21. $2b \cdot 4b$
22. $-3d \cdot -4d^2$
23. $-2a \cdot 3a^4$
24. $6c \cdot 4c$
25. $xy \cdot x^2y^2$
26. $s^2t \cdot st^2$
27. $3w \cdot 2r^2$
28. $-5r \cdot -rt$
29. $ab^2 \cdot a^2b^2$
30. $3bc \cdot b^2c^3$

Divide:

31. y^5 by y^2
32. b^7 by b^4
33. r^8 by r^5
34. z^5 by z
35. s^6 by s^4
36. b^9 by b^7
37. $8b^2$ by $2b$
38. $-9a^2b$ by $3a$
39. $12x^3y^2$ by $-6xy$
40. $-16n^4$ by $-4n$
41. $14z^5$ by $-7z^2$
42. $24a^2b^3$ by $6ab$
43. $18s^2t^6$ by $-9st^5$
44. $-36x^3y^2z^2$ by $12xy$
45. $30r^3s^3t^2$ by $-6rs$
46. $16m^4n^5$ by $-8mn^2$
47. $-12c^2d^4$ by $-4cd^3$
48. $6xy^3z^4$ by $2xz$
49. $-15a^5b^6c$ by $5a^2b^2$
50. $5cd^2x^2$ by dx
51. $12a^2$ by $3a^2$
52. $-16m$ by $-4m^3$
53. $-18r^2s^4$ by $6r^5s^2$
54. $5a^3$ by $15a$
55. $-9ab^3$ by $3a^2$
56. $24x^6y$ by $-8xy^2$
57. $-18z^4m$ by $6z^3m^2$
58. x^2y^2 by $9x$
59. $15m^3n^6$ by $-3m^4n^2$
60. $30a^2bc^2$ by $6ab^2$

B

Multiply:

1. $rst \cdot r^2st$
2. $-m^2n^4 \cdot 3mn^3$
3. $(-3x)(-5x^2)$
4. $(4p)(-2p^2)$
5. $(8m^2n)(-5mn^5)$
6. $(2abc)(-4ab^2c)$
7. $(-6x^3)(-3x)$
8. $(-ab^2)(-a^2b)$
9. $(5cd^4)(2c^3d^3)$
10. $(-3x^2y)(2x^2y^3)$
11. $(8z)(3xz)$
12. $(abc)(abc)$
13. $(x^2yz)(-xyz^3)$
14. $(-3abx)(-2bx)$
15. $(7mnp)(-3mp^2)$
16. $(9c^2dx)(2dx)$
17. $(-4abd)(-2a^2bd^3)$
18. $(3ab)(2a^2b)(a^2b^2)$
19. $(-xy^2)(-x^2y)(-xy)$
20. $(-3st^2)(2s^2t^3)(-2s^2t)$

Divide:

21. $-3m^2np^2$ by $-mp$
22. $28rst^4$ by $7t^3$
23. $-27w^3z^2$ by $-3wz$
24. $20cdx$ by -5
25. $-18x^9y^6$ by $-6x^5y$
26. $21r^2x^5$ by $7rx^4$
27. $-15a^4b^5$ by $-5ab^4$
28. $12cx^2y^3$ by $3xy^2$
29. $-8b^3y^5$ by $-2by^3$

30. $24xyz^3$ by $-8z^2$ 31. r^3s^5 by $3r^4s$ 32. $-p^3q^5$ by $6p^5q^3$
33. $-36x^4y^4z$ by $-9xyz^2$ 34. $8c^3d$ by $16cd^3$ 35. w^3x^2 by $-4wx^5$

19. MULTIPLICATION OF A MULTINOMIAL BY A MULTINOMIAL

The multiplication of one multinomial by a second multinomial involves the distributive law. If we wish to multiply $3x + 2$ by $2x - 5$, we may write this problem as $(2x - 5)(3x + 2)$. Then, by the distributive law, we have

$$(2x - 5)(3x + 2) = 2x(3x + 2) - 5(3x + 2)$$
$$= 6x^2 + 4x - 15x - 10$$
$$= 6x^2 - 11x - 10$$

Example 1. Multiply $(x + y)$ by $(x + y)$.

$$(x + y)(x + y) = x(x + y) + y(x + y)$$
$$= x^2 + xy + xy + y^2$$
$$= x^2 + 2xy + y^2$$

Example 2. Multiply $(4a + 2b)$ by $(a - b)$.

$$(4a + 2b)(a - b) = 4a(a - b) + 2b(a - b)$$
$$= 4a^2 - 4ab + 2ab - 2b^2$$
$$= 4a^2 - 2ab - 2b^2$$

Example 3. Multiply $(a^3 - 2a^2b + ab^2)$ by $(a - b)$.

$$(a - b)(a^3 - 2a^2b + ab^2) = a(a^3 - 2a^2b + ab^2) - b(a^3 - 2a^2b + ab^2$$
$$= (a^4 - 2a^3b + a^2b^2) - (a^3b - 2a^2b^2 + ab^3)$$
$$= (a^4 - 2a^3b + a^2b^2) + (-a^3b + 2a^2b^2 - ab^3)$$
$$= a^4 - 2a^3b + a^2b^2 - a^3b + 2a^2b^2 - ab^3$$
$$= a^4 - 2a^3b - a^3b + a^2b^2 + 2a^2b^2 - ab^3$$
$$= a^4 - 3a^3b + 3a^2b^2 - ab^3$$

Multiplication of one multinomial by another multinomial may be done vertically as shown in the following example.

Example 4. Multiply $3a + 2b$ by $2a - 5b$.

$$
\begin{array}{r}
3a + 2b \\
2a - 5b \\
\hline
6a^2 + 4ab \\
-15ab - 10b^2 \\
\hline
6a^2 - 11ab - 10b^2
\end{array}
$$

This method also makes use of the distributive law since we have multiplied each term in the multiplicand by each term in the multiplier. In other words, we have distributed the multiplier over each of the addends in the multiplicand. Finally, we added algebraically those terms that were similar.

Example 5.   Multiply $3x^2 + x + 1$ by $2x + 1$.

$$
\begin{array}{r}
3x^2 + x + 1 \\
2x + 1 \\
\hline
6x^3 + 2x^2 + 2x \\
3x^2 + x + 1 \\
\hline
6x^3 + 5x^2 + 3x + 1
\end{array}
$$

It can be observed in Examples 4 and 5 that each time a term in the multiplicand was multiplied by a term in the multiplier, the terms were arranged in columns consisting of similar terms. It is then much simpler to find the algebraic sum of the similar terms. The terms in both the multiplicand and multiplier should be arranged in either descending or ascending powers of the same variable before the multiplication is attempted. In the expression $x^3 + x^2 + x + 1$, the terms are in descending order with respect to the powers of x. That means that the term with the largest exponent is in first place and the exponent of each succeeding term is smaller than the one in the preceding term. If the expression were reversed, it would read: $1 + x + x^2 + x^3$. In this order it is said to be in ascending powers of the variable x.

Example 6.   Arrange the terms in the expression $x^5 - x^2 + 3x^3 - x^4$ in descending order of the exponents.

$$x^5 - x^2 + 3x^3 - x^4 = x^5 - x^4 + 3x^3 - x^2$$

Example 7.   Arrange the terms in Example 6 in ascending order of the powers of x.

$$x^5 - x^2 + 3x^3 - x^4 = -x^2 + 3x^3 - x^4 + x^5$$

Example 8.   Arrange the terms in the expression $a^2 + b^2 + 2ab$ in descending powers of a.

$$a^2 + b^2 + 2ab = a^2 + 2ab + b^2$$

In the answer to Example 8 the expression is also arranged in ascending powers of b.

If both the multiplicand and multiplier are arranged in either descending or ascending order of the same letter, the multiplication is more easily accomplished. The reason why this is true is that the similar terms have a tendency to fall into the same column. Otherwise one would have to look for the correct column into which each part of the product was to be placed.

A

Rearrange the terms in the following problems in descending order of the unknown. If more than one unknown appears in the problem, place the terms in descending order of the letter that comes first in the alphabet.

1. $7x - x^3 - 3 + x^4 - 3x^2$
2. $4a - 2 + 3a^2 + 2a^4$
3. $3 - 4m^2 + m^4 - 2m^3$
4. $x^4 - 3 + 7x - 7x^3 + x^2$
5. $3ab - b^2 + a^2$
6. $c^3 - 3cd + d^2 - 5c^2$
7. $b^3 + x^3 + 3b^2x + 3bx^2$
8. $9 - x^2 - x^3 + x^4 - 3x$
9. $5xy^4 + 10x^3y^2 + x^5 - y^5 - 5x^4y - 10x^2y^3$
10. $6m^2n^2 + 4m^3n + 4mn^3 + m^4 + n^4$

Multiply:

11. $a - b$ by $a - b$
12. $c + d$ by $c + d$
13. $s + 2t$ by $s + 2t$
14. $2w - x$ by $3w - x$
15. $a - 2$ by $a + 3$
16. $6x - y$ by $x + 3y$
17. $t - s$ by $t + s$
18. $a + 5b$ by $a - 5b$
19. $7u - 1$ by $3u + 4$
20. $-4c - d$ by $-2c + 3d$
21. $5n - 2$ by $-3n + 7$
22. $8p + q$ by $2p + 3q$
23. $4s - w$ by $-2s + w$
24. $x - y$ by $3y + x$
25. $t^2 + 3$ by $t - 1$
26. $4x^2 + x$ by $x + 2$
27. $t^3 + 5$ by $t - 1$
28. $a^4 - b^4$ by $a + b$
29. $y + 2z^2$ by $z - y$
30. $9w^2 + w$ by $4 + w^2$
31. $c - 3d + e^2$ by $d - e$
32. $w^2 - x + 3$ by $w + x$
33. $3a^2 + b^2 + c^2$ by $2a - 3b$
34. $x + y - 1$ by $x - 3$
35. $x^2y^2 + xy + z$ by $x + 3y$
36. $x^2 + 2xy + y^2$ by $x + y$
37. $a + b + c + d$ by $a + b$
38. $x^3 + x^2 + 3x - 2$ by $x - 5$
39. $ab + bc - cd - 2$ by $a + b$
40. $x + 2y - 3z - 1$ by $-2z - 3$

B

Multiply:

1. $m^3 + 3m^2 - 4m + 1$ by $2m - 3$
2. $2w^3 - 5w^2 + 3w - 5$ by $-w + 4$
3. $r^3 + 2r^2s - 3rs^2 + 2s^3$ by $r - s$

4. $d^3 + d^3c + d^2c^2 + dc^3$ by $2d - c$
5. $3b^2 + 2bx + 3by + bz$ by $b + 3z$
6. $ax + by + cz - 2$ by $a + 1$
7. $x^2 + 2x + 1$ by $x^2 + 2x + 1$
8. $a + b + c$ by $a + b + c$
9. $m^2 - 2mn + n^2$ by $m - n - 2$
10. $2x^2 - x - 1$ by $x^2 + x + 1$
11. $s^4 + s^3 + 2s^2 - s$ by $3s + 2$
12. $a^2 + 2ab + b^2$ by $a + b - 1$
13. $x^2 + 5x + 6$ by $x^2 + 3x + 2$
14. $p^3 + p^2 - p - 6$ by $p^2 - p - 1$
15. $x^2y^2 + 2xyz + z^2$ by $xy + z$
16. $y^2 - 7y + 12$ by $y^2 - 5y + 6$

20. THE COEFFICIENT OF GROUPED EXPRESSIONS

No coefficient has been shown with any of the grouping symbols previously used. In all such cases it was understood that the coefficient was 1. Many times a coefficient other than 1 is used, as, for example, when we introduced the distributive law with respect to addition. By that law the expression $2(x - y)$ becomes $2x - 2y$. In the expression $m - 3[a - 2b]$ we convert the subtraction problem to one of addition by the usual method; thus the expression becomes $m + [6b - 3a]$ and removal of the brackets gives us $m + 6b - 3a$.

Example 1. Simplify $4 + 3(x - y) - x - 2(y - x)$.

$$
\begin{aligned}
4 + 3(x - y) - x - 2(y - x) &= 4 + 3(x - y) - x + 2(x - y) \\
&= 4 + 3x - 3y - x + 2x - 2y \\
&= 3x + 2x - x - 3y - 2y + 4 \\
&= (3 + 2 - 1)x + (-3 - 2)y + 4 \\
&= 4x + (-5)y + 4 \\
&= 4x - 5y + 4
\end{aligned}
$$

Example 2. Simplify $m - [m + 2n] - n + 5[m - 2n]$.

$$
\begin{aligned}
m - [m + 2n] - n + 5[m - 2n] &= m + [-m - 2n] - n + 5m - 10n \\
&= m - m - 2n - n + 5m - 10n \\
&= m - m + 5m - 2n - n - 10n \\
&= [1 - 1 + 5]m + [-2 - 1 - 10]n \\
&= [5]m + [-13]n \\
&= 5m - 13n
\end{aligned}
$$

Example 3. Simplify $3\{-2[a - 3b - 1] + 3[2a + 4b - 6]\} - 3$.

$3\{-2[a - 3b - 1] + 3[2a + 4b - 6]\} - 3$
$$= 3\{+2[3b - a + 1] + 3[2a + 4b - 6]\} - 3$$
$$= 3\{6b - 2a + 2 + 6a + 12b - 18\} - 3$$
$$= 18b - 6a + 6 + 18a + 36b - 54 - 3$$
$$= (18a - 6a) + (36b + 18b) + (6 - 54 - 3)$$
$$= (18 - 6)a + (36 + 18)b + (-51)$$
$$= 12a + 54b - 51$$

Example 4. Simplify $7 + \{-p - 2(q + 3[p - q] + 4p) - 2q\}$.

$7 + \{-p - 2(q + 3[p - q] + 4p) - 2q\}$
$$= 7 + \{-p - 2(q + 3p - 3q + 4p) - 2q\}$$
$$= 7 + \{-p + 2(-q - 3p + 3q - 4p) - 2q\}$$
$$= 7 + \{-p - 2q - 6p + 6q - 8p - 2q\}$$
$$= 7 - p - 2q - 6p + 6q - 8p - 2q$$
$$= 7 - p - 6p - 8p + 6q - 2q - 2q$$
$$= 7 + (-1 - 6 - 8)p + (6 - 2 - 2)q$$
$$= 7 + (-15)p + (2)q$$
$$= 7 - 15p + 2q$$

Example 5. Simplify $x[3 - 2(x - y) + 4y]$.

$x[3 - 2(x - y) + 4y] = x[3 + 2(y - x) + 4y]$
$$= x[3 + 2y - 2x + 4y]$$
$$= 3x + 2xy - 2x^2 + 4xy$$
$$= 3x + 6xy - 2x^2$$

21. EVALUATION OF EXPRESSIONS CONTAINING GROUPING SYMBOLS

Solving for the numerical value of algebraic expressions containing grouping symbols is illustrated in the following examples:

Example 1. If $a = 2$, $b = 1$, and $c = 4$, evaluate the expression $a - (b - c) + 2a + b$.

$a - (b - c) + 2a + b = a + (c - b) + 2a + b$
$$= a + c - b + 2a + b$$
$$= 3a + c$$

Now substitute the given values in the expression $3a + c$.

$$3a + c = 3(2) + 4$$
$$= 6 + 4$$
$$= 10$$

The problem could also be solved by substituting the values before the algebraic form is simplified.

$$\begin{aligned} a - (b - c) + 2a + b &= 2 - (1 - 4) + 2(2) + 1 \\ &= 2 + (4 - 1) + 4 + 1 \\ &= 2 + 3 + 4 + 1 \\ &= 10 \end{aligned}$$

Example 2. Find the value of $x^2 - (x - 3) + (y - x)$ if $x = 2$ and $y = -2$.

$$\begin{aligned} x^2 - (x - 3) + (y - x) &= x^2 + (3 - x) + (y - x) \\ &= x^2 + 3 - x + y - x \\ &= x^2 - 2x + y + 3 \\ &= (2)^2 - 2(2) + (-2) + 3 \\ &= 4 - 4 - 2 + 3 \\ &= 1 \end{aligned}$$

22. INSERTING GROUPING SYMBOLS

As we progress in the study of algebra, it is often necessary or convenient to combine certain terms into a unit and enclose that unit within one of the usual forms of symbols used for grouping. If the unit is in a form that can be used as it appears, the symbols used for grouping must have a positive sign placed before them. If the unit, to be dealt with properly, needs all of the signs reversed, a negative sign must precede the grouping symbols.

Example 1. In the expression $x^2 + x + 1$ enclose within parentheses the $x + 1$ and precede the symbols with a positive sign.

$$x^2 + x + 1 = x^2 + (x + 1)$$

Example 2. In the expression $4 - x^2 + x + a - b$ enclose the $a - b$ within parentheses that are preceded by a negative sign.

$$4 - x^2 + x + a - b = 4 - x^2 + x - (-a + b)$$

Since the order in which terms are placed may be changed by use of the commutative law for addition, the above expression may be written as

$$4 - x^2 + x - (b - a)$$

Example 3. Indicate by use of parentheses that the sum of x and y is to be subtracted from twice the sum of a and b.

Twice the sum of a and b would be written $2(a + b)$ and the sum of

x and y would be written $(x + y)$. Then, by following the instructions in the problem, we would have

$$2(a + b) - (x + y)$$

Example 4. Indicate by use of parentheses that the remainder when n is subtracted from m is to be added to the sum of c and d.

$$(m - n) + (c + d)$$

Example 5. Indicate by use of parentheses that twice the sum of $2a$ and $3b$ is to be subtracted from four times the difference obtained when a is subtracted from $2b$.

$$4(2b - a) - 2(2a + 3b)$$

EXERCISE 15

A

Simplify:

1. $4a - 2(a + 3b) - (3 + 2a)$
2. $\{x - 3(y - 2x) + 7y - 2(2y + 3)\} - y$
3. $c - d - 6[-2c - (c + d)] + 4c$
4. $2\{r - s + t - 3(-r + 2s + 3t) - 5s\}$
5. $2z + \{y - 3z - (y - z - [z + 3y] - 2y)\}$
6. $m + [n - 3 - 4m + \{3m - (-n - 1) + 2n\} - 3m]$
7. $a^2 - [a + 3b - (2a^2 + b) - 4b]$
8. $x - 2y + [3x - 6y - (4x - 2y)]$
9. $y - x - y - [x^2 + x - (y + 2x)]$
10. $[m^2 + n^2] - [2m - n^2 - 2(m^2 - 2n^2)]$
11. $-(4a + 3b) - (b - 2[7a - 5b] - a)$
12. $c^2 - 4[c + 3d - (c^2 - c - d)]$
13. $-3[-x - 4 - x(x - 5)] + 3x$
14. $-[s - t - s(s - 4) - 2t]$
15. $a[a - 3b - 2(b - 4a) + 3b]$

Evaluate the following if $x = 3$, $y = 1$, $a = 2$, and $b = -1$:

16. $-[x - y^2] - [y - x^2]$
17. $3[x - (y + 3) - y - x]$
18. $a^2 - 3[b^2 - b - (a^2 - a - b) + 4]$
19. $x - (b - a[a - 1] + x^2 - 2)$
20. $-[-(x + y) - 3(x - 1)]$
21. $3a^2 - b^2 - (1 - b + a) - 6$

22. $x^2 - [2(x - y) - (y^2 - x^2)]$
23. $3x - 2y(y - 1) + x(2x - 6)$
24. $(a^2 + b^2) - (x^2 - y^2)$
25. $7y - 3(xy - 6) + 2x^2$

In Exercises 26 through 37 enclose all terms containing x and y within parentheses preceded by a positive sign and those containing m and n within parentheses preceded by a negative sign.

26. $x - y - m + n$
27. $y - 2x + m - n$
28. $4x - m - 3y + n$
29. $x^2 - 2xy + y^2 - m^2 - 2m + n^2$
30. $x^2 - y^2 + n - m$
31. $7n - m^2 - y^2 + 2x^2$
32. $-2xy + y^2 + x^2 - n^2 - 7mn - 12m^2$
33. $n - y - mn - m + x$
34. $x^2y^2 - y^2 + m^2n^2 - m^2$
35. $y + 3n - m - 3x$
36. $y^2 - 5xy + 6x^2 - m^2 - 5mn - 6n^2$
37. $x^2 - 4mn - xy + 12y^2 - m^2 + 21n^2$

B

1. By use of parentheses show that the sum of a and b^2 is subtracted from c^2.
2. Indicate by use of parentheses that the difference obtained by subtracting 3 from $2a$ is to be added to the sum of $2x$ and $3y$.
3. What is the result of subtracting the sum of $3p$ and q from the sum of r and $3s$?
4. Show that $3n$ is subtracted from $2m$ and that the difference is subtracted from the sum of $2w$ and z.
5. Indicate that the sum of $2b$ and $5d$ is subtracted from the remainder when $3y$ is subtracted from $4z$.
6. Indicate that the sum of a, b, and c is added to the difference obtained when $4m$ is subtracted from $3p$.
7. If two angles of a triangle are $2x°$ and $y°$, what represents the third angle? (*Hint:* The sum of the three angles of any triangle is 180°.)
8. If the first angle of a triangle is $x°$ and the second one is twice the first one, what represents the third angle of the triangle?
9. A young man bought two shirts at x dollars each and three ties at y dollars each. If he presented the clerk with a twenty-dollar bill in payment for the merchandise, illustrate by the use of grouping symbols the change he received.

10. A merchant offered a boxed Thanksgiving dinner consisting of one turkey, eight potatoes, four individual pumpkin pies, one can of cranberry sauce, two cans of creamed corn, two heads of lettuce, and four fresh tomatoes. He originally boxed 50 such packages and on Thanksgiving eve found that 8 packages remained. If we designate each turkey by the letter t, each potato by p, each pie by m, each can of cranberry sauce by c, each can of corn by f, each head of lettuce by d, and each tomato by x, indicate by the use of grouping symbols an algebraic expression that represents the merchandise sold in the boxes.

23. DIVIDING A MULTINOMIAL BY A MULTINOMIAL

When dividing a multinomial by a multinomial, the problem is set up as a long division problem in arithmetic. In order to get the solution to work out easily and conveniently, both the dividend and divisor must be arranged in either descending or ascending order of the powers of the same variable.

The process of long division can best be explained by the steps completed in the following example:

Example 1.   Divide $x^2 - 5x + 6$ by $x - 3$.

$$x - 3 \,\big|\, x^2 - 5x + 6$$

Divide the first term in the dividend by the first term in the divisor and place the result above the division symbol as is done in arithmetic. When x^2 is divided by x, we get x.

$$\begin{array}{r} x \phantom{{}-5x+6} \\ x - 3 \,\big|\, \overline{x^2 - 5x + 6} \end{array}$$

The next step requires that the term in the quotient (the x) be used as a multiplier for each term in the divisor. The result of that multiplication is placed under the dividend and subtracted from the dividend. Be sure to keep similar terms in each column. Remember that when subtracting the signs of all terms in the subtrahend are changed. After the subtraction has been done, bring down the next term in the dividend.

$$\begin{array}{r} x \phantom{{}- 5x + 6} \\ x - 3 \,\big|\, \overline{x^2 - 5x + 6} \\ \underline{x^2 - 3x \phantom{{}+ 6}} \\ -2x + 6 \end{array}$$

The next step requires that the remainder ($-2x + 6$) be treated as a new dividend. The $-2x$ is divided by the first term in the divisor and that part of the quotient is found to be -2. Place the -2 in the second place (it is the second term) in the quotient. Then use the -2 as a multiplier and multiply each term in the divisor by the -2 and place that product under the new dividend and subtract.

$$
\begin{array}{r}
x - 2 \\
x - 3 \overline{\smash{\big)}\ x^2 - 5x + 6} \\
\underline{x^2 - 3x} \\
-2x + 6 \\
\underline{-2x + 6}
\end{array}
$$

Hence $x - 2$ is the quotient. Since there was nothing left after the second subtraction, there is no remainder.

Division may be checked in the same manner as in arithmetic. If the product of the divisor and quotient is equal to the dividend, the solution is correct.

Check:
$$
\begin{aligned}
(x - 3)(x - 2) &= x(x - 2) - 3(x - 2) \\
&= x(x - 2) + 3(2 - x) \\
&= x^2 - 2x + 6 - 3x \\
&= x^2 - 2x - 3x + 6 \\
&= x^2 + (-2 - 3)x + 6 \\
&= x^2 - 5x + 6
\end{aligned}
$$

Example 2. Divide $a^2 + 7a + 15$ by $a + 3$.

$$
\begin{array}{r}
a + 4 \\
a + 3 \overline{\smash{\big)}\ a^2 + 7a + 15} \\
\underline{a^2 + 3a} \\
4a + 15 \\
\underline{4a + 12} \\
3
\end{array}
$$

The quotient to this problem is $a + 4$ with a remainder of 3. As in arithmetic, the remainder may be placed over the divisor to make a fraction. In this case the quotient is $a + 4 + \dfrac{3}{a + 3}$.

When checking a division problem in which a remainder appears, again we do as is done in arithmetic. To the product of the quotient and divisor add the remainder. The sum of the product (of the divisor and the quotient) and the remainder should equal the dividend.

Check:
$$
\begin{aligned}
(a + 3)(a + 4) + 3 &= a(a + 4) + 3(a + 4) + 3 \\
&= a^2 + 4a + 3a + 12 + 3 \\
&= a^2 + (4 + 3)a + 15 \\
&= a^2 + 7a + 15
\end{aligned}
$$

Example 3. Divide $6x^2 + x - 2$ by $2x - 1$.

$$
\begin{array}{r}
3x + 2 \\
2x - 1 \overline{\smash{\big)}\ 6x^2 + x - 2} \\
\underline{6x^2 - 3x} \\
4x - 2 \\
\underline{4x - 2}
\end{array}
$$

Check:
$$
\begin{aligned}
(3x + 2)(2x - 1) &= 3x(2x - 1) + 2(2x - 1) \\
&= 6x^2 - 3x + 4x - 2 \\
&= 6x^2 + 4x - 3x - 2 \\
&= 6x^2 + (4 - 3)x - 2 \\
&= 6x^2 + x - 2
\end{aligned}
$$

Example 4. Divide $2a^2 - 5a^3 - 1 + 6a^4$ by $1 + 2a^2 - a$.

Rearrange both the dividend and divisor so that both are in descending powers of a. The problem then reads: Divide $6a^4 - 5a^3 + 2a^2 - 1$ by $2a^2 - a + 1$. (*Hint:* It can be observed that there is no a term in the dividend. Leave a space for such a term.)

$$
\begin{array}{r}
3a^2 - a - 1 \\
2a^2 - a + 1 \overline{\smash{\big)}\ 6a^4 - 5a^3 + 2a^2 - 1} \\
\underline{6a^4 - 3a^3 + 3a^2} \\
- 2a^3 - a^2 \\
\underline{- 2a^3 + a^2 - a} \\
- 2a^2 + a - 1 \\
\underline{- 2a^2 + a - 1}
\end{array}
$$

Check:
$$
\begin{aligned}
(2a^2 &- a + 1)(3a^2 - a - 1) \\
&= 2a^2(3a^2 - a - 1) - a(3a^2 - a - 1) + 1(3a^2 - a - 1) \\
&= 2a^2(3a^2 - a - 1) + a(1 + a - 3a^2) + (3a^2 - a - 1) \\
&= 6a^4 - 2a^3 - 2a^2 + a + a^2 - 3a^3 + 3a^2 - a - 1 \\
&= 6a^4 + (-2a^3 - 3a^3) + (3a^2 - 2a^2 + a^2) + (a - a) - 1 \\
&= 6a^4 - 5a^3 + 2a^2 - 1
\end{aligned}
$$

EXERCISE 16

A

Divide:

1. $x^2 + 8x + 12$ by $x + 2$
2. $a^2 + 8a + 15$ by $a + 5$
3. $y^2 - 2y - 15$ by $y - 5$
4. $m^2 - 10m + 24$ by $m - 4$

5. $b^2 + 12b + 27$ by $b + 3$

6. $x^2 - 6x + 9$ by $x - 3$

7. $x^2 + 12x + 32$ by $x + 4$

8. $c^2 - c - 42$ by $c - 7$

9. $r^2 - r - 12$ by $r + 3$

10. $y^2 - 7y - 18$ by $y + 2$

11. $2m^2 + 3m - 2$ by $m + 2$

12. $3y^2 + 7y - 6$ by $3y - 2$

13. $8s^2 - 6s - 5$ by $2s + 1$

14. $6z^2 - 17z - 3$ by $z - 3$

15. $6t^2 + 13t + 6$ by $2t + 3$

16. $20b^2 - 3b - 2$ by $5b - 2$

17. $8a^2 + 2a - 15$ by $2a + 3$

18. $4n^2 + 3nm - m^2$ by $n + m$

19. $5a^2 + 9ab - 2b^2$ by $a + 2b$

20. $3p^2 - 5pt - 2t^2$ by $p - 2t$

21. $3r^2 - 5rs + 2s^2$ by $r - s$

22. $6y^2 - 11y - 9$ by $2y + 1$

23. $4x^2 - 21x + 2$ by $x - 6$

24. $7y^2 + 32y - 17$ by $y + 5$

25. $8m^2 + 10m - 4$ by $2m + 3$

26. $a^3 - b^3$ by $a - b$

27. $8a^3 + 1$ by $2a + 1$

28. $27x^3 - 1$ by $3x - 1$

29. $64y^3 + 8b^3$ by $4y + 2b$

30. $125 - 27z^3$ by $5 - 3z$

B

Divide:

1. $x^4 + 5x^3 + 6x^2 + x - 1$ by $x^2 + 2x + 1$

2. $2a^4 + a^3 - 2a^2 + 2a - 1$ by $a^2 + a - 1$

3. $2x^4 - 5x^3 - 7x^2 + 9x + 9$ by $x^2 - 2x - 3$

4. $3a^4 + 4a^3 - 2a^2 - 4a - 1$ by $3a^2 - 2a - 1$

5. $6r^4 + 5r^3 + 8r^2 + 3r + 2$ by $3r^2 + r + 2$

6. $8m^4n^4 + 6m^3n^3 + 8m^2n^2 - 5mn - 3$ by $4m^2n^2 - mn - 1$

7. $5c^4d^4 + 7c^3d^3 + c^2d^2 + cd + 2$ by $c^2d^2 + 2cd + 1$

8. $7m^2 + 72m - 8m^3 + m^4 - 144$ by $m^2 - m - 12$

9. $-x^2 - 2x - 1 + x^4$ by $x^2 - x - 1$

10. $3r - r^2 - 1 - 3r^3 + 2r^4$ by $2r^2 - 1 + r$

EXERCISE 17

Multiply:

1. $7x^2 + x - 1$ by $2x - 5$

2. $-3p^3 - 7p^2 + 3p - 2$ by $-3p + 1$

3. $x^2y^2 - 2xy - 5$ by $xy - 7$

4. $m^2n + mn^2 + n^3$ by $m + n$

5. $-6s^2 - 4s + 1$ by $-3s + 5$

6. $3w^2 - w + 1$ by $2w^2 - 3w - 1$

7. $8z^2 - 2z + 3$ by $z^2 - 5z - 2$

8. $3y^2 - 4y + 7$ by $2y^2 + 3y - 1$

Divide:

9. $12x^2 - 5x - 2$ by $4x + 1$ 10. $1 - 4x + 3x^2 + 2x^3$ by $1 - 2x$

11. $x^4 - 8x^2 + 16$ by $x^2 - 4$ 12. $x^4 - 16$ by $x^2 - 4$

13. $x^4 - 9x^2 + 14$ by $x^2 - 2$

14. $y^4z^4 - 4y^2z^2a - 21a^2$ by $y^2z^2 - 7a$

15. $a^4b^4 - 5a^2b^2c^2d^2 + 6c^4d^4$ by $a^2b^2 - 2c^2d^2$

Simplify:

16. $4a - (a - b + c) + (2a - b)$

17. $x^2 + 3(x - y) + 2y^2 - 2(x - y)$

18. $4 - [a - 3b - 2(a - b) + 7]$

19. $-[-4x - 3y - 5(x - 3) - 2(y + 3)]$

20. $m^2 - \{-m + n - 2[m - 3] + 2n\} - 4$

21. $4x - y - [x - 2(x + 3y) - 4(y - 2x) + y]$

22. $3c - (c + 4d - 2[d - c] + 5 - c)$

23. $x^2 - 3(3 - x[x - 2] + x^2) - 3x + 1$

24. $a + b - c - (a + b - c) - 3(a + b - c)$

25. $-[p + q] - [-p - q - (4p + 3) - q]$

Insert within parentheses preceded by a negative sign all terms containing x, y, and z, and within parentheses preceded by a positive sign all terms containing m, n, and p:

26. $x - y + m - 3p$

27. $n - m^2 - 2x - 3y^2$

28. $x^2 - y^2 - p^2 - n^2 + z^2$

29. $x^2y^2 - z^2 - m^2n^2 - p^2$

30. $z^2 - 6xyz - m^2 + 4mnp + 9x^2y^2 - 4n^2p^2$

Evaluate the following if $c = 2$, $d = 1$, and $x = -2$.

31. $-(c - d) - (c - x) + c + (d + x)$

32. $c - x^2 - (c^2 - d^2 - [c + d + x] - 2)$

33. $-[-c - d + x - (x - d) + x^2] - d^2$

34. $4d - [-x + c^2] + 4d$

35. $c^2 + d^2 + x^2 - [d^2 + x^2 + c^2] + 3$

REVIEW TEST 7

On a sheet of paper write the numbers 1 through 15 to correspond to the numbered statements below. After each number place T (true) or F (false) to indicate if each statement is true or false. (Indicate that a statement is false unless it is *always* true.)

1. If two numbers are added together, their sum is positive.

2. If the divisor is negative and the dividend positive, the quotient is negative.

3. If three factors are all negative numbers, the product is a negative number.

4. If two numbers are added together, the unsigned value of their sum is equal to the sum of the unsigned values of the original numbers.

5. The unsigned value of the difference of two numbers is smaller than the unsigned value of either the minuend or the subtrahend.

6. The quotient obtained by dividing a negative number by a negative number is a negative number.

7. The sum of two negative numbers is a negative number.

8. The product obtained by multiplying two positive numbers together is a positive number.

9. The sum of a positive number and a negative number divided by a negative number results in a quotient that is a positive number.

10. The unsigned value of the subtrahend must be smaller than the unsigned value of the minuend if a difference can be obtained.

11. If two numbers have unlike signs, their product is a negative number.

12. If a negative number is subtracted from a negative number, the remainder is a negative number.

13. If a positive number is added to a positive number and their sum divided by a negative number, the resulting quotient is a negative number.

14. If two negative numbers are added together and from their sum another negative number is subtracted, the result is a negative number.

15. If two positive numbers are added together and from their sum a positive number is subtracted, the remainder is a positive number.

REVIEW TEST 8

On a sheet of paper write the numbers 1 through 20 to correspond to the numbered expressions in the left-hand column below. After each number place the letter that correctly matches the item in the left-hand column with that in the right-hand column. Do not use any letter more than once.

1. $(x^2)(-x^3)$	a. $-10bd^2$
2. $(3a^2)(2a)$	b. $12c^6d^6$
3. $(-xy)(-x^2y)$	c. $-2p^2q^2$
4. $\dfrac{-x^7}{-x^2}$	d. $-x^5$
	e. $2st^2$
5. $(-5)(2bd^2)$	f. $-3xy$
6. $(9m^2n^4)(2mn)$	g. $2p^2q^2$

7. $\dfrac{x^2y^2}{xy}$

8. $14p^4q^2 \div -7p^2$

9. $(3c^2d^2)(4c^3d^3)$

10. $\dfrac{-27x^2y^3}{-9xy^2}$

11. $\dfrac{2st^4}{2t^2}$

12. $\dfrac{30bd^3}{3d^2}$

13. $\dfrac{-24p^2q^5}{8pq^3}$

14. $(-2pq)(-pq)$

15. $(x^2y^2z^2)(xy)$

16. $(-ab)(-ab^2)(a^2b)$

17. $\dfrac{12c^7d^9}{-c^2d^4}$

18. $(-3)(xy)$

19. $\dfrac{-6a^7b^5}{6a^3b}$

20. $(-6mn)(-4m^2n^2)$

h. x^5

i. $x^3y^3z^2$

j. x^3y^2

k. $-12c^5d^5$

l. $24m^3n^3$

m. $-x^6$

n. $3pq^2$

o. $10bd$

p. a^4b^4

q. $6a^3$

r. $-24m^3n^3$

s. $18m^3n^5$

t. $-3pq^2$

u. xy

v. $-a^4b^4$

w. st^2

x. $12c^5d^5$

y. $x^2y^2z^2$

z. $3xy$

REVIEW TEST 9

On a sheet of paper write the numbers 1 through 20 to correspond to the numbered statements in the left-hand column below. After each number place the letter that correctly indicates which algebraic expression in the right-hand column matches the statement in the left-hand column. A letter may be used more than once.

1. The sum of the square of one number and the cube of another number.

   a. $\dfrac{x^2 + x}{x^2 + 2}$

2. The product obtained by multiplying a number by the square of the number represented by the next letter in the alphabet.

   b. $r^2 - s^2$

   c. d^2

3. The quotient obtained by dividing the sum of a number and its square by the sum of that number and 2.

   d. $\dfrac{r^2}{r - 1}$

4. A negative number squared.

   e. $x^2 + y^3$

5. Three times a number subtracted from the number.

   f. $\dfrac{1}{b - 3}$

6. The square of one number subtracted from the square of another number.

7. A number added to its square and then divided by 2 more than the square of the number.

8. Three subtracted from a number.

9. The product of three negative numbers.

10. Zero added to the square of a number.

11. The square of one number added to the cube of the next letter in the alphabet.

12. The square of a number divided by 1 less than that number.

13. One divided by 3 less than some number.

14. The square of a number subtracted from the square of the number that alphabetically immediately precedes the first number.

15. Zero subtracted from the square of a number.

16. The product of a number and the sum of the square of that number and 2.

17. A number diminished by 3.

18. The product of two negative numbers.

19. One divided by a number diminished by 3.

20. The product of a negative number and two positive numbers.

g. $\dfrac{x^2 + x}{x + 2}$

h. $s^2 - r^2$

i. $b - 3$

j. $x(x^2 + 2)$

k. $-2t^2$

l. mn^2

m. $p - 3p$

REVIEW TEST 10

In each of the following cases write either *positive* or *negative* in the blank to make a true statement.

1. If two negative numbers are added, their sum is a _____ number.

2. If two numbers with unlike signs are multiplied together, their product is a _____ number.

3. If a positive number is subtracted from a negative number, the remainder is a _____ number.

4. If a negative number is added to a larger negative number, their sum is a _____ number.

5. If a negative number is added to a smaller negative number, their sum is a _____ number.

6. If a positive number is divided into a positive number, the quotient is a _____ number.

7. If a negative number is multiplied by a negative number, the product is a _____ number.

8. If a negative number is subtracted from a negative number whose unsigned value is smaller than the unsigned value of the subtrahend, the remainder is a _____ number.

9. If a negative number is added to a positive number and the unsigned value of the negative number is larger than that of the positive number, their sum is a _____ number.

10. If a negative number is subtracted from a positive number, the difference is a _____ number.

11. If a negative number is divided by a negative number, the quotient is a _____ number.

12. If a positive number is multiplied by a positive number, the product is a _____ number.

13. If two positive numbers the sum of whose unsigned values is less than the unsigned value of a negative number are added to the negative number, the result is a _____ number.

14. If two negative numbers the sum of whose unsigned values is more than the unsigned value of a positive number are subtracted from the positive number, the result is a _____ number.

15. If two negative numbers are added and their sum divided by a negative number, the quotient is a _____ number.

16. If two negative numbers are multiplied together and their product multiplied by a third negative number, the final result is a _____ number.

17. If two negative numbers are added together and then a negative number whose unsigned value is smaller than their sum is subtracted from that sum, the final result is a _____ number.

18. If two numbers with like signs are multiplied together and their product divided by a negative number, the final result is a _____ number.

REVIEW TEST 11

On a sheet of paper write the numbers 1 through 20 to correspond to the numbered problems in the left-hand column below. After each number place the letter that properly identifies the answer as found in the right-hand column. Do not use any letter more than once. (Some of the expressions in the right-hand column are not answers to the problems found in the left-hand column.)

1. Remove the parentheses in $-(x - y)$.

2. Simplify $2[y - 3x]$.

3. If $a = -1$ and $b = 2$, evaluate the expression $(a^2 - b^2)$.

4. Simplify $(c + d) - (-c + d)$.

5. Evaluate the expression $-(a^2 - b^2)$ if $a = -1$ and $b = 2$.

a. $3 - 2a + b$

b. $-3n$

c. -2

d. $y - x$

e. $2r^2 + r + s$

f. $3 - b$

6. Insert within parentheses $r - 3s$ and place a negative sign before the parentheses.

7. Simplify $3 - (a - b) - a$.

8. Simplify $m - (n - [m + 3n] - n)$.

9. Simplify $-(c - d) + (d - c)$.

10. Evaluate $p^2 - (p + q) - q^2$ if $p = 2$ and $q = -3$.

11. Simplify $3 - a - (b - a)$.

12. Insert within parentheses $r - 3s$ and place a positive sign before the parentheses. From that value subtract $r - 3s$, placed within parentheses preceded by a positive sign.

13. Simplify $m - n - [(m + 3n) - n]$.

14. If $p = 2$ and $q = -3$, evaluate the expression $p^2 - (p + q - q^2)$.

15. Simplify $3 - (4 - 3) + 2$.

16. Simplify $-[r^2 - (r + s + r^2)]$.

17. If $x = 3$ and $y = -2$, evaluate the expression $3x - (y^2 - x) + x$.

18. Evaluate the expression $m - (n - p + m) - (n - p)$ if $m = -1$, $n = 1$, and $p = 2$.

19. Simplify $r - [r + s - (r + s)] - s$.

20. Simplify $r - s - [s - 2r - (r + s)]$.

g. 4

h. $2y - 6x$

i. 6

j. 3

k. zero

l. $-(r + 3s)$

m. $r - s$

n. $2c$

o. -4

p. $r + s$

q. -3

r. 14

s. $s - 4r$

t. $6x - 2y$

u. $4r - s$

v. 11

w. $-(3s - r)$

x. 2

y. $2d - 2c$

z. $3n + 2m$

REVIEW TEST 12

On a sheet of paper write the numbers 1 to 10 to correspond to the numbers of the statements below. After each number write the letter a, b, c, or d to indicate which of the answers given after each statement is correct.

1. If zero is subtracted from x^2, the answer is: (a) zero; (b) x^2; (c) $-x^2$; (d) none of these.

2. If $-x^2$ is subtracted from $5x^2$, the answer is: (a) $4x^2$; (b) $5x^0$; (c) $5x^4$; (d) $6x^2$.

3. If $-4a$ is added to $4a^2$, the answer is: (a) zero; (b) $4a^2 - 4a$; (c) $8a^3$; (d) $-8a^3$.

4. If $7m$ is subtracted from zero, the answer is: (a) zero; (b) $7m$; (c) $-7m$; (d) none of these.

5. In the expression $(7x)(0) + 3$, the answer is: (a) $10x$; (b) 3; (c) $7x + 3$; (d) none of these.

6. If $4a$ is divided by zero and subtracted from b, the answer is: (a) b; (b) $b - 4a$; (c) zero; (d) none of these.

7. If $-7m$ is subtracted from $-3m$, the answer is: (a) $4m$; (b) 4; (c) $-10m$; (d) $-4m$.

8. If the sum of a and a^2 is divided by zero, the result is: (a) zero; (b) $a + a^2$; (c) $a^2 + a$; (d) none of these.

9. Four times the sum of m and n added to negative three times the sum of m and n gives: (a) $12(m + n)$; (b) $-(m + n)$; (c) $(m + n)$; (d) $7(m + n)$.

10. If $-3a^2b$ is subtracted from $-3ab^2$, the result is (a) $6a^2b$; (b) $-6ab^2$; (c) zero; (d) none of these.

4

First-Degree Equations

24. DEFINITION OF THE EQUATION

One of the most meaningful techniques in the study of mathematics is that of converting the conditions stated in a problem into mathematical language. Consider the problem

$$x + 2 = 7$$

We could state this in words in the following manner: *2 added to the number represented by x is equal to 7.*

Since x is a variable, it might assume many values. Some of those values would produce a false statement. As an example, if we replace x with the number 3, our statement would read $3 + 2 = 7$, which obviously is a false statement. Many other replacements for x would also produce false statements. However, if we replace x with 5, we have a true statement. Thus we cannot say whether the above statement, $x + 2 = 7$, is a true statement unless we have the information as to what we are using as a value for x. Any statement such as the example we have been using is called an *open sentence* and in some cases may be false and in other cases (depending upon what we use as a replacement for the variable) may be true.

In the present discussion we shall be concerned with those open sentences which produce a true statement. Thus our task will be to find the replacement for the variable that will make the statement true.

An equation is a statement that two expressions are equal. The expression

$$x + 2 = 7$$

is an equation. The two parts, one on either side of the equals sign, are called the *members of the equation*. The $x + 2$ is referred to as the *left member* of the equation and the 7 is called the *right member* of the equation.

In solving the above equation, we are asked to find the value of x. We might ask: "What number added to 2 is equal to 7?" It can be seen that 5 must be added to 2 to give 7. This means that the value of x in the equation is 5. If we add 2 and 5, we get 7. When a number is substituted for the variable and makes the equation a true statement, then that number is a *root* of the equation.

A first-degree equation is one in which the exponent of the variable for which we are solving is 1.

In Chapter 1 we stated in Law 11 that "if equals are added to equals, then the sums are equal" and in Law 12 that "if equals are multiplied by equals, then the products are equal." We shall be using these laws extensively in the study of equations.

Previously we defined the additive identity as 0. When we add the negative of a number to that given number, their sum is zero. Thus $(a) + (-a) = 0$. In this case we say that $-a$ is the additive inverse of a. Likewise, a is the additive inverse of $-a$. Thus:

> The *additive inverse* of a number is the opposite of that number.

We must keep in mind, then, that any number and its additive inverse are at equal distances from zero on the number line, one of them to the left and the other to the right of zero.

The *reciprocal* of a number is another number such that the product of the two numbers is 1. The reciprocal of a is $1/a$ since

$$a \cdot \frac{1}{a} = \frac{a}{a} = 1.$$

Likewise, $\frac{1}{4}$ is the reciprocal of 4 since their product $(4 \cdot \frac{1}{4})$ is 1. If we multiply $\frac{1}{3}$ by 3, the product is 1. Hence 3 is the reciprocal of $\frac{1}{3}$.

> The *multiplicative inverse* of any number except zero is the reciprocal of the given number.

The number zero does not have a multiplicative inverse as this would involve division by zero, which, as we previously discussed, is never permitted.

The solutions of a great many types of simple equations require the use of Laws 10 and 11, the additive inverse, and the multiplicative inverse.

Frequently it is necessary to simplify the form of the equation in order to find the root of the equation.

Equivalent equations are any two or more equations that have the same solution set. It will be recalled that in Chapter 1 we defined the *solution set* as the set that contains all the elements from U that satisfy the condition placed upon the variable. Any equation containing a variable poses a condition placed upon that variable. Consider the equation

$$2x + 3 = 15 \tag{1}$$

We can readily see that if x is equal to 6 the equation is a true statement. Thus $\{6\}$ is the solution set or the only root of the equation.

Now observe the equation

$$2x = 15 - 3 \tag{2}$$

Again, if we substitute 6 for x, we have a true statement and $\{6\}$ is the solution set or the only root of equation (2).

Finally, consider the equation

$$x = \frac{15 - 3}{2} \tag{3}$$

If we subtract 3 from 15 and divide the remainder by 2, we have $x = 6$ and $6 = \dfrac{15 - 3}{2}$ is a true statement.

The above three equations, $2x + 3 = 15$, $2x = 15 - 3$, and $x = \dfrac{15 - 3}{2}$, are all equivalent equations since in each case x must have the value 6 to make the equation a true statement and in each case $\{6\}$ is the solution set.

An equation can be classified as one of two general types of equations. An *identical equation*, often referred to as an *identity*, is that equation which holds true for any permissible values of the variable. Observe the equation

$$3x - 4 = 3(x - 1) - 1$$

It can be shown that this equation makes a true statement regardless of what value we assign to x in each complete operation.

We mentioned above that only permissible values may be used. It has been shown that we cannot divide by zero. Thus in the equation

$$x - 3 = \frac{x + 2}{x - 1}$$

we would not be permitted to use 1 as a value of x as that would make the denominator in the right member of the equation equal to zero. In a later discussion we shall discover other cases in which certain real values cannot be used.

The second general type of equation is the *conditional equation*, which is defined as an equation which is true only for a certain value or for certain values of the variable involved. The three equations discussed earlier in this chapter, all of which had {6} as the solution set, are conditional equations because they all become true statements upon the condition that we replace x with the number 6.

In Chapter 1 we discussed the set builder. It will be recalled from that discussion that the part following the vertical line in the set builder was called "the condition imposed upon the variable." The following examples will illustrate how simple conditional equations are solved.

Example 1. Find the solution set in the equation $x - 3 = 5$.

By use of the set builder, the additive inverse, and the additive identity, we have

$$
\begin{aligned}
\{x \mid x - 3 = 5\} &= \{x \mid x + (-3) + (+3) = 5 + (+3)\} \\
&= \{x \mid x + [(-3) + (+3)] = 5 + 3\} \\
&= \{x \mid x + 0 = 8\} \\
&= \{x \mid x = 8\} \\
&= \{8\}
\end{aligned}
$$

The last step in this succession is the solution set. In other words, the 8 is assumed to be the root of the equation. However, before we can say that 8 is a root of the original equation, we must show that 8 satisfies that equation. This is shown in the check below.

Check:
$$
\begin{aligned}
x - 3 &= 5 \\
8 - 3 &= 5 \\
5 &= 5
\end{aligned}
$$

Example 2. Solve for y in the equation $y + 2 = 6$.

Again we use the set builder and the additive identity:

$$
\begin{aligned}
\{y \mid y + 2 = 6\} &= \{y \mid y + [(+2) + (-2)] = 6 + (-2)\} \\
&= \{y \mid y + [0] = 4\} \\
&= \{y \mid y = 4\} \\
&= \{4\}
\end{aligned}
$$

Check:
$$
\begin{aligned}
y + 2 &= 6 \\
4 + 2 &= 6 \\
6 &= 6
\end{aligned}
$$

Example 3. Solve for m in the equation $m + 4 = 2$.

$$
\begin{aligned}
\{m \mid m + 4 = 2\} &= \{m \mid m + [(+4) + (-4)] = 2 + (-4)\} \\
&= \{m \mid m + [0] = -2\} \\
&= \{m \mid m = -2\} \\
&= \{-2\}
\end{aligned}
$$

Check:
$$m + 4 = 2$$
$$(-2) + 4 = 2$$
$$2 = 2$$

Example 4. Solve for x in the equation $\frac{1}{3}x = 2$.

In this problem we shall use the multiplicative inverse of $\frac{1}{3}$ to eliminate the fractional coefficient of x. This, of course, involves the use of Law 11. If we multiply the left member of the equation by the multiplicative inverse of $\frac{1}{3}$, this implies that we are multiplying that left member by 3. Then, to maintain our equality, we must also multiply the right member of the equation by 3. Then

$$\{x \mid \tfrac{1}{3}x = 2\} = \{x \mid 3 \cdot \tfrac{1}{3}x = 3 \cdot 2\}$$
$$= \{x \mid x = 6\}$$
$$= \{6\}$$

Check:
$$\tfrac{1}{3}x = 2$$
$$\tfrac{1}{3}(6) = 2$$
$$2 = 2$$

Example 5. Solve for y in the equation $3y - 1 = 8$.

Again we shall use the multiplicative inverse of the coefficient of y in order to make that coefficient 1. The multiplicative inverse of 3 is $\frac{1}{3}$. Thus we shall multiply both members of the equation by $\frac{1}{3}$. We shall also use the additive inverse before introducing the multiplicative inverse into the solution.

$$\{y \mid 3y - 1 = 8\} = \{y \mid 3y + (-1) = 8\}$$
$$= \{y \mid 3y + [(+1) + (-1)] = 8 + (+1)\}$$
$$= \{y \mid 3y + [0] = 9\}$$
$$= \{y \mid 3y = 9\}$$
$$= \{y \mid \tfrac{1}{3} \cdot 3y = \tfrac{1}{3} \cdot 9\}$$
$$= \{y \mid y = 3\}$$
$$= \{3\}$$

Check:
$$3y - 1 = 8$$
$$3(3) - 1 = 8$$
$$9 - 1 = 8$$
$$8 = 8$$

Example 6. Solve for m in the equation $\frac{2}{3}m = 6$.

In Examples 4 and 5 we were concerned with arriving at an equation in which the coefficient of the variable was 1 (understood to be such but omitted, as was agreed earlier in this text). In the present example this may be accomplished by making use of the multiplicative inverse twice. Thus

$$2 \cdot \tfrac{1}{3} \cdot m = 2 \cdot \tfrac{1}{3} \cdot m \qquad \text{(Symmetric relation)}$$

$$2 \cdot \tfrac{1}{3} \cdot m = \tfrac{1}{3} \cdot 2 \cdot m \qquad \text{(Commutative law for multiplication)}$$

$$3 \cdot 2 \cdot \tfrac{1}{3} \cdot m = 3 \cdot \tfrac{1}{3} \cdot 2 \cdot m \qquad \text{(Both members of the equation multiplied by 3)}$$

$$3 \cdot 2 \cdot \tfrac{1}{3} \cdot m = 1 \cdot 2 \cdot m \qquad \text{(Multiplicative inverse)}$$

$$3 \cdot 2 \cdot \tfrac{1}{3} \cdot m = 2 \cdot m \qquad \text{(Multiplicative identity)}$$

$$\tfrac{1}{2} \cdot 3 \cdot 2 \cdot \tfrac{1}{3} \cdot m = \tfrac{1}{2} \cdot 2 \cdot m \qquad \text{(Both members of the equation multiplied by $\tfrac{1}{2}$)}$$

$$\tfrac{1}{2} \cdot 3 \cdot 2 \cdot \tfrac{1}{3} \cdot m = 1 \cdot m \qquad \text{(Multiplicative inverse)}$$

$$\tfrac{1}{2} \cdot 3 \cdot 2 \cdot \tfrac{1}{3} \cdot m = m \qquad \text{(Multiplicative identity)}$$

$$\tfrac{1}{2} \cdot 2 \cdot 3 \cdot \tfrac{1}{3} \cdot m = m \qquad \text{(Commutative law for addition)}$$

$$[\tfrac{1}{2} \cdot 2] \cdot [3 \cdot \tfrac{1}{3}] \cdot m = m \qquad \text{(Associative law for multiplication)}$$

$$[1] \cdot [1] \cdot m = m \qquad \text{(Multiplicative inverse)}$$

$$1 \cdot m = m \qquad (1 \cdot 1 = 1)$$

$$m = m \qquad \text{(Multiplicative identity)}$$

In the above discussion we have used two multiplicative inverses— that of 2, which is $\tfrac{1}{2}$, and that of $\tfrac{1}{3}$, which is 3. Each of these multiplicative inverses is a factor in the left member of the equation. The product of these two multiplicative inverses, $\tfrac{1}{2}$ and 3, is $\tfrac{3}{2}$ since $3 \cdot \tfrac{1}{2} = \tfrac{3}{2}$. Originally in Example 5 we found the coefficient $\tfrac{2}{3}$ with which we were confronted. We have found that $\tfrac{3}{2}$ times that $\tfrac{2}{3}$ gives us a coefficient of 1. Thus the multiplicative inverse of $\tfrac{2}{3}$ is $\tfrac{3}{2}$. From this discussion we shall define the multiplicative inverse of a fraction made up of any nonzero real numbers as the inversion of that fraction. In general, then, the multiplicative inverse of a/b for all nonzero real values of a and b is b/a.

Returning to Example 6, we shall proceed as follows:

$$
\begin{aligned}
\{m \mid \tfrac{2}{3}m = 6\} &= \{m \mid \tfrac{3}{2} \cdot \tfrac{2}{3}m = \tfrac{3}{2} \cdot 6\} \\
&= \{m \mid 1 \cdot m = \tfrac{1}{2} \cdot 3 \cdot 6\} \\
&= \{m \mid m = \tfrac{1}{2} \cdot 18\} \\
&= \{m \mid m = 9\} \\
&= \{9\}
\end{aligned}
$$

Check:

$$\tfrac{2}{3}m = 6$$
$$\tfrac{2}{3}(9) = 6$$
$$6 = 6$$

Example 7. Solve for d in the equation $2d + 5 = 3d + 2$.

It will be noted that the variable is included in both members of this equation. In order to simplify the solution of such an equation, we substitute for the original equation an equivalent equation in which the variable is found in only one member of the equation. It is usually deemed preferable to have that variable in the left member of the equation. We utilize the methods introduced in the previous examples to accomplish this substitution of an equivalent equation for the original equation. Thus

$$\{d \mid 2d + 5 = 3d + 2\} = \{d \mid (2d) + (-3d) + 5 = (3d) + (-3d) + 2\}$$
$$= \{d \mid -d + 5 = 2\}$$
$$= \{d \mid -d + (5) + (-5) = 2 + (-5)\}$$
$$= \{d \mid -d = -3\}$$

The left member of the conditional equation is $-d$ whereas we need d. If both members of that conditional equation, $-d = -3$, are multiplied by -1, we obtain the d in the left member of the equation. Our solution then continues as

$$= \{d \mid (-1)(-d) = (-1)(-3)\}$$
$$= \{d \mid d = 3\}$$
$$= \{3\}$$

Check:
$$2d + 5 = 3d + 2$$
$$2(3) + 5 = 3(3) + 2$$
$$6 + 5 = 9 + 2$$
$$11 = 11$$

EXERCISE 18

A

Solve for the variable in each of the following:

1. $y - 4 = 2$
2. $x + 3 = 7$
3. $m - 1 = 5$
4. $a + 3 = 11$
5. $x - 5 = 9$
6. $b + 3 = 1$
7. $d - 6 = 3$
8. $y + 5 = 6$
9. $z - 9 = 11$
10. $x + 5 = 5$
11. $n - 3 = 2$
12. $b - 17 = 19$
13. $x + 14 = 38$
14. $a - 13 = 21$
15. $y - 9 = -9$
16. $2a = 10$
17. $3x = 12$
18. $\frac{1}{4}y = 3$
19. $\frac{1}{3}b = 2$
20. $6d = 24$
21. $4c = 12$
22. $9z = 36$
23. $4m = 20$
24. $4n = -28$
25. $\frac{1}{2}z = -2$

Solve for the variable in each of the following:

1. $\frac{3}{4}x = 18$ 2. $\frac{2}{3}n = 12$

3. $\frac{3}{5}b = -6$ 4. $\frac{5}{6}c = 25$

5. $5a + 6 = 2a - 3$ 6. $a^2 + a = 3 + a^2$

7. $m - 2 = 4 - 2m$ 8. $3p - 5 = 3 - p$

9. $4 = 5 - p$ 10. $7 = 17 - 2x$

11. $\frac{1}{4}x = 3$ 12. $\frac{2}{3}y = 1 - \frac{1}{3}y$

13. $\frac{1}{4}x = 5 - \frac{1}{4}x$ 14. $\frac{3}{2}d = 12$

15. $\frac{3}{2}y - 2 = 10 - \frac{1}{2}y$ 16. $\frac{1}{5}w = 5$

17. $3 = \frac{1}{6}x$ 18. $x - 2 = \frac{1}{2}x + 1$

19. $\frac{5}{3}y = -10$ 20. $\frac{3}{7}c = c - 12$

21. $\frac{1}{4}w - 2 = 4 - \frac{3}{4}w$ 22. $x - 5 = \frac{1}{3}x + 7$

23. $\frac{5}{3}z - 2 = 5 + \frac{2}{3}z$ 24. $x + \frac{1}{3}x = 20$

25. $y - \frac{1}{3}y + 1 = 3 - \frac{1}{3}y$ 26. $\frac{3}{8}c - 3 = 6$

27. $\frac{1}{2}x + \frac{1}{2}x - 1 = 3x + 7$ 28. $\frac{2}{3}s - 5 = 3 + \frac{1}{3}s$

29. $\frac{5}{6}y + 3 = \frac{1}{6}y - 9$ 30. $\frac{4}{3}b - \frac{1}{3}b - 1 = \frac{1}{3}b - 7$

If an equation has some of the terms enclosed within grouping symbols, remove those symbols first and then solve for the variable, as was done in the preceding exercises.

Example 8.   Solve for x in the equation $3(x - 2) = 2x + 3$.

Remove the parentheses and the equation becomes $3x - 6 = 2x + 3$. Then

$$\{x \mid 3x - 6 = 2x + 3\} = \{x \mid (3x) + (-2x) - 6 = (2x) + (-2x) + 3\}$$
$$= \{x \mid x - 6 = 3\}$$
$$= \{x \mid x + (-6) + (+6) = 3 + (+6)\}$$
$$= \{x \mid x = 9\}$$
$$= \{9\}$$

Check: $3(x - 2) = 2x + 3$
$$3(9 - 2) = 2(9) + 3$$
$$3(7) = 18 + 3$$
$$21 = 21$$

Example 9.   Solve for x in the equation $x(x - 2) + x = x^2 - 2$.

Remove the parentheses and the equation becomes $x^2 - 2x + x = x^2 - 2$. Then

$\{x \mid x^2 - 2x + x = x^2 - 2\}$
$$= \{x \mid (x^2) + (-x^2) - 2x + x = (x^2) + (-x^2) - 2\}$$
$$= \{x \mid -2x + x = -2\}$$
$$= \{x \mid x + (-2x) = -2\}$$
$$= \{x \mid -x = -2\}$$
$$= \{x \mid (-1)(-x) = (-1)(-2)\}$$
$$= \{x \mid x = 2\}$$
$$= \{2\}$$

Check:
$$x(x - 2) + x = x^2 - 2$$
$$2(2 - 2) + 2 = (2)^2 - 2$$
$$2(0) + 2 = 4 - 2$$
$$0 + 2 = 2$$
$$2 = 2$$

EXERCISE 19

A

Solve for the given variable in each of the following:

1. $y(y + 3) = y^2 + 6$
2. $2(y - 3) = 4$
3. $2x - (x - 2) = 3$
4. $2x(x + 1) = 4 + 2x^2$
5. $-(3 - x) = -1$
6. $4 - (m + 3) = -5$
7. $8z - (3 + 5z) = 3$
8. $c(c + 5) = c^2 - 10$
9. $n - 3 + 2(n - 2) = 2n - 1$
10. $a^2 - (a + 1) = 3 + a^2$
11. $4(b - 3) = b + 6$
12. $p(p + 3) - 6 = p^2 + 6$
13. $x^2 - x(x - 3) = 18$
14. $4 - 2(3 - x) = 8$
15. $z(3z + 2) - 4 = 7 + 3(z^2 - 1)$

B

Solve for the given variable in each of the following:

1. $w + (2w - 3) = 5 - w$
2. $-(a + 5) = 2a + 4$
3. $3(4m - 2) = 2(3m + 6)$
4. $a - (2a + 5) = 7 - (4 - a) + 10$
5. $x - 3(4 - x) + 5 = -2(3 - 2x) - x$
6. $-5(3 - z) = 5 - (z + 10)$

7. $3 - s(s - 2) = 5 - s^2$

8. $-5t(t + 3) + 4 = 3t(4 - t) - 5 - 2t^2$

9. $3a^2 - 2a(a - 3) + 6 = a^2 + 4(a - 13)$

10. $y - y(3y - 5) = y - 2(y^2 + y) - y^2 - 14$

25. STATED PROBLEMS

Stated, or verbal, problems occur extensively in mathematics, science, and business. One of the aims in a first course in algebra is to teach the student to set up and solve stated problems. The following examples illustrate the formal solution of stated problems. It will be observed that the use of the set builder has been omitted in these solutions. The format used is the more traditional one for the solution of simple equations.

Example 1. If one number is 3 more than another number and their sum is 35, what are the numbers?

Let x be the smaller number and $x + 3$ be the larger number. Then

$$x + (x + 3) = 35$$
$$x + x + 3 = 35$$
$$2x + 3 + (-3) = 35 + (-3)$$
$$2x = 32$$
$$x = 16 \quad \text{(the smaller number)}$$
$$x + 3 = 19$$

Check:
$$16 + 19 = 35$$
$$35 = 35$$

Example 2. The sum of two consecutive numbers is 49. What are the numbers?

Let x be the smaller number and $x + 1$ be the next consecutive number. Then

$$x + (x + 1) = 49$$
$$x + x + 1 = 49$$
$$2x + 1 + (-1) = 49 + (-1)$$
$$2x = 48$$
$$x = 24 \quad \text{(the smaller number)}$$
$$x + 1 = 25 \quad \text{(the larger number)}$$

Check:
$$24 + 25 = 49$$
$$49 = 49$$

Example 3. If the sum of two consecutive even numbers is 86, what are the numbers? (*Hint:* The larger of two consecutive even or two consecutive odd numbers is always 2 greater than the smaller one.)

Let x be the smaller number and $x + 2$ be the larger number. Then

$$x + (x + 2) = 86$$
$$x + x + 2 = 86$$
$$2x + 2 + (-2) = 86 + (-2)$$
$$2x = 84$$
$$x = 42 \quad \text{(the smaller number)}$$
$$x + 2 = 44 \quad \text{(the larger number)}$$

Check:
$$42 + 44 = 86$$
$$86 = 86$$

Example 4. If the length of a garden plot is 12 feet more than its width and the perimeter is 192 feet, what are the dimensions of the garden? (*Hint:* Remember the perimeter of a rectangle is the sum of twice the length and twice the width.)

Let w be the number of feet in the width and $w + 12$ be the number of feet in the length. Then, from the formula, we have

$$2(w + 12) + 2(w) = 192$$
$$2w + 24 + 2w = 192$$
$$4w + 24 + (-24) = 192 + (-24)$$
$$4w = 168$$
$$w = 42 \text{ feet} \quad \text{(the width)}$$
$$w + 12 = 54 \text{ feet} \quad \text{(the length)}$$

Check:
$$2(54) + 2(42) = 192$$
$$108 + 84 = 192$$
$$192 = 192$$

Example 5. A man buys two pieces of property for which he pays $26,000. If one of them cost $1,200 more than the other, what did each cost him?

Let x be the cost of the less expensive property and $x + \$1,200$ be the cost of the more expensive property. Then

$$x + (x + \$1,200) = \$26,000$$
$$x + x + \$1,200 = \$26,000$$
$$2x + \$1,200 + (-\$1,200) = \$26,000 + (-\$1,200)$$
$$2x = \$24,800$$
$$x = \$12,400 \quad \text{(cost of the less expensive property)}$$
$$x + \$1,200 = \$13,600 \quad \text{(cost of the more expensive property)}$$

Check: $$\$12,400 + \$13,600 = \$26,000$$
$$\$26,000 = \$26,000$$

Example 6. A hardware merchant bought a garden plow for $20. If he priced it so he could make 20 percent profit on the cost, what was the selling price of the plow? (*Hint:* Remember that the selling price of an article is equal to the sum of the cost and the profit.)

Let x be the selling price. Then

$$x = \$20 + 0.20(\$20)$$
$$x = \$20 + \$4$$
$$x = \$24$$

Example 7. A purse contains 82 cents in pennies, nickels, and dimes. There are 4 more pennies than nickels and twice as many dimes as nickels. How many of each type of coin are there in the purse?

Let x be the number of nickels, $x + 4$ be the number of pennies, and $2x$ be the number of dimes. The value of each, in terms of cents, would be represented as follows:

$$5(x) = 5x \quad \text{(the value of the nickels)}$$
$$1(x + 4) = x + 4 \quad \text{(the value of the pennies)}$$
$$10(2x) = 20x \quad \text{(the value of the dimes)}$$

Then

$$5x + x + 4 + 20x = 82$$
$$26x = 82 - 4$$
$$26x = 78$$
$$x = 3 \quad \text{(the number of nickels)}$$
$$x + 4 = 7 \quad \text{(the number of pennies)}$$
$$2x = 6 \quad \text{(the number of dimes)}$$

Check: $$\$0.01(7) + \$0.05(3) + \$0.10(6) = \$0.82$$
$$\$0.07 + \$0.15 + \$0.60 = \$0.82$$
$$\$0.82 = \$0.82$$

In the study of physics the lever is often used in problem situations. The *lever* may be a board or bar that is balanced on an object called the *fulcrum.* A frequent use of the lever is in raising or moving an object by placing one end of the lever under the object and using it as a prying bar. The object placed under the lever to assist in the moving or raising is again called the fulcrum. The seesaw or teeter board is another illustration of the lever.

By experimentation in physics it has been proved that the lever is balanced if the weight on one end times its distance from the fulcrum is equal to the weight on the other end multiplied by its distance from the fulcrum. This is expressed as follows:

$$w_1 d_1 = w_2 d_2$$

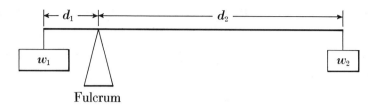

Fulcrum

If there are two or more weights on either side, each weight must be multiplied by its distance from the fulcrum. The sum of the weights times the distances on one side must equal the sum of the weights times the distances on the other side if the lever is to be balanced. Thus

$$w_1 d_1 = w_2 d_2 + w_3 d_3$$

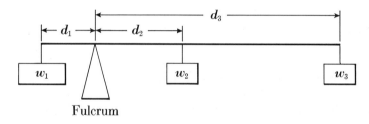

Fulcrum

Figure 17

Example 8. Two boys sit on opposite ends of a seesaw. The first boy weighs 150 pounds and is 10 feet from the fulcrum. If the second boy weighs 125 pounds, how far must he be from the fulcrum if the board is to be balanced?

Let x be the distance the second boy is from the fulcrum. Then

$$125(x) = 10(150)$$
$$125x = 1500$$
$$x = 1500 \div 125$$
$$x = 12 \text{ feet}$$

Check:
$$12(125) = 10(150)$$
$$1500 = 1500$$

Example 9. A man uses a 10-foot steel bar to raise a 200-pound box from the ground. If he places a block of wood under the bar and 2 feet from the end of the bar, how much energy will he have to exert on the end of the bar to raise the box from the ground?

In this type of problem the force exerted is the weight on that end of the bar. Let x be the force exerted. Then

$$(x)(8) = 2(200)$$
$$8x = 400$$
$$x = 50 \text{ pounds}$$

Check: $\qquad\qquad 8(50) = 2(200)$
$$400 = 400$$

Mixture problems provide typical situations in which a more detailed type of linear equation leads to the solution. The following example illustrates this type of problem and its solution:

Example 10. How many pounds each of walnuts that sell for 45 cents per pound and pecans that sell for 65 cents per pound must be used to provide 60 pounds of mixture to sell for 60 cents per pound?

Some students find it helpful to illustrate the problem with a diagram similar to the one shown below:

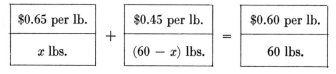

Let

$x =$ the number of pounds of pecans needed
$60 - x =$ the number of pounds of walnuts needed
$0.65(x) =$ the value of the pecans used
$0.65x =$ the value of the pecans used
$0.45(60 - x) =$ the value of the walnuts used
$\$27.00 - 0.45x =$ the value of the walnuts used
$\$27.00 - 0.45x + 0.65x =$ the value of both the pecans and walnuts used
$0.60(60) = \$36.00$ (the value of the mixture)

Since the value before mixing the nuts is equivalent to the value after they are mixed, we form an equation (as shown by the diagram above) by stating that the value before mixing is equal to the value after mixing.

$$0.65x + \$27.00 - 0.45x = \$36.00$$
$$0.65x - 0.45x + (\$27.00) + (-\$27.00) = \$36.00 + (-\$27.00)$$
$$0.65x - 0.45x = \$9.00$$
$$0.20x = \$9.00$$
$$x = \frac{\$9.00}{0.20}$$
$$x = 45 \text{ lbs. of pecans}$$
$$60 - x = 60 - 45$$
$$= 15 \text{ lbs. of walnuts}$$

Check:
$$15(\$0.45) + 45(\$0.65) = 60(\$0.60)$$
$$\$6.75 + \$29.25 = \$36.00$$
$$\$36.00 = \$36.00$$

Stated problems vary considerably and consequently there is no uniform pattern to follow in completing their solutions. The following suggestions will be helpful in working toward the solution:

a. Read the problem carefully.

b. Learn what facts are given or stated.

c. Determine what is asked for in the problem.

d. Make a statement that some letter will be used to represent the quantity or value to be found.

e. Using that same letter, make statements representing other given facts in the problem.

f. Set up an equation in which the relationship between the unknown and the given facts is expressed.

g. By use of Laws 10 and 11, the additive inverse and the multiplicative inverse, solve the equation.

h. Check the answer found. Observe the answer found and compare it with the facts stated in the problem. Does it appear to be a reasonable answer in terms of the facts stated in the problem? If so, substitute that value in the original equation to see if it does check.

EXERCISE 20

A

Solve the following problems:

1. The sum of two numbers is 78. One of the numbers is 4 more than the other number. What are the two numbers?

2. One number is 21 more than another number. Their sum is 107. What are the numbers?

3. The sum of two numbers is 111. If one of the numbers is 5 less than the other number, what are the two numbers?

4. A certain number is 8 less than three times another number. If their sum is 80, what are the two numbers?

5. If twice a certain number is increased by 26, the result is the same as if 2 were added to four times the number. What is the number?

6. If 10 is subtracted from six times a certain number, the result is the same as if 10 were added to four times the number. What is the number?

7. A and B sit on opposite ends of a seesaw. A weighs 120 pounds and sits 6 feet from the fulcrum. If B weighs 90 pounds, how far from the fulcrum must he sit if the seesaw is to be balanced?

8. A and B sit on opposite ends of a seesaw, A 9 feet from the fulcrum and B 12 feet from the fulcrum. If A weighs 160 pounds, what is the weight of B if they balance each other?

9. A and B sit on opposite ends of a 22-foot seesaw. If A weighs 120 pounds and B weighs 100 pounds, how far from the fulcrum must B sit to balance A?

10. A man uses a 12-foot steel bar to lift a 300-pound stone from the ground. If the fulcrum is placed 2 feet from the stone, how much force must be exerted to lift the stone?

11. A and B sit on opposite ends of a 30-foot seesaw that has a fulcrum 15 feet from either end. A weighs 175 pounds and B weighs 125 pounds. How far from the fulcrum will C, who weighs 125 pounds, have to sit if C and B are to balance A?

12. Two men use a 10-foot steel bar to lift a 500-pound box. The fulcrum is placed 2 feet from the end of the bar on which the box sits. The first man exerts a force of 75 pounds on the other end of the bar. If the second man exerts a force 3 feet from the first man, what is the force exerted by the second man?

13. The length of a rectangle is 8 feet more than its width. If the perimeter of the rectangle is 100 feet, what is its width?

14. A rectangle is twice as long as it is wide. If the perimeter is 108 inches, what are the dimensions of the rectangle?

15. The perimeter of a triangle is 29 inches. If the second side is 2 inches more than the first side and the third side is 1 inch more than the second side, what is the length of each side of the triangle?

16. The first angle of a triangle is 10 degrees more than the second angle,

and the third angle is 10 degrees more than the first angle. How many degrees are there in each angle of the triangle?

17. The length of a rectangle is 4 inches greater than its width. If the length and width are each increased by 2 inches, the area is increased by 32 square inches. What were the dimensions of the original rectangle?

18. A man has 240 yards of wire with which to fence a rectangular garden. If he makes the garden three times as long as it is wide, what are the dimensions of the garden if he uses all the wire?

19. The length of a rectangle is 5 inches greater than its width. If the width is doubled and the length remains the same, the perimeter is increased by 8 inches. What were the dimensions of the original rectangle?

20. A house and lot are assessed by the tax department for $13,800. If the house is assessed at $200 more than three times the assessment of the lot, for how much is each assessed?

21. A man bought a new automobile and a small trailer for $3200. If he paid three times as much for the automobile as for the trailer, how much did each cost?

22. A man invested $12,000 in two types of bonds. One investment paid 5 percent and the other 4 percent interest. If he made $520 annually from the two, how much did he have invested in each?

23. A man bought an automobile on which the mortgage was $285 more than twice the down payment. If, when the car is paid for, it has cost him $3585, how much was his down payment?

24. A used car sold for $1320, which was 55 percent of the cost when it was sold as a new car. For how much did it sell as a new car?

25. The sum of the ages of two boys is 16 years. If the older one is three times as old as the younger one, how old is each boy?

B

Solve the following problems:

1. A student has $1.12 made up of an equal number of pennies, nickels, and dimes. How many of each type of coin does he have?

2. Fred has $1.46 in his pocket. If he has twice as many dimes as quarters, twice as many nickels as dimes, and twice as many pennies as nickels, how many of each type of coin does he have?

3. An automobile averaged 40 miles per hour for the first three hours of a trip and then increased its speed to average 45 miles per hour for the next two hours. How far did it travel during the five hours?

4. An automobile averaged 40 miles per hour in traveling from one city to another. On the return trip it averaged 50 miles per hour. If the return trip was made in one hour less than the original trip, what was the distance between the two cities?

5. The symphony hall charged $.65 for students to attend a concert. For the same concert others paid $1.00 admission. A total of 255 tickets were sold. If the receipts were $213, how many of each type ticket were sold?

6. At a circus performance adults were charged $1.50 and children paid $.75. There were 300 more children's tickets sold than adult tickets. If the total receipts for the performance were $3600, how many of each type of admission ticket were sold?

7. A grocer mixes 30 pounds of a brand of coffee that sells for 70 cents per pound with a quantity of coffee that sells for 90 cents per pound. If the mixture is to sell for 85 cents per pound, how many pounds of the 90-cent coffee must be used?

8. A motorist traveling in a cold climate found that his antifreeze was too weak to prevent radiator damage. The solution in the 15-gallon radiator tested 30 percent pure antifreeze. How much of the solution would have to be removed and replaced with pure antifreeze to secure a 60 percent solution?

9. Divide $10,000 into four parts such that the first part is twice the second part, the third part is $500 more than the first part, and the fourth part is $1,000 less than the first part.

10. A man's deductions on his federal income tax amount to $1700. If his total income is $6300, how much tax does he pay if the rate is 12 percent after deductions?

REVIEW TEST 13

On a sheet of paper write the numbers 1 through 15 to correspond to the numbered equations in the left-hand column below. After each number place a letter to match the answers from the right-hand column with the problems in the left-hand column. Each letter is to be used only once.

1. $3x - 1 = 5$	a. -1
2. $2y - 3 = y + 1$	b. 3
3. $\frac{1}{2}x = 4$	c. -8
4. $\frac{2}{3}a = -4$	d. 6
5. $3b + 2 = b - 4$	e. -5

6. $2m - 1 = 2 + m$ f. 0

7. $\frac{2}{3}p + 4 = 2 - \frac{1}{3}p$ g. 2

8. $2z + 3 = 4 + 3z$ h. 1

9. $4 - 2d = 5 - 3d$ i. -3

10. $3c - 1 = c - 1$ j. -4

11. $2(2n - 6) = 3n - 16$ k. 5

12. $n(n - 2) = n^2 - (n + 6)$ l. 4

13. $3n(n - 1) = 3n^2 - 2(n - 4)$ m. -2

14. $2x + x(x - 4) = x^2 - 10$ n. -6

15. $y - 2(3y + 5) = y - 2(y - 5)$ o. 8

REVIEW TEST 14

In the left-hand column below are stated problems. In the right-hand column are algebraic equations that state the facts given in those problems. On a sheet of paper write the numbers 1 through 20 to correspond to the numbers of the stated problems. After each number place a letter matching the problem with the algebraic equation that would lead to the correct solution. Some of the equations found in the right-hand column will not lead to a solution for any of the problems.

H 1. The sum of two consecutive numbers is 35. What are those numbers?

E 2. The sum of two consecutive even numbers is 34. What are those numbers?

L 3. Carol is 3 years older than Barbara. If their combined age is 35 years, how old is each girl?

C 4. George is 4 years older than Clifford and Clifford is twice as old as Wayne. If their combined ages total 24 years, how old is each?

J 5. The sum of three consecutive even numbers is 24. What are the numbers?

M 6. On a certain project John lacked 6 days of working twice as many days as did Jack. If the sum of the days they worked is 24, how many days did each work?

a 7. If the length of a rectangle is 2 feet more than twice the width and the

a. $2x + 2(2x + 2) = 34$

b. $3x - \$23.00 = \$78.00$

c. $5x + 4 = 24$

d. $x + (x + 1) + (x + 3) = 88$

e. $2x + 2 = 34$

f. $x = 0.25(30)$

g. $x + x + 2 = 34$

h. $2x + 1 = 35$

i. $0.75x + 1.25(315 - x)$ $= \$321.25$

j. $3x + 6 = 24$

k. $x + 0.25x = 30$

l. $2x + 3 = 35$

m. $2x - 6 = 24$

n. $2x - \$23.00 = \$78.00$

o. $3x + \$1,500 = \$17,500$

p. $3x - 6 = 24$

q. $x + 0.20x = \$36.00$

perimeter is 34 feet, what are the dimensions of the rectangle?

8. If the width of a rectangle is 2 feet more than one-half the length and the perimeter is 34 feet, what are the dimensions of the rectangle?

9. A merchant makes a profit of 25 percent on the cost of a radio that sells for $30. What is the cost of the radio?

10. A merchant buys a chair for $30 and marks it to sell for 25 percent above the cost to him. What will be the selling price of the chair?

11. A man pays $23 more state income tax than he does property tax. If the two cost him $78, how much state income tax and how much property tax does he pay?

12. A man pays two insurance policies whose premiums total $78. If one premium is $23 less than twice the other one, how much is each premium?

13. Two boys who weigh 110 and 125 pounds respectively sit on opposite ends of a 16-foot seesaw. If they balance each other, how far is each from the fulcrum?

14. A and C weigh 100 and 150 pounds respectively and sit on opposite ends of a 22-foot seesaw whose fulcrum is midway between the ends of the board. Where must B, who weighs 110 pounds, sit to balance the seesaw?

15. Jack has 88 cents consisting of pennies, nickels, and dimes in his pocket. He has two more pennies than nickels and one more nickel than dimes. How many of each coin does he have?

16. At a sports event the adult tickets sold for $1.25 and the student tickets for $.75. If a total of 315 tickets were sold and amounted to $321.25 in admissions, how many of each type of ticket were sold?

17. A realtor sold two properties for $17,500. If one sold for $1,500 more

r. $2(x + 2) + 2(2x) = 34$

s. $x = \$30 + 0.25(\$30)$

t. $110x + 1,100 = 1,650$

u. $110(x - 16) = 125x$

v. $2x + \$1,500 = \$17,500$

w. $2x - 3 = 35$

x. $x - 0.20x = \$36.00$

y. $10x + 5(x + 1) + x + 3 = 88$

z. $125x = 110(16 - x)$

than the other one, for how much did each sell?

Q 18. At a sale a merchant advertised that everything would sell at 20 percent less than the marked price. What would be the regular price of an article that was marked to sell for $36?

19. A man paid $17,500 for a vacant lot and another lot with a house on it. If the property with the house on it cost him $1,500 more than twice the cost of the vacant lot, how much did he pay for each?

20. A merchant buys a lawn mower and sells it at 20 percent above cost. If he sells it for $36, what did the mower cost him?

5

Inequalities

In Chapter 1 we stated the law of trichotomy, which tells us that if a and b are any real numbers, then $a = b$, or $a < b$, or $a > b$. It will also be recalled that we stated in Chapter 1 that if $a \leq b$, this is read: "a is less than or equal to b," and if $a \geq b$, we say that "a is greater than or equal to b."

On the number line the greater of two numbers is located to the right of the smaller number. Thus if $a > b$, then a would be to the right of b.

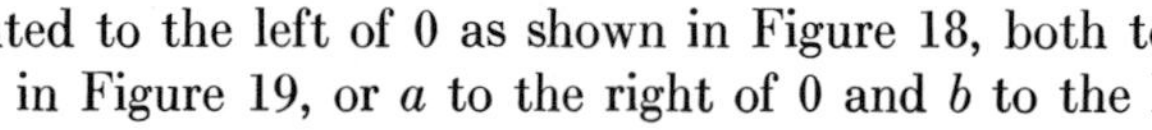

Figure 18

Observe in Figures 18, 19, and 20 that it makes no difference where a and b are located with respect to 0. In each case, if $a > b$, both numbers may be located to the left of 0 as shown in Figure 18, both to the right of 0 as seen in Figure 19, or a to the right of 0 and b to the left of 0 as

$$\begin{array}{ccc} & & \\ \overline{} \bullet \bullet \bullet \\ 0 b a \end{array}$$

Figure 19

98

shown in Figure 20. In each case a is greater than b, and so is located to the right of b.

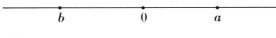

Figure 20

To graph an inequality we use the number line and indicate the solution by heavy dots at each number on the line that satisfies the condition expressed by the inequality.

The set of numbers with which we are concerned at a given time or which applies to a given problem is called the *universal set*. To indicate the universal set we may use the letter U. Thus if we are concerned with only the one-digit natural numbers, we would indicate this by writing $U = \{1, 2, 3, 4, 5, 6, 7, 8, 9\}$. For the sake of brevity this may also be written $U = \{1, 2, 3, \ldots, 9\}$. This expression is read: "U is the set of one-digit natural numbers" or "U is the set of natural numbers up to and including 9." The expression $U = \{1, 2, 3, \ldots\}$ means the entire set of natural numbers. Likewise, $U = \{1, 3, 5, \ldots\}$ would read: "The set of all odd natural numbers."

If U is the set of natural numbers and $A = \{x \mid x < 7\}$, this expression means that x can be any natural number less than 7 and the solution set is $\{1, 2, 3, 4, 5, 6\}$. We would graph this as shown in Figure 21.

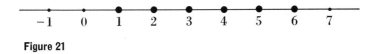

Figure 21

In a similar manner, if $U = \{-2, -1, 0, 1, 2, 3\}$ and $B = \{x \mid x < 1\}$, the solution set would be $\{-2, -1, 0\}$. The graph of this is shown in Figure 22.

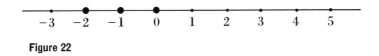

Figure 22

When two inequality symbols point in the same direction, the two inequalities are said to be unequal in the *same order* or *same sense*. Thus the two inequalities $a > b$ and $x > y$ are unequal in the same sense. If the symbols point in opposite directions, as $a > b$ and $x < y$, the inequalities are unequal in the *opposite sense*.

If U is the set of all natural numbers and $A = \{x \mid 3 < x < 7\}$, this means that 3 is less than x (or that x is greater than 3) and that x is less than 7. The graph of this is shown in Figure 23.

Figure 23

In a similar manner, if U is the set of all natural numbers and $B = \{x \mid 1 < x \le 5\}$, we would read this: "The set of all x such that 1 is less than x and x is less than or equal to 5." To graph this we must include the 5 as shown in Figure 24.

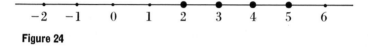

Figure 24

When U includes all the real numbers, then we are, of course, concerned with every number on the number line, integers as well as every number between each set of any two consecutive integers. In order to show this we use a heavy line in the graph. Thus if U is the set of all real numbers and $C = \{x \mid x > 2\}$, we would shade in the entire line to the right of 2. To indicate that all such numbers are included and that the line extends infinitely far to the right, we use an arrow at the end of the line. A problem arises in the construction of this graph: How can we show that 2 is not included but that every number to the right of 2 is included? In such cases we circle the 2 to mean that 2 is not included. If it is to be included, we use the heavy dot rather than the circle. The graph of set C above, then, is shown in Figure 25.

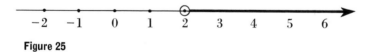

Figure 25

In a similar manner, if U is the set of all real numbers and $A = \{x \mid -2 < x \le 4\}$, the graph of A would be as shown in Figure 26.

In some of the problems we have under consideration, there are two parts in the condition imposed on the variable. In the problem above, $\{A = \{x \mid -2 < x \le 4\}$, the $-2 < x \le 4$ is the condition imposed on

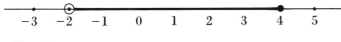

Figure 26

the variable x. We could very well write this in the set builder as $A = \{x \mid -2 < x \text{ and } x \leq 4\}$. In this case x must satisfy the first condition *and* the second condition.

Set A could have been written as two sets and then the intersection of those two sets would be the solution set. Thus if $A = \{x \mid -2 < x \leq 4\}$, we might say that $M = \{x \mid -2 < x\}$ and $N = \{x \mid x \leq 4\}$, and then $M \cap N = A$. In Figure 26 set M would include all the real numbers to the right of -2 and set N would include all the real numbers less than or equal to 4. Thus $M \cap N = A$ and includes only those elements common to both set M and set N.

In a similar manner, set B (associated with Figure 24) could be written as two sets. If we let $R = \{x \mid 1 < x\}$ and $S = \{x \mid x \leq 5\}$, then $R = \{2, 3, 4, \ldots\}$ and $S = \{1, 2, 3, 4, 5\}$. Since the intersection of two sets consists of those elements common to the two sets, $R \cap S = \{2, 3, 4, 5\}$, as shown in Figure 24. It must be kept in mind that any set in the form $\{x \mid a < x < b\}$ means $a < x$ and $x < b$.

Again, if U is the set of all real numbers and $B = \{x \mid x < 3 \text{ or } x > 5\}$, notice that we have used the word *or* rather than *and*. The graph of set B is shown in Figure 27. The word *or* used above implies that either the

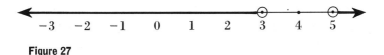

Figure 27

first condition ($x < 3$) *or* the second condition ($x > 5$) is the replacement for our variable x. We could very well write two sets from set B — $D = \{x \mid x < 3\}$ or $E = \{x \mid x > 5\}$—and set B is the union of sets D and E.

Since the word *and* implies intersection of the sets, we can observe from Figure 27 that there are no elements in common and that $\{x \mid x < 3 \text{ and } x > 5\} = \varnothing$.

Similarly, with this type of problem we may use the $\leq$ or $\geq$ symbols. If $C = \{x \mid x \geq 2 \text{ or } x < -1\}$, the graph is as shown in Figure 28 (note the circle and the heavy dot).

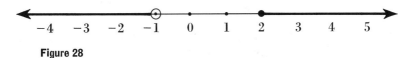

Figure 28

A

Graph the following inequalities where U is the set of natural numbers:

1. $\{x \mid x > 3\}$
2. $\{x \mid x < 3\}$
3. $\{x \mid -1 < x < 4\}$
4. $\{x \mid x \geq 0\}$
5. $\{x \mid 3 < x < 6\}$
6. $\{x \mid 0 < x < 1\}$
7. $\{x \mid x > 5 \text{ or } x < 3\}$
8. $\{x \mid x > 3 \text{ and } x < 6\}$

Graph the following inequalities where U is the set of all integers:

9. $\{x \mid x < 1\}$
10. $\{x \mid x > -4\}$
11. $\{x \mid x < 4 \text{ and } x > -4\}$
12. $\{x \mid 2 < x < 5\}$
13. $\{x \mid x < -5 \text{ or } x > 5\}$
14. $\{x \mid x > 0 \text{ or } x \leq -2\}$
15. $\{x \mid -5 < x < -1\}$

B

Graph the following inequalities where U is the set of all real numbers:

1. $\{x \mid -2 < x < 1\}$
2. $\{x \mid -5 < x < -1\}$
3. $\{x \mid 3 < x \leq 7\}$
4. $\{x \mid x < 1 \text{ or } x \geq 3\}$
5. $\{x \mid x > 2 \text{ and } x < 4\}$
6. $\{x \mid x \geq 0 \text{ or } x \leq -2\}$
7. $\{x \mid x < 4 \text{ and } x \geq 1\}$
8. $\{x \mid -3 \leq x \leq 3\}$
9. $\{x \mid x > 6\}$
10. $\{x \mid 3 < x \leq 0\}$

26. ALGEBRAIC SOLUTION OF INEQUALITIES

Before we undertake the solution of inequalities by algebraic methods, let us consider once more the number line as shown in Figure 29. Keep

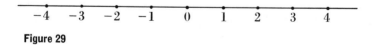

Figure 29

in mind that any number to the right of another is the larger of the two numbers. Furthermore, if we subtract the smaller number from the larger number, the difference will always be a positive number. To show that this holds for all numbers, first consider Figure 30, in which a is larger than b and both $-a$ and $-b$ are negative numbers. Algebraically, $(-a) - (-b) = (-a) + (b)$. The distance from $-b$ to 0 is greater than the distance from $-a$ to 0. Algebraically, we are adding a positive b to a negative a and since the distance represented by $-b$ to 0 is greater than the distance represented by $-a$ to 0, the result will be a positive number.

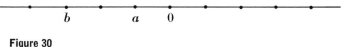

$$b \qquad a \qquad 0$$

Figure 30

If a is a positive number and $-b$ is a negative number, as shown in Figure 31, algebraically we have $(a) - (-b) = a + b$ and, by the law of

$$b \qquad 0 \qquad a$$

Figure 31

closure for addition, we have a positive number. The only case left for consideration is that in which both a and b are positive; since a is larger than b, if we subtract b from a, the difference will obviously be a positive number. From this discussion, we are prepared for the following definition:

Definition 1. If a and b are any real numbers and $a > b$, then $a - b$ is positive, and if $a < b$, then $b - a$ is positive. In other words, if $a > b$, then $a - b > 0$, and if $a < b$, then $b - a > 0$. *Also*, if $a < b$, then $a - b < 0$ or $a - b$ is negative.

To solve inequalities of the first degree, it will be necessary to prove the following theorems:

Theorem 1. If a, b, and c are any real numbers and $a > b$ and $b > c$, then $a > c$.

Proof:

        1. $a > b$ and $b > c$ (Given)
        2. $a - b > 0$ (Definition 1)
        3. $b - c > 0$ (Definition 1)

Let x and y be positive numbers and substitute them in steps 2 and 3 above. Then

4. $a - b = x$ (Substitution)
5. $b - c = y$ (Substitution)
6. $a - c = x + y$ (If equals are added to equals, the sums are equal [adding the corresponding members of the equations in steps 4 and 5].)
7. $x + y > 0$ (Law of closure for addition)
8. $a - c > 0$ (Substitution)
9. $a > c$ (Definition 1)

Theorem 1 tells us, then, that if the first of three numbers is larger than the second, and the second larger than the third, then the first number is larger than the third number.

A somewhat less complicated proof of Theorem 1 is shown in the following:

Proof:
1. $a > b$ and $b > c$ (Given)
2. $a - b > 0$ (Definition 1)
3. $b - c > 0$ (Definition 1)
4. $(a - b) + (b - c) > 0$ (The sum of two positive numbers is a positive number)
5. $(a - b + b - c) > 0$ (The associative law for addition)
6. $(a - c) > 0$ (Additive inverse)
7. $a > c$ (Definition 1)

Theorem 2. If a, b, and c are any real numbers and $a > b$, then $a + c > b + c$.

Proof:
1. $a > b$ (Given)
2. $a - b > 0$ (Definition 1)

Let x be any positive number; then

3. $a - b = x$ (Substitution)
4. $a - b + [c + (-c)] = x$ (The sum of any number and its negative is zero)
5. $a - b + c - c = x$ (Associative law)
6. $a + c - b - c = x$ (Commutative law for addition)
7. $(a + c) - (b + c) = x$ (If any numbers are grouped within parentheses and a negative sign placed before the parentheses, the signs of the numbers included are changed)
8. $a + c > b + c$ (Definition 1)

This theorem states that if a real number is added to both members of an inequality, the resulting inequality is in the same sense.

Theorem 3. If a and b are any real numbers, $a > b$, and c is a positive real number, then $ac > bc$.

Proof:
1. $a > b$ (Given)
2. $c > 0$ (Given)
3. $a - b > 0$ (Definition 1)

Let x be any positive number; then

4. $a - b = x$ (Substitution)
5. $ac - bc = xc$ (If equals are multiplied by equals, the products are equal)
6. xc is positive   (Law of closure)
7. $ac > bc$ (Definition 1)

This theorem states that if both members of an inequality are multiplied by the same positive number, the resulting inequality is in the same sense. Since we define division as the inverse of multiplication, this same theorem would apply. Thus if both members of an inequality are divided by the same positive number, the resulting quotients are unequal in the same sense.

Theorem 4. If a and b are any real numbers, $a > b$, and c is any negative real number, then $ac < bc$.

Proof:
1. $a > b$ (Given)
2. $c < 0$ (Given)
3. $a - b > 0$ (Definition 1)

Let x be any positive number; then

4. $a - b = x$ (Substitution)
5. $ac - bc = xc$ (If equals are multiplied by equals, the products are equal)
6. $xc < 0$ (The product of two numbers with unlike signs is negative)
7. $ac - bc < 0$ (Substitution)
8. $ac < bc$ (Definition 1)

This theorem states that if both members of an inequality are multiplied (or divided) by a negative number, the resulting inequality is in the opposite sense.

Example 1. Solve the following inequality: $\{x \mid 3x + 2 > 8\}$.

$$\{x \mid 3x + 2 > 8\} = \{x \mid 3x > 6\} \qquad \text{(Theorem 2. Add } -2 \text{ to both members of the inequality.)}$$
$$= \{x \mid x > 2\} \qquad \text{(Theorem 3. Divide both members of the inequality by the same positive value, 3 in this case.)}$$
$$= \{x > 2\}$$

Example 2. Solve the following inequality: $\{x \mid \frac{1}{3}x + 3 < 2\}$.

$$\{x \mid \tfrac{1}{3}x + 3 < 2\} = \{x \mid \tfrac{1}{3}x < -1\} \qquad \text{(Theorem 2. Add } -3 \text{ to both members of the inequality.)}$$
$$= \{x \mid x < -3\} \qquad \text{(Theorem 3. Multiply both members of the inequality by 3.)}$$
$$= \{x < -3\}$$

Example 3. Solve the following inequality: $\{x \mid 3x + 1 \geq x + 7\}$.

$$\{x \mid 3x + 1 \geq x + 7\} = \{x \mid 3x \geq x + 6\} \qquad \text{(Theorem 2. Add } -1 \text{ to both members of the inequality.)}$$
$$= \{x \mid 2x \geq 6\} \qquad \text{(Theorem 2. Add } -x \text{ to both members of the inequality.)}$$
$$= \{x \mid x \geq 3\} \qquad \text{(Theorem 3. Divide both members of the inequality by } +2.)$$
$$= \{x \geq 3\}$$

Example 4. Solve the following inequality: $\{x \mid 2 - x < 4\}$.

$$\{x \mid 2 - x < 4\} = \{x \mid -x < 2\} \qquad \text{(Theorem 2. Add } -2 \text{ to both members of the inequality.)}$$
$$= \{x \mid x > -2\} \qquad \text{(Theorem 4. Multiply both members of the inequality by } -1.)$$
$$= \{x > -2\}$$

Example 5. Solve the following inequality: $\{x \mid -1 < x + 1 < 5\}$.

$$\{x \mid -1 < x + 1 < 5\} = \{x \mid -2 < x < 4\} \qquad \text{(Theorem 2. Add } -1 \text{ to each of the three members of the double inequality.)}$$
$$= \{-2 < x < 4\}$$

27. ABSOLUTE VALUE

There are times when we are concerned only with the magnitude of a number and have no interest in its direction. Let us suppose that from a given intersection of two streets one automobile drove 4 miles east and a second one drove 4 miles west. From the starting position each of these numbers, as far as direction is concerned, is the opposite of the other or one is the additive inverse of the other. However, in this case we are concerned only with the distance traveled, which in each case is 4 miles. In both cases we say this 4 is the *absolute value*. In a similar manner, on the number line 4 and -4 each is a distance of 4 units from 0.

To indicate the absolute value of a number, we flank it with a vertical line on both sides, for example, as, $|4|$.

Definition 2. If a is any real number, its absolute value $|a|$ is defined by

$$|a| = a \quad \text{(if } a > 0)$$
$$|a| = -a \quad \text{(if } a < 0)$$
$$|a| = 0 \quad \text{(if } a = 0)$$

We recall from an earlier discussion that if a is a positive number, the $-a$ is negative and $|-a| = a$, whereas $|a| = a$. Thus $|-a| = |a|$. It must be kept in mind that absolute value is always nonnegative.

The linear inequalities we previously worked with involved either a positive or a negative variable. What impact does using the absolute value of the variable have on the solution? In the expression $|x| < m$, where $m > 0$, either $x < m$ or $-x < m$. If $-x < m$, then, by Theorem 4, $x > -m$ since we have multiplied both members of the inequality by -1. Hence $|x| < m$ means that $x < m$ and $x > -m$; this may be written $-m < x < m$. Thus $|x| < m$ and $-m < x < m$ mean the same thing.

Likewise, if $|x| > m$, this means that $x > m$ and $-x > m$. Again, if we multiply both members of the inequality $-x > m$ by -1, this becomes $x < -m$. Thus $|x| > m$ and $x < -m$ or $x > m$ mean the same thing.

Example 1. Solve the following inequality: $|x - 1| < 3$.

The inequality $|x - 1| < 3$ may be written as $-3 < x - 1 < 3$.

1. $-3 < x - 1 < 3$ (Given)
2. $-2 < x < 4$ (Theorem 2. Add 1 to each member of the double inequality.)

Example 2. Solve the following inequality: $|2x/3| < 4$.

The inequality $|2x/3| < 4$ may be written $-4 < 2x/3 < 4$.

1. $-4 < \dfrac{2x}{3} < 4$ (Given)

2. $-12 < 2x < 12$ (Theorem 3. Multiply each member of the double inequality by $+3$.)

3. $-6 < x < 6$ (Theorem 3. Divide each member of the double inequality by $+2$)

Example 3. Solve the following inequality: $|2 - x| > 3$.

1. $|2 - x| > 3$ (Given)

2. $-3 > 2 - x$ or   (Substitution of an equivalent form)
   $2 - x > 3$

3. $-5 > -x$ or   (Theorem 2. Add -2 to all three mem-
   $-x > 1$ bers of the inequality.)

4. $5 < x$ or $x < -1$ (Theorem 4. Multiply all three members of the double inequality by -1.)

A

Solve the following inequalities:

1. $x - 5 > 1$ 2. $2x + 3 > 5$

3. $1 - x < 6$ 4. $2x - 4 > x + 3$

5. $\dfrac{x}{2} < 3$ 6. $2x - \frac{1}{2} > 3$

                           8. $\dfrac{1 - 2x}{5} > 3$

7. $\dfrac{x + 3}{3} < 1$

9. $|4 - x| < 1$ 10. $|1 - 2x| > 5$

B

Solve the following inequalities:

1. $\left|\dfrac{x - 2}{4}\right| < 3$ 2. $|4 - 3x| > 5$

3. $|2 + 3x| < 7$ 4. $\left|\dfrac{1 - x}{2}\right| > 5$

5. $\left|\dfrac{3 - x}{3}\right| > 2$

If a, b, and c are any real numbers, prove the following inequalities:

6. If $a > b$ and $c < 0$, then $\dfrac{a}{c} < \dfrac{b}{c}$.

7. If $a < b$ and $c > 0$, then $a - c < b - c$.

8. If $a > b$ and $c < 0$, then $c - a < c - b$.

The algebraic equivalent of each of the following graphs is included in the statements that follow the graphs. On a sheet of paper write the numbers 1 through 10 and after each number place the capital letter accompanying the statement that matches each graph. Some of the statements do not match any of the given graphs. In all cases assume that U is the set of all real numbers.

1.

2.

3.

4.

5.

6.

7.

8.

9.

10.

A. $x > -1$ and $x < 3$ B. $x < 8$ C. $x > 0$ or $x \le -4$

D. $|x - 1| > 2$ E. $3 < x < 8$ F. $2 < x < 5$

G. $x \le 3$ or $x \ge 8$ H. $3 \le x \le 8$ I. $x \ge 3$

J. $|2x + 1| < 3$ K. $-4 < x \le 0$ L. $-1 \le x \le 3$

M. $-4 \le x < 0$ N. $x < 2$ or $x > 5$ O. $x \le -1$ or $x \ge 3$

6

Special Products
and Factorization

28. INTRODUCTION

As one continues with the study of mathematics, much of his success depends upon his ability to recognize certain forms or concepts and to perform some of the computations mentally. One of the most useful techniques in working with algebra is that of converting an algebraic expression of two or more terms into factored form.

The techniques and skills utilized in making this conversion to factored form is known as *factorization*. A great many of the algebraic expressions with which we are confronted may be factored. These expressions tend to fall into certain types of products whose factors are of certain classifications, as we shall observe throughout the discussion in the present chapter.

A *prime integer* is any natural number greater than 1 that has no integral factors except itself and 1. Thus the only integral factors of 3 are 3 and 1 and of 7 are 7 and 1. Then we say that 3 and 1 are the prime factors of 3 and that 7 and 1 are the prime factors of 7. Algebraic expressions such as x, $x + 1$, $x - y$, and $x - y + z$ have no factors except themselves and 1. We should refrain from saying that they are prime numbers as we have no information about the values of the various letters that are used. It will be our purpose in this discussion to convert algebraic expressions into factors that have no factors except themselves and 1.

As explained earlier in this text, *factors* are two or more numbers or expressions that result in a product when they are multiplied together. Examples of this are: $(3)(4) = 12$, $(5)(2) = 10$, and $(6)(7) = 42$. In each case the numbers enclosed within parentheses are factors that, when multiplied together, result in the product that is in the right member of the equation. In the first example, $(3)(4)$, the 4 could be rewritten as $(2)(2)$. Thus the factors, instead of being 3 and 4, could be 3, 2, and 2. Likewise, the 6 and 7 in the last example could be 3, 2, and 7. The factors as shown in the latter form cannot be simplified.

In general, monomial algebraic factors are not usually converted into prime factors. The expression $6x^2$ could be expressed as $(3)(2)(x)(x)$ but such an expression is usually kept in its original form for the sake of brevity and simplicity.

To find the prime factors of a given larger natural number, we may start by dividing it by prime numbers.

Example 1. Find the prime factors of 248.

We know that any number whose right-hand digit is an even number is divisible by 2. Since 2 is a prime number, then we may proceed as follows:

$$248 = (2)(124)$$
$$= (2)(2)(62)$$
$$= (2)(2)(2)(31)$$

Since the above four factors are all prime numbers, we have the prime factors of 248.

Example 2. Find the prime factors of 120.

$$120 = (2)(60)$$
$$= (2)(2)(30)$$
$$= (2)(2)(2)(15)$$
$$= (2)(2)(2)(3)(5)$$

Example 3. Find the prime factors of 225.

$$225 = (3)(75)$$
$$= (3)(3)(25)$$
$$= (3)(3)(5)(5)$$

Find the prime factors of the following numbers:

1. 15	2. 20	3. 18	4. 24
5. 28	6. 36	7. 35	8. 60
9. 72	10. 100	11. 112	12. 150
13. 224	14. 512	15. 750	16. 1000
17. 1600	18. 3200	19. 4860	20. 7224

29. THE DIFFERENCE OF TWO SQUARES

The product of the sum and difference of two numbers introduces a unique pattern of algebraic expressions. If x and y are any real numbers, then their sum is denoted by $x + y$ and their difference by $x - y$. The product of this sum and difference is found by use of the distributive law. Thus

$$\begin{aligned}(x + y)(x - y) &= x(x - y) + y(x - y) \\ &= x^2 - xy + xy - y^2 \\ &= x^2 + (-xy) + (xy) - y^2 \\ &= x^2 + 0 - y^2 \\ &= x^2 - y^2\end{aligned}$$

Since x and y represent any real numbers, this pattern holds for the product of the sum and difference of all real numbers. We observe from the above solution that

$$(x + y)(x - y) = x^2 - y^2$$

By the law of symmetry, this may be written

$$x^2 - y^2 = (x + y)(x - y)$$

Thus the factors of $x^2 - y^2$ are $(x + y)$ and $(x - y)$.

The x^2 and y^2 we call *perfect squares* because each is obtained by multiplying a number by itself ($x \cdot x = x^2$ and $y \cdot y = y^2$). Likewise, $16a^2b^2$ and $49m^2n^2$ are perfect squares since $(4ab)(4ab) = 16a^2b^2$ and $(7mn)(7mn) = 49m^2n^2$. We should also observe that $(-4ab)(-4ab) = 16a^2b^2$ and that $(-7mn)(-7mn) = 49m^2n^2$.

The *square root* of a number is one of two identical factors that when multiplied together give us the original number. In the first of the above examples $4ab$ is the square root of $16a^2b^2$ since $(4ab)(4ab) = 16a^2b^2$. We observed also that $(-4ab)(-4ab) = 16a^2b^2$. Thus $16a^2b^2$ has two square roots,

$-4ab$ and $4ab$. The two are sometimes combined and we say that the square root of $16a^2b^2$ is $\pm 4ab$, which is read: "The square root of $16a^2b^2$ is *either* $4ab$ or $-4ab$." In a similar manner, the square root of $49m^2n^2$ is $\pm 7mn$.

The symbol "$\sqrt{}$" is called a *radical* and is used to denote the square root of a number under the radical. Thus $\sqrt{16a^2b^2}$ means $\pm 4ab$ if a and b represent positive numbers. In this case we do not know whether a and b represent positive or negative numbers. When such is the case, we express the answer as $\sqrt{16a^2b^2} = 4|ab|$ and $-\sqrt{16a^2b^2} = -4|ab|$. The square root is always the *principal* or *positive* square root designated by $\sqrt{}$. Its opposite is designated by $-\sqrt{}$.

The *cube root* of a number is one of three identical factors that when multiplied together give the original number. Thus the cube root of 8 is 2, since $2 \cdot 2 \cdot 2 = 8$. In radical form, $\sqrt[3]{8} = 2$. In a similar manner, the cube root of -8 is -2 since $(-2)(-2)(-2) = -8$. The small number placed in the crook of the radical tells us which root is to be found. Thus $\sqrt[4]{16}$ means we want the fourth root of 16 and $\sqrt[5]{32}$ states that we wish to find the fifth root of 32. If no number is placed in the crook of the radical, it is understood that square root is implied. In all cases in which a radical is used, the number under the radical is called the *radicand*.

From the above discussion we observe that to factor the difference of two perfect squares we simply take the square roots of the two numbers and form one factor by expressing the sum of those square roots and the other factor by expressing the difference of the two square roots.

Example 1. Find the product of $(2x - 3y)(2x + 3y)$.

$$
\begin{aligned}
(2x - 3y)(2x + 3y) &= 2x(2x + 3y) - 3y(2x + 3y) \\
&= 4x^2 + 6xy - 6xy - 9y^2 \\
&= 4x^2 + 0 - 9y^2 \\
&= 4x^2 - 9y^2
\end{aligned}
$$

Example 2. Find the product of $(xy + z)$ and $(xy - z)$.

$$
\begin{aligned}
(xy + z)(xy - z) &= xy(xy - z) + z(xy - z) \\
&= x^2y^2 - xyz + xyz - z^2 \\
&= x^2y^2 - z^2
\end{aligned}
$$

Example 3. Factor $t^2 - r^2$.

$$t^2 - r^2 = (t + r)(t - r)$$

Example 4. Factor $25a^2 - 9b^2$.

The square root of $25a^2$ is $5a$ and of $9b^2$ is $3b$. Then

$$25a^2 - 9b^2 = (5a + 3b)(5a - 3b)$$

Example 5. Factor $(x + y)^2 - (m - n)^2$.

This problem expresses the difference of two squares since $(x + y)^2$ is the square of $(x + y)$ and $(m - n)^2$ is the square of $(m - n)$. We proceed as in the previous examples, the only difference being that we are using larger units than in the former cases. Then

$$(x + y)^2 - (m - n)^2 = [(x + y) + (m - n)][(x + y) - (m - n)]$$
$$= [x + y + m - n][x + y - m + n]$$

A technique frequently used in solutions of large or cumbersome mathematical expressions is that of substituting simpler expressions for those larger units. We use these simplified forms to accomplish the computations and then substitute the larger equivalents in the answer obtained.

In Example 5 let us, for the time being, substitute as follows: Let

$$a = x + y \qquad \text{and} \qquad b = m - n$$

Then

$$a^2 = (x + y)^2 \qquad \text{and} \qquad b^2 = (m - n)^2$$

Now our problem becomes that of factoring $a^2 - b^2$, which, of course, is

$$a^2 - b^2 = (a + b)(a - b)$$

The next step then requires that we substitute back into the solution the values for a and b. Hence in the above solution we substitute $(x + y)$ for each a and $(m - n)$ for each b. Then

$$(a + b)(a - b) = [(x + y) + (m - n)][(x + y) - (m - n)]$$
$$= [x + y + m - n][x + y - m + n]$$

This answer is identical to that we obtained in the original solution.

Example 6. Factor $s^4 - t^4$.

$$s^4 - t^4 = (s^2 + t^2)(s^2 - t^2)$$

It can be observed that the second factor is, again, the difference of two squares. To factor completely, our answer must consist of factors each of which has no factors except itself and 1. The complete solution of the above problem, then, is shown as follows:

$$s^4 - t^4 = (s^2 + t^2)(s^2 - t^2)$$
$$= (s^2 + t^2)(s + t)(s - t)$$

The student may possibly observe the first factor—that of $(s^2 + t^2)$—and consider the possible factorization of it. In most cases the sum of two squares has no factors except itself and 1. There are certain cases of the sum of two squares in which factorization is possible, but in this course we shall not consider such cases. In a subsequent course in algebra this type of factoring will be developed.

A

Multiply:

1. $(p + q)(p - q)$
3. $(2a + 1)(2a - 1)$
5. $(4z - 3y)(4z + 3y)$
7. $(mn - p)(mn + p)$
9. $(2ab - c)(2ab + c)$
11. $(xyz + 2)(xyz - 2)$
13. $(3c - mn)(3c + mn)$
15. $(bd - 7c)(bd + 7c)$

2. $(d + 4)(d - 4)$
4. $(3s + 5)(3s - 5)$
6. $(m - 6)(m + 6)$
8. $(rs - t)(rs + t)$
10. $(9a + bc)(9a - bc)$
12. $(cd - 3f)(cd + 3f)$
14. $(rst - y)(rst + y)$

Factor:

16. $d^2 - 4c^2$
19. $16m^2 - 49n^2$
22. $4 - z^2$
25. $4c^2d^2 - 49$
28. $16a^2b^2 - 25c^2$
31. $a^2b^2 - c^2d^2$
34. $16c^2d^2 - 81a^2b^2$

17. $x^2 - 9y^2$
20. $9a^2 - 64b^2$
23. $p^2q^2 - 1$
26. $1 - z^2$
29. $1 - 49m^2$
32. $4x^2y^2 - z^2$
35. $m^2n^2p^2 - 1$

18. $4t^2 - 25s^2$
21. $36y^2 - 25w^2$
24. $x^2 - 81$
27. $n^2 - 100$
30. $100a^2 - 81c^2$
33. $25r^2s^2 - 1$

B

Factor:

1. $d^4 - c^4$
3. $81x^4 - 16y^4$
5. $16 - p^4$
7. $a^8 - b^8$
9. $(4a^2 - b^2)^2 - (x^2 - y^2)^2$

2. $4m^4 - n^2$
4. $36a^4 - 1$
6. $81x^8 - 16y^4$
8. $(d - c)^2 - (p + q)^2$
10. $(x^2 - y^2)^2 - (m^2 + n^2)^2$

30. THE QUADRATIC TRINOMIAL

The trinomial $ax^2 + bx + c$ is called the *general quadratic trinomial*—quadratic because the highest power of the variable x is 2. In that trinomial a, b, and c are constants. The development of multiplication in a previous chapter frequently led to a product in the form of the general quadratic trinomial. The product obtained by multiplying together certain types of two binomial expressions is of this form. Consider the multiplication of $(a + 3)$ and $(2a + 1)$. By the distributive law, this becomes

$$(2a + 1)(a + 3) = 2a(a + 3) + 1(a + 3)$$
$$= 2a^2 + 6a + a + 3$$
$$= 2a^2 + 7a + 3$$

Then, by the law of symmetry, we have

$$2a^2 + 7a + 3 = (2a + 1)(a + 3)$$

To factor a trinomial such as the one above, we first state the trinomial as the product of two binomials in the form

$$2a^2 + 7a + 3 = (? + ?)(? + ?)$$

The product of the two first terms in the binomials must produce the first term in the trinomial, $2a^2$ in this case. The only nonfractional factors that will produce $2a^2$ are $2a$ and a. Then our partial solution becomes

$$2a^2 + 7a + 3 = (2a + ?)(a + ?)$$

The product of the last two terms must equal the third term in the trinomial, 3 in this case. Our solution then may be

$$2a^2 + 7a + 3 = (2a + 1)(a + 3)$$

This may or may not be the correct set of factors since we could very well have set the factors as $(2a + 3)(a + 1)$. In either case we would obtain the proper first and third terms in the given trinomial.

We must test the factors established to see if they will give us the proper second term. To do this we multiply together the *two outer terms* and the *two inner terms*, as shown below, and if the algebraic sum of those two products is identical to the second term in the trinomial, then the factors are correctly formed. Observe the factors we have in the following:

$$\overset{\text{outer}}{2a^2 + 7a + 3 = (2a + 1)(a + 3)}$$
$$\underset{\text{inner}}{}$$

The product of the two outer terms is $6a$ and of the two inner terms is a. The algebraic sum of $6a$ and a is $7a$. Since this is the second term in the trinomial, our factors are correct.

Example 1.   Find the product of $(2x - y)(3x + 4y)$.

$$(2x - y)(3x + 4y) = 2x(3x + 4y) - y(3x + 4y)$$
$$= 6x^2 + 8xy - 3xy - 4y^2$$
$$= 6x^2 + 5xy - 4y^2$$

If we wish to factor this $6x^2 + 5xy - 4y^2$, we proceed as in the previous example. The $6x^2$, again, must be the product of the first terms in each of the binomial factors. Here we could use $6x$ and x or $3x$ and $2x$. Until the student has had considerable practice in factoring, the selection of possible factors will, in all probability, become a trial-and-error procedure. Let us use the $3x$ and $2x$. Then

$$6x^2 + 5y - 4y^2 = (3x \quad ?)(2x \quad ?)$$

It will be noted that the signs have been omitted in this set of binomial factors. We can readily see that the last term in the trinomial follows a negative sign. When this occurs, the signs between the terms in the binomial factors will be unlike (one positive and one negative). This can be explained by changing the product to read

$$6x^2 + 5xy + (-4y^2)$$

Then to obtain a $-4y^2$ we must multiply together two terms with unlike signs. Again, that last term could be the product of $4y$ and $-y$, $-4y$ and $+y$, or $2y$ and $-2y$. Let us use $4y$ and $-y$. Then, to proceed,

$$6x^2 + 5xy - 4y^2 = (3x + 4y)(2x - y)$$

The product of the two outer terms is $(3x)(-y)$, or $-3xy$, and of the two inner terms is $(4y)(2x)$, or $8xy$. Then the algebraic sum is $8xy - 3xy$, or $5xy$. Since this $5xy$ is the second term of the original trinomial, our solution is correct.

It will be observed that above we used, for the last factor, a $-y$. The negative sign between the $2x$ and the y is a sign of operation. However, if we wrote the last factor as $[2x + (-y)]$, then we are justified in using the $-y$.

Example 2. Factor $24x^2 - 14x - 3$.

$$24x^2 - 14x - 3 = (4x - 3)(6x + 1)$$

Example 3. Factor $x^2 - 7x + 12$.

In this example it will be noted that the $7x$ follows a negative sign. This means that both signs between the terms in the binomial factors will be negative. It will be seen in the solution below that the product of the two outer terms will be negative, as will be the product of the two inner terms. The algebraic sum of these two products is the sum of two negative numbers.

$$x^2 - 7x + 12 = (x - 3)(x - 4)$$

In retrospect, we can see that in a general quadratic trinomial if the first and last terms follow positive signs, the signs between the terms in the binomial factors will be alike and will be the same as the sign preceding the second term in the trinomial. If the third term in the trinomial follows a negative sign, one of the binomial factors will be a sum and the other one a difference of two numbers.

A special type of quadratic trinomial is what we call a *perfect square trinomial*. Before we define this kind of trinomial, let us consider the following multiplication problems:

Example 4. Multiply $(x + y)(x + y)$.

$$\begin{aligned}(x + y)(x + y) &= x(x + y) + y(x + y) \\ &= x^2 + xy + xy + y^2 \\ &= x^2 + 2xy + y^2\end{aligned}$$

Example 5. Multiply $(x - y)(x - y)$.

$$\begin{aligned}(x - y)(x - y) &= x(x - y) - y(x - y) \\ &= x^2 - xy - xy + y^2 \\ &= x^2 - 2xy + y^2\end{aligned}$$

Example 6. Multiply $(3p + 2q)(3p + 2q)$.

$$\begin{aligned}(3p + 2q)(3p + 2q) &= 3p(3p + 2q) + 2q(3p + 2q) \\ &= 9p^2 + 6pq + 6pq + 4q^2 \\ &= 9p^2 + 12pq + 4q^2\end{aligned}$$

Each of the three examples above consists of a binomial multiplied by itself. This is equivalent to saying that we are squaring a binomial. Example 4 could have been written $(x + y)^2$. Likewise, Examples 5 and 6 could have been stated with only one binomial factor having the notation that it was to be squared. Each of the expansions above resulted in a trinomial whose first and third terms were perfect squares and followed positive signs and whose second term was twice the product of the square roots of the first and third terms. This statement, then, is the definition of a perfect square trinomial.

It can be seen that in the perfect square trinomial both the first and third terms follow positive signs. The sign preceding the second term may be either positive or negative and that sign governs the sign between the two terms in each of the identical binomial factors.

From this discussion, then, we can state the general procedure for squaring a binomial as follows: *To square a binomial, square the first term, then plus or minus (as the case may be) twice the product of the two terms, then plus the square of the second term.*

To determine if a trinomial is a perfect square trinomial, we check to see if both the first and last terms are perfect squares and if each follows a positive sign. If so, then we take the square roots of the first and last terms; if twice their product is equivalent to the second term in the trinomial, then the original is a perfect square trinomial and the two binomial factors will be identical.

Example 7. Factors $x^2 - 6x + 9$.
$$x^2 - 6x + 9 = (x - 3)(x - 3)$$

Example 8. Factor $1 + 14b + 49b^2$.
$$1 + 14b + 49b^2 = (1 + 7b)(1 + 7b)$$

Example 9. Factor $x^4 - 6x^2y + 9y^2$.
$$x^4 - 6x^2y + 9y^2 = (x^2 - 3y)(x^2 - 3y)$$

Trinomials may become somewhat more complicated when larger units are used. Consider the following trinomial and its factorization:

Example 10. Factor $(x + 1)^2 + 4(x + 1) + 3$.
$$\begin{aligned}(x + 1)^2 + 4(x + 1) + 3 &= [(x + 1) + 3][(x + 1) + 1] \\ &= [x + 1 + 3][x + 1 + 1] \\ &= [x + 4][x + 2]\end{aligned}$$

We could use the substitution method utilized earlier in this chapter by letting
$$u = (x + 1) \qquad \text{and} \qquad u^2 = (x + 1)^2$$

Then we substitute these values in the given problem and have
$$u^2 + 4u + 3$$

Then we factor $u^2 + 4u + 3$ as we have been doing in the general trinomials.
$$u^2 + 4u + 3 = (u + 3)(u + 1)$$

Now for each u we substitute the $x + 1$ and obtain
$$(x + 1 + 3)(x + 1 + 1) = (x + 4)(x + 2)$$

A third method for solving this problem is to simplify the original expression and then factor. Thus
$$\begin{aligned}(x + 1)^2 + 4(x + 1) + 3 &= x^2 + 2x + 1 + 4x + 4 + 3 \\ &= x^2 + 6x + 8\end{aligned}$$

Then we factor this expression and obtain
$$x^2 + 6x + 8 = (x + 4)(x + 2)$$

Example 11. Factor $3(x + 2y)^2 - 13(x + 2y) - 10$.

Letting
$$m = x + 2y \qquad \text{and} \qquad m^2 = (x + 2y)^2$$

we have

$$3m^2 - 13m - 10 = (3m + 2)(m - 5)$$

Then we substitute $x + 2y$ for each m in the above solution and get

$$(3m + 2)(m - 5) = [3(x + 2y) + 2][(x + 2y) - 5]$$
$$= [3x + 6y + 2][x + 2y - 5]$$

We must remember that it is always possible to check our solution by multiplying the factors together and if their product is the given expression our solution is correct. Example 11 above should be expanded in order to make this check. Thus

$$3(x + 2y)^2 - 13(x + 2y) - 10 = 3(x^2 + 4xy + 4y^2) - 13x - 26y - 10$$
$$= 3x^2 + 12xy + 12y^2 - 13x - 26y - 10$$

Then, to check,

$$(3x + 6y + 2)(x + 2y - 5)$$
$$= 3x(x + 2y - 5) + 6y(x + 2y - 5) + 2(x + 2y - 5)$$
$$= 3x^2 + 6xy - 15x + 6xy + 12y^2 - 30y + 2x + 4y - 10$$
$$= 3x^2 + 12xy + 12y^2 - 13x - 26y - 10$$

EXERCISE 25

A

Multiply:

1. $(y - 1)(y - 2)$ 2. $(b + 3)(b + 5)$ 3. $(m + 2)(m + 7)$
4. $(s - 1)(s - 5)$ 5. $(z + 3)(z + 3)$ 6. $(a + 4)(a + 2)$
7. $(b - 2)(b - 8)$ 8. $(x + 3)(x + 7)$ 9. $(n - 4)(n - 7)$
10. $(b + 1)(b - 6)$ 11. $(y - 4)(y + 6)$ 12. $(z - 5)(z + 8)$
13. $(2s + 3t)(3s + t)$ 14. $(3x - y)(2x + y)$ 15. $(2a - 5b)(a + 3b)$
16. $(a - 1)(5a + 6)$ 17. $(x - 3y)(5x + 2y)$ 18. $(3m - 5)(5m + 2)$
19. $(1 + a)^2$ 20. $(c - m)^2$ 21. $(x + 2y)^2$
22. $(3d + 2)^2$ 23. $(y - 3z)^2$ 24. $(2y + 3x)^2$
25. $(z - 5)^2$

Factor:

26. $x^2 + 7x + 6$ 27. $y^2 + 8y + 15$ 28. $m^2 + 9m + 18$
29. $a^2 + 14a + 48$ 30. $x^2 + 11x + 18$ 31. $t^2 - 4t + 3$
32. $b^2 - 10b + 21$ 33. $a^2 - 8a + 15$ 34. $x^2 - 12x + 35$

35. $y^2 - 13y + 36$ 36. $m^2 - m - 6$ 37. $c^2 + 2c - 24$

38. $y^2 - 5y - 24$ 39. $b^2 - 3b - 10$ 40. $a^2 - 2a - 24$

41. $b^2 + 11b + 28$ 42. $m^2 + 4m + 4$ 43. $c^2 - 6c + 9$

44. $z^2 - 8z + 16$ 45. $y^2 - 2y + 1$ 46. $1 - 8z + 16z^2$

47. $9y^2 - 12y + 4$ 48. $t^2 + 12t + 36$ 49. $p^2 - 18p + 81$

50. $64x^2 + 16x + 1$

B

Factor:

1. $4x^2 - 12xy + 9y^2$ 2. $c^2 - 18c + 81$

3. $49t^2 - 14t + 1$ 4. $64 - 16b + b^2$

5. $q^2 - 24q + 144$ 6. $121x^2 - 44x + 4$

7. $y^2 + 2y - 63$ 8. $d^2 - 12d + 32$

9. $d^2 - 6d - 27$ 10. $8a^2 - 34a + 21$

11. $12c^2 + 7c - 12$ 12. $15a^2 - 7a - 30$

13. $24z^2 + 30z - 9$ 14. $30p^2 + 49p - 9$

15. $(x + y)^2 + 5(x + y) + 6$ 16. $(2m + 3n)^2 - 8(2m + 3n) + 12$

17. $4(c - d)^2 - 5(c - d) - 6$ 18. $1 - (p + q) - 12(p + q)^2$

19. $(m - n)^2 - 2(m - n) - 63$ 20. $(2c - d)^2 + 3(2c - d) - 18$

31. THE SUM OR DIFFERENCE OF TWO CUBES

The expression $a^3 + b^3$ is referred to as the *sum of two cubes* and $a^3 - b^3$ as the *difference of two cubes*. Let us consider the problem of dividing $a^3 + b^3$ by $a + b$.

Leave a space, as shown below, for the a^2 and a terms that are missing in the dividend. This gives room for the exponents to appear (as they sometimes do) in descending order of the powers of a.

$$
\begin{array}{r}
a^2 - ab + b^2 \\
a + b \,\overline{\smash{\big)}\, a^3 + b^3} \\
\underline{a^3 + a^2b} \\
- a^2b \\
\underline{- a^2b - ab^2} \\
ab^2 + b^3 \\
\underline{ab^2 + b^3}
\end{array}
$$

Then divide $a^3 - b^3$ by $a - b$.

$$
\begin{array}{r}
a^2 + ab + b^2 \\
a - b \,\overline{\smash{\big)}\, a^3 - b^3} \\
\underline{a^3 - a^2b} \\
a^2b \\
\underline{a^2b - ab^2} \\
ab^2 - b^3 \\
\underline{ab^2 - b^3}
\end{array}
$$

Since the product of the divisor and the quotient is equal to the dividend, from the two illustrations above we can say

$$a^3 + b^3 = (a + b)(a^2 - ab + b^2)$$
$$a^3 - b^3 = (a - b)(a^2 + ab + b^2)$$

This is a special case of factoring. It can be observed that when we factor either the sum of two cubes or the difference of two cubes, we get two factors. One of them is a binomial and the other is a trinomial. The following rule can be used for factoring the sum or difference of two cubes.

Rule. *When factoring the sum or difference of two cubes, for the first factor take the cube root of each of the terms and join them by the sign that appears between the two cubes. The second factor, a trinomial, is formed from the first factor. The first term of the trinomial factor is the square of the first term of the binomial factor. The second term is the product of the two terms in the binomial factor and is preceded by the sign opposite that which joins the two terms in the binomial factor. The third term in the trinomial factor is the square of the second term in the binomial factor. The fact that a number squared is always positive ensures that the first and third terms of the trinomial factor are positive.*

Example 1.   Factor $m^3 + n^3$.

$$m^3 + n^3 = (m + n)(m^2 - mn + n^2)$$

Example 2.   Factor $c^3 - d^3$.

$$c^3 - d^3 = (c - d)(c^2 + cd + d^2)$$

Example 3.   Factor $x^3y^3 + z^3$.

$$x^3y^3 + z^3 = (xy + z)(x^2y^2 - xyz + z^2)$$

Example 4.   Factor $b^3 - 8c^3$.

$$b^3 - 8c^3 = (b - 2c)(b^2 + 2bc + 4c^2)$$

Example 5.   Factor $27b^6 - a^3$.

$$27b^6 - a^3 = (3b^2 - a)(9b^4 + 3ab^2 + a^2)$$

Factor:

1. $m^3 - d^3$	2. $x^3 + y^3$	3. $r^3 + s^3$
4. $t^3 + 8$	5. $27 - w^3$	6. $x^3y^3 + a^3$
7. $64 + m^3$	8. $a^3b^3 - c^3$	9. $r^3s^3 + x^3y^3$
10. $1 - z^3$		

32. THE COMMON FACTOR

In our discussion of the distributive law it will be recalled that we distributed one factor over the addends of a second factor. The following problem illustrates, once more, the distributive law.

Example 1.   Find the product of $a(b + 2c + 4d)$.

$$a(b + 2c + 4d) = ab + 2ac + 4ad \tag{1}$$

Then, by the law of symmetry, this may be written

$$ab + 2ac + 4ad = a(b + 2c + 4d) \tag{2}$$

The left member of equation (2) represents a series of *three terms* or *addends*, each made up of *two* or *three factors*, whereas the right member contains the *two factors* a and $(b + 2c + 4d)$. It will be noted that each of the three terms in the left member of equation (2) contains the factor a. When each term of an expression contains the same factor, we say that factor is *common* to all terms. Thus if each term is divided by that common factor, we obtain the second factor, $(b + 2c + 4d)$, in equation (2). The a, then, is a factor of the original expression, as is the other factor, $(b + 2c + 4d)$, resulting from the dividing of each term or addend by that common factor.

Example 2.   Factor $2am + 6an + 10ap$.

$$2am + 6an + 10ap = 2a(m + 3n + 5p)$$

Example 3. Factor $2ab^2 - 4a^2b^2 - 8a^2b$.

In this problem each term can be divided exactly by $2ab$. Hence $2ab$ is a common factor.

$$2ab^2 - 4a^2b^2 - 8a^2b = 2ab(b - 2ab - 4a)$$

Example 4. Factor $10m^2n^2 + 25m^3n^3 - 40m^4n^4$.

$$10m^2n^2 + 25m^3n^3 - 40m^4n^4 = 5m^2n^2(2 + 5mn - 8m^2n^2)$$

A common monomial factor is not ordinarily separated into its prime factors.

Example 5. Factor $ax^2 - ay^2$.

$$ax^2 - ay^2 = a(x^2 - y^2)$$

As in the previous examples, we have a common monomial factor. Observe the second factor, $(x^2 - y^2)$. This is the difference of two squares and, of course, can be factored. To factor an expression completely, we must have every factor in a form which is divisible only by itself and by 1. Then the complete factorization of Example 5 is

$$ax^2 - ay^2 = a(x^2 - y^2)$$
$$= a(x + y)(x - y)$$

and we have the three factors shown.

Example 6. Factor $3bx^4 - 3by^4$.

$$3bx^4 - 3by^4 = 3b(x^4 - y^4)$$
$$= 3b(x^2 + y^2)(x^2 - y^2)$$
$$= 3b(x^2 + y^2)(x + y)(x - y)$$

Trinomials may also contain a common factor. This should be removed from the trinomial before we attempt to factor the trinomial into its two binomial factors. In the first place, this will give us a more simplified trinomial and its factorization will therefore usually be somewhat more easily accomplished. Secondly, if this is not done, at least one of the binomial factors will contain a common factor which we may neglect to remove.

Example 7. Factor $6ay^2 + 40ay + 24a$.

$$6ay^2 + 40ay + 24a = 2a(3y^2 + 20y + 12)$$
$$= 2a(3y + 2)(y + 6)$$

The sum or difference of two cubes may also contain a common factor which, if not removed, will allow little insight into the fact that the sum or difference of two cubes is involved.

Example 8. Factor $3ax^3 - 24ay^3$.

$$3ax^3 - 24ay^3 = 3a(x^3 - 8y^3)$$
$$= 3a(x - 2y)(x^2 + 2xy + 4y^2)$$

Example 9. Factor $128m^2x^3 + 2m^2y^3$.

$$128m^2x^3 + 2m^2y^3 = 2m^2(64x^3 + y^3)$$
$$= 2m^2(4x + y)(16x^2 + 4xy + y^2)$$

Example 10. Factor $(x + y)a^3 - (x + y)b^3$.

A common factor certainly may be other than a monomial. Observe that the first term consists of the two factors $(x + y)$ and a^3 while the second term is made up of the two factors $(x + y)$ and b^3. Thus $(x + y)$ is a common factor in both terms. Then

$$(x + y)a^3 - (x + y)b^3 = (x + y)(a^3 - b^3)$$
$$= (x + y)(a - b)(a^2 + ab + b^2)$$

Example 11. Factor $x^2 - 5x + 6 + x^2 - 6x + 8$.

This problem may be factored by using the associative law and grouping as $(x^2 - 5x + 6) + (x^2 - 6x + 8)$. Each of these trinomials may be factored and then we observe a common factor in each term. Thus

$$x^2 - 5x + 6 + x^2 - 6x + 8 = (x^2 - 5x + 6) + (x^2 - 6x + 8)$$
$$= (x - 2)(x - 3) + (x - 2)(x - 4)$$

At this stage we discover the common factor $(x - 2)$, and the second factor is found by dividing each term by the common factor. Then we continue as follows:

$$= (x - 2)(x - 3 + x - 4)$$
$$= (x - 2)(2x - 7)$$

This problem could very well be solved by an alternate method. To do this we take the original expression, $x^2 - 5x + 6 + x^2 - 6x + 8$, and combine algebraically the similar terms, which gives us the expression $2x^2 - 11x + 14$. Then, to factor the equivalent expression, we have

$$2x^2 - 11x + 14 = (2x - 7)(x - 2)$$

There are times when the student may have difficulty in visualizing larger units in some of the types of factoring. As he progresses through the sequence of courses in the mathematics curriculum, he will find the technique of substituting a single expression for a more complex one used during the solution process. Let us consider for a moment the expression $125y^3 - 64x^3z^6$ which we wish to factor. If we let

$$u = 5y \quad \text{and} \quad v = 4xz^2$$

then

$$u^3 = 125y^3 \quad \text{and} \quad v^3 = 64x^3z^6$$

Substituting these values in the original expression, we have $u^3 - v^3$ to be factored. Then

$$u^3 - v^3 = (u - v)(u^2 + uv + v^2)$$

For each u we shall substitute its equivalent, the $5y$. Likewise, for each v we shall substitute the value $4xz^2$. Then, to proceed with the above, we have

$$125y^3 - 64x^3z^6 = [5y - 4xz^2][(5y)^2 + (5y)(4xz^2) + (4xz^2)^2]$$
$$= [5y - 4xz^2][25y^2 + 20xyz^2 + 16x^2z^4]$$

Now that we have introduced the method of factoring out a common factor, let us consider an alternate approach to the factoring of the difference of two squares. If we are given $a^2 - b^2$ and wish to find the factors of the expression, we proceed as follows:

1. $a^2 - b^2 = a^2 - b^2$ (Reflexive relation)

2. $a^2 - b^2 = a^2 + 0 - b^2$ (Additive identity)

3. $a^2 - b^2 = a^2 + ab - ab - b^2$ (Additive inverse)

4. $a^2 - b^2 = (a^2 + ab) + (-ab - b^2)$ (Associative law for addition)

5. $a^2 - b^2 = a(a + b) - b(a + b)$ (Factoring out a common factor by the distributive law)

6. $a^2 - b^2 = (a + b)(a - b)$ (Factoring out a common factor by the distributive law)

EXERCISE 27

A

Factor:

1. $3a - ab$

2. $xy + xz$

3. $2m + 2n + 2p$

4. $ab + ac + ad$

5. $2st - 2sr$

6. $m^2 + mn$

7. $4b + 2c$

8. $-am - an - ap$

9. $m^2x - m^2y$

10. $mnp + np$

11. $12a - 9b$

12. $8ax - 6ay + 4az$

13. $cd - dm$

14. $r^2s^2t - rst^2$

15. $15m^2 - 18m$

16. $12ab + 18b$

17. $30y^2z^2 + 20z^2$

18. $12ab - 6ac + 24ad$

19. $p^2q^3 - pq^2$

20. $8b^4 - 6b^3 + 10b^2$

21. $-3a^2b^2 - 6a^3b^3 - 9ab$ 22. $16x^2y + 8xy^2 - 40xy$

23. $4mp^3 - 12mp^2 - 16mp$ 24. $abx^2 - ab^2x^2 - a^2bx^2$

25. $28r^2t - 35rt^2 - 63r^3t^3$

26. $mx^2 - my^2$ 27. $cdx^2 - cdy^2$ 28. $2m^2 - 8n^2$

29. $4ar^2 - 36as^2$ 30. $3m^2n^2 - 27p^2$ 31. $8by^2 - 18bz^2$

32. $48pd^2 - 75pe^2$ 33. $2axb^2 - 50axc^2$ 34. $d - 9dy^2$

35. $12m^2n^2 - 27p^2$ 36. $zx^2 - z$ 37. $mnp - mnpd^2$

38. $a^2x^2b - bz^2$ 39. $27d^2 - 75c^2$ 40. $24am^2 - 54an^2$

41. $m^4 - n^4$ 42. $a^4 - b^4$ 43. $3x^4 - 3z^4$

44. $4ad^4 - 4ax^4$ 45. $2mn^5 - 2m^5n$

B

Factor completely:

1. $36my^2 + 12my - 15m$ 2. $4amy^2 - amy - 3am$

3. $24z^2 + 30z - 9$ 4. $2m^2n - 5mn - 12mn^2$

5. $6b^2 + 14b + 4$ 6. $8ax^2 - 2ax - 3a$

7. $3mb^3 - 3mc^3$ 8. $2y^3 - 16z^3$

9. $16x^3 + 2y^3$ 10. $54m^3 - 2$

11. $2a^2c^3 - 16a^2d^3$ 12. $(x^2 - y^2) - (x^2 + xy - 2y^2)$

13. $(x - y)^2 - (2x^2 + xy - 3y^2)$

14. Show that $x^2 - y^2 - z^2 + 2yz$ is equal to $(x - y + z)(x + y - z)$.

15. Show that $x^2 - y^2 \neq (x - y)^2$.

33. FACTORING BY GROUPING

In the previous section we made use of the associative law for addition and grouped together certain terms. In this section we shall extend this idea. Consider the following problem:

Factor $ax + ay + bx + by$.

We group the first two terms together and place the group in parentheses. We repeat this process for the last two terms.

$$ax + ay + bx + by = (ax + ay) + (bx + by)$$

By application of the distributive law to each group, the right member of the equation becomes

$$a(x + y) + b(x + y)$$

Now we have two terms each of which contains the common factor $(x + y)$. Again by the distributive law, the right member of the equation will be
$$(x + y)(a + b)$$
Thus
$$ax + ay + bx + by = (ax + ay) + (bx + by)$$
$$= a(x + y) + b(x + y).$$
$$= (x + y)(a + b)$$

This answer may be checked as follows:

$$x + y$$
$$\underline{a + b}$$
$$ax + ay$$
$$\underline{ + bx + by}$$
$$ax + ay + bx + by$$

Example 1. Factor $am + an + bm + bn$.
$$am + an + bm + bn = (am + an) + (bm + bn)$$
$$= a(m + n) + b(m + n)$$
$$= (m + n)(a + b)$$

Example 2. Factor $3x + 3y - bx - by$.

Notice that if the second parentheses is preceded by a negative sign, the signs of the terms included within are changed and we have a common factor in the two terms.
$$3x + 3y - bx - by = (3x + 3y) - (bx + by)$$
$$= 3(x + y) - b(x + y)$$
$$= (x + y)(3 - b)$$

Example 3. Factor $3am - 3an - 2bm + 2bn$.
$$3am - 3an - 2bm + 2bn = 3a(m - n) - 2b(m - n)$$
$$= (m - n)(3a - 2b)$$

Example 4. Factor $3acx + 3bcx + 3adx + 3bdx$.

Factor out the common factor $3x$.
$$3acx + 3bcx + 3adx + 3bdx = 3x[ac + bc + ad + bd]$$
$$= 3x[c(a + b) + d(a + b)]$$
$$= 3x(a + b)(c + d)$$

Example 5. Factor $a^2 + 2ab + b^2 - x^2 - 2xy - y^2$.
$$a^2 + 2ab + b^2 - x^2 - 2xy - y^2 = [a^2 + 2ab + b^2] - [x^2 + 2xy + y^2]$$
$$= [a + b]^2 - [x + y]^2$$
$$= ([a + b] + [x + y])([a + b] - [x + y])$$
$$= (a + b + x + y)(a + b - x - y)$$

Another type of larger unit with which we sometimes work is similar to the larger units that appeared when we were factoring by grouping. Those larger units may appear after certain expressions have been factored. Consider the following problem:

Factor $(x + 3)^2 + x^2 + 5x + 6$.

We factor the expression $x^2 + 5x + 6$ and write $(x + 3)^2$ as $(x + 3)(x + 3)$. Then

$$(x + 3)^2 + x^2 + 5x + 6 = (x + 3)(x + 3) + (x + 3)(x + 2)$$

Now in each of the two terms we observe a common factor, $(x + 3)$.

$$\begin{aligned} (x + 3)^2 + x^2 + 5x + 6 &= (x + 3)(x + 3) + (x + 3)(x + 2) \\ &= (x + 3)(x + 3 + x + 2) \\ &= (x + 3)(2x + 5) \end{aligned}$$

The answer may be checked as follows:

$$\begin{array}{r} x + 3 \\ 2x + 5 \\ \hline 2x^2 + 6x \\ + 5x + 15 \\ \hline 2x^2 + 11x + 15 \end{array}$$

This answer is not in the same form as the original expression, but is equal to it. If we change the form of the original problem, this equality will be evident.

$$\begin{aligned} (x + 3)^2 + x^2 + 5x + 6 &= x^2 + 6x + 9 + x^2 + 5x + 6 \\ &= 2x^2 + 11x + 15 \end{aligned}$$

It will be observed that this quantity is the same as the product when the problem was checked above.

This problem could have been simplified to start with, as follows:

$$\begin{aligned} (x + 3)^2 + x^2 + 5x + 6 &= x^2 + 6x + 9 + x^2 + 5x + 6 \\ &= 2x^2 + 11x + 15 \end{aligned}$$

Now we factor as a straight trinomial:

$$= (2x + 5)(x + 3)$$

Example 6. Factor $x^2 + 10x + 24 + (x + 4)^2$.

$$\begin{aligned} x^2 + 10x + 24 + (x + 4)^2 &= x^2 + 10x + 24 + x^2 + 8x + 16 \\ &= 2x^2 + 18x + 40 \\ &= 2(x^2 + 9x + 20) \\ &= 2(x + 4)(x + 5) \end{aligned}$$

A

Factor:

1. $xz + yz + ax + ay$ 2. $bc + b + cd + d$
3. $mp - np + mq - nq$ 4. $rt - st - ru + su$
5. $ab + b + ac + c$ 6. $3ac + ad + 3cb + bd$
7. $mp - np - mq + nq$ 8. $ab + bd - ac - cd$
9. $3xz - 2yz + 3x - 2y$ 10. $ad - 4a - cd + 4c$
11. $uw + vw - 5u - 5v$ 12. $bxy - by + bxz - bz$
13. $2ab + 4bc + 2ad + 4cd$ 14. $2art + 3ast - 2ar - 3as$
15. $6bc - 2ac + 9bd - 3ad$ 16. $s - 3st + 2x - 6xt$
17. $3ab - ac - 6bd + 2cd$ 18. $d - e + df - ef$
19. $24amn - 6anx - 16amy + 4axy$ 20. $6bxz - 24bx - 3bzy - 12by$

B

Factor:

1. $(r + s)^2 - 1$ 6. $4 - m^2n^2 - 2mnp - p^2$
2. $b^2 - (s + t)^2$ 7. $a + b + (a + b)^2$
3. $m^2 - 4mn + 4n^2 - p^2$ 8. $9 + (3x + 3y)$
4. $x^2 - a^2 - 10ab - 25b^2$ 9. $c^2 + 2cd + d^2 + 2c + 2d$
5. $c^2 - 6cd + 9d^2 - a^2 + 12ab - 36b^2$ 10. $x^2 + 4x + 4 + (x + 2)$

34. NUMERICAL MULTIPLICATION BY USE OF BINOMIAL FACTORS

Multiplication of arithmetical numbers can often be simplified by changing those numbers into binomials. The following examples illustrate this concept:

Example 1.   Multiply 53 by 47.

Write 53 as $(50 + 3)$ and 47 as $(50 - 3)$. Use these two binomials as the sum and difference of two numbers and find their product as was done in Exercise 24.

$$(50 + 3)(50 - 3) = (50)^2 - (3)^2$$
$$= 2500 - 9$$
$$= 2491$$

Example 2. Multiply 64 by 56.

$$(64)(56) = (60 + 4)(60 - 4)$$
$$= 3600 - 16$$
$$= 3584$$

Example 3. Multiply 57 by 57.

Change 57 to $(50 + 7)$ and, since there would be two identical binomials, use the rule for squaring a binomial.

$$(57)(57) = (50 + 7)(50 + 7)$$
$$= (50 + 7)^2$$
$$= 2500 + 700 + 49$$
$$= 3249$$

This problem could be solved by squaring a binomial represented by the difference of two numbers, as follows:

$$(57)(57) = (60 - 3)(60 - 3)$$
$$= (60 - 3)^2$$
$$= 3600 - 360 + 9$$
$$= 3249$$

Example 4. Multiply 38 by 62.

Change 38 to $(50 - 12)$ and 62 to $(50 + 12)$. Then

$$(38)(62) = (50 - 12)(50 + 12)$$
$$= 2500 - 144$$
$$= 2356$$

EXERCISE 29

Find the following products by converting the numbers into binomial factors:

1. $(17)(23)$ 2. $(26)(34)$ 3. $(35)(45)$
4. $(12)(28)$ 5. $(59)(41)$ 6. $(72)(68)$
7. $(87)(87)$ 8. $(59)(59)$ 9. $(96)(96)$
10. $(75)(75)$ 11. $(21)(39)$ 12. $(43)(57)$
13. $(92)(92)$ 14. $(69)(69)$ 15. $(45)(75)$

16. $(37)(43)$
19. $(62)(78)$
22. $(111)(89)$
25. $(125)(75)$

17. $(77)(77)$
20. $(29)(29)$
23. $(115)(85)$

18. $(24)(36)$
21. $(109)(109)$
24. $(130)(130)$

EXERCISE 30

A

Factor completely:

1. $bm + cm + dm$
3. $12cdm + 3cm + 18dm$
5. $x^2 - 4z^2$
7. $m^2n^2 - p^2$
9. $x^2z^2 - a^2c^2$
11. $3m^2 - 27n^2$
13. $12ap^2 - 75aq^2$
15. $121s^2 - 144t^2$
17. $32mb^2 - 50mc^2$
19. $axy^3 - axy$
21. $t^2 - 4t + 4$
23. $9 - 6s + s^2$
25. $p^2 + 3p - 18$
27. $bc^2 + 6bc + 8b$
29. $t^2 - 11t + 10$
31. $2w^2 - 17w + 8$
33. $24c^2 - 2c - 15$
35. $24md^2 - 29md - 4m$
37. $3m^3 + 12m^2 + 18m$
39. $4cx^2 - 8cxy - 12cy^2$
41. $12t^2 + 52t + 35$
43. $a^3b^3 - ab$
45. $t^3 - 16t$
47. $30am^2 - 35am - 15a$
49. $36a^2 - 3a - 5$

2. $2ax + 4ay + 10az$
4. $12az - 18ay - 42ax$
6. $9a^2 - 1$
8. $36 - 25z^2$
10. $49 - 81w^2$
12. $25 - 4a^2$
14. $7bz^2 - 28by^2$
16. $a^3 - ab^2$
18. $c^2d^3 - db^2$
20. $t - 9tx^2$
22. $m^2 - 2m + 1$
24. $ad^2 + 10ad + 25a$
26. $d^2 + 9d - 22$
28. $3m^2 - 9m - 84$
30. $r^2 - 10r + 21$
32. $5m^2 + 29m - 6$
34. $12a^2 + 14a - 6$
36. $5x^2 - 125y^2$
38. $14a^3m + 35a^2m + 7am$
40. $a - 100az^2$
42. $9by - byx^2$
44. $18c^2 + 77c - 18$
46. $p^2q^3 - p^2q$
48. $4z^2 - 25z + 6$
50. $12abn^2 - 4a^2n^2$

Factor completely:

1. $12c^2 + 23c - 9$
2. $8b^2 - 59b + 21$
3. $12r^2 - 25r + 12$
4. $18b^2 + 15bd + 2d^2$
5. $2x^2 + 5xy - 3y^2$
6. $4r^2 - 13rt + 9t^2$
7. $6m^2 + 43mn - 15n^2$
8. $6a^2 + 17a - 10$
9. $4c^2d^2 - 9cdx + 5x^2$
10. $12r^2 - r - 63$
11. $m^3 - n^3$
12. $y^3 + z^3$
13. $ad^3 - a$
14. $27 + 8b^3$
15. $x^2 - (y + z)^2$
16. $(y - x)^2 - 1$
17. $x^2 - a^2 - 4a - 4$
18. $(a + b)^2 - (x + y)^2$
19. $54 - 16p^3$
20. $am^3n^3 - a$
21. $125q^3 - 1$
22. $(d - a)^2 - x^2$
23. $2(x + y)^2 - 8z^2$
24. $16a^4 - 2ab^3$
25. $12ab - 20ac + 8ad - 28am + 4an$
26. $2ad^2 + 6bcd^2 - 10cd^2 + 12c^2d^2$
27. $12m^2n^2p^2 - mnp - 6$
28. $ay - yz + ax - xz$
29. $mp - 3m - pq + 3q$
30. $dc + cx - dy - xy$

Evaluate each of the following by first factoring the expression:

31. $4^3 - 3^3$
32. $\frac{1}{4} - \frac{1}{9}$
33. $9^2 - 7^2$
34. $\frac{25}{16} - \frac{4}{25}$
35. $12^2 - 6^2$

REVIEW TEST 16

In the left-hand column below are algebraic expressions each of which has common factors. The common factors are found in the right-hand column. On a sheet of paper write the numbers 1 through 20 to correspond to the numbered expressions in the left-hand column. After each number place the letter that indicates which common factor correctly matches the expression. Be sure it is the largest common factor. Some of the answers in the right-hand column do not match any of the expressions in the left-hand column. Do not use any of the letters more than once.

1. $ax + bx + yx$
   a. y
2. $3a^2y - 4a^3x + 7az$
   b. $a^2b^2c^2$

3. $4amz - 8nmp - 16amb$ c. $3t$

4. $a^2b^2c^2 - 3abc^2 - 12a^2b^2c$ d. mnp

5. $5cdx - 15abx + 35mnx$ e. $(x + y)$

6. $axy + bxy - cy$ f. x

7. $12c^2d - 4cd^2 - 24c^2d^2$ g. $(m + n)$

8. $m^2n^2p - mn^2p^2 + m^2np^2$ h. $3pq$

9. $2abc + 8abd + 12bde$ i. $4cd$

10. $27t^3 + 36t^2 + 63t$ j. $5mnp$

11. $3pq^2 - 15p^2q - 24pq$ k. $4m$

12. $3abc + 8a^2b^2c^2 + 11b^2c^2$ l. $m^2n^2p^2$

13. $10m^2np + 25mn^2p + 30mnp^2$ m. abc

14. $4pq^2 - 12pq + 15p^2q$ n. $9t$

15. $16c^2d^2 - 24c^3d^3 + 32c^4d^4$ o. pq

16. $(x + y)^2 - (x + y)^3$ p. a

17. $(m^3 + n^3) + (m^2 + 2mn + n^2)$ q. $(x + 2)$

18. $(x^2 + 4xy + 4y^2) - (x + 2y)$ r. $8c^2d^2$

19. $m^3n^3p^3 + m^4n^2p^2 + 6m^2n^3p^3$ s. $(x + 2y)$

20. $(x^2 + 4x + 4) + (x^2 + 5x + 6)$ t. $(x + y)^2$

    u. bc

    v. $5x$

    w. $2c^2d^2$

    x. $(m^2 + n^2)$

    y. $m^2n^2p^3$

    z. $2b$

REVIEW TEST 17

Some of the algebraic expressions listed below are perfect square trinomials and others are not. On a sheet of paper write the numbers 1 through 30 to correspond to the numbered expressions below. After each number write Y (yes) or N (no) to indicate which ones are and which ones are not perfect square trinomials.

1. $x^2 - 3x + 1$ 2. $x^2 + 5x + 25$

3. $x^2 + 8x + 4$ 4. $x^2 - 2x + 1$

5. $a^2 - 12a + 36$ 6. $b^2 + 10b + 100$

7. $y^2 - 14y + 49$ 8. $z^2 + 2z + 1$

9. $c^2 + 16c + 16$ 10. $m^2 - m + 1$

11. $p^2 + 2p - 1$ 12. $r^2 - 18r + 81$

13. $a^2 - 12a - 36$ 14. $1 - 2z + z^2$

15. $n^2 - 6n + 9$ 16. $c^2 - 2cd + d^2$

17. $x^2y^2 - 4xyz + 4z^2$ 18. $m^2n^2 + 2mn - 1$

19. $r^2 - 8rst + 16s^2t^2$ 20. $a^2b^2 - 2ab + 1$

21. $4x^2 - 4x + 1$ 22. $9x^2 - 12x - 4$

23. $2x^2 + 12x + 9$ 24. $t^2 + 16t + 64$

25. $25c^2 + 20c + 4$ 26. $r^2s^2 + 8rs + 16$

27. $p^2q^2 - 10pq - 25$ 28. $36b^2 - 36b + 9$

29. $4y^2 - 28y + 49$ 30. $9m^2 - 36m - 36$

7

Fractions

A common fraction is a mathematical expression so written as to show that division is indicated. The expression $\frac{2}{3}$ means that 2 is divided by 3. Another way to view this is to consider that we have something that has been divided into thirds and $\frac{2}{3}$ means that we have under consideration two of those thirds.

The expression $\frac{x+y}{m+n}$ means that the sum of x and y is to be divided by the sum of m and n. The $x+y$ is called the *numerator* and the $m+n$ the *denominator* of the fraction.

35. SIMPLIFICATION OF FRACTIONS

Before we begin the computational processes associated with fractions, there are certain basic principles that must be developed.

Definition 1. If a is an integer, then $\frac{a}{1} = a$.

Definition 2. If $\frac{a}{b}$ and $\frac{c}{d}$ are any rational numbers and $b \neq 0$ and $d \neq 0$,

then $\frac{a}{b} = \frac{c}{d}$ if and only if $ad = bc$.

Definition 3. If $\dfrac{a}{b}$ ($b \neq 0$) is a rational number, then $-1\left(\dfrac{a}{b}\right) = -\left(\dfrac{a}{b}\right) = -\dfrac{a}{b}.$

Theorem 1. If $\dfrac{a}{b}$ ($b \neq 0$) is a rational number and x is any nonzero real number, then $\dfrac{a}{b} = \dfrac{ax}{bx}.$

Proof:

1. $(ab)(x) = (ab)(x)$ (Reflexive relation)
2. $(a)(bx) = (ab)(x)$ (Associative law for multiplication)
3. $ = (ba)(x)$ (Commutative law for multiplication)
4. $ = (b)(ax)$ (Associative law for multiplication)
5. $\dfrac{a}{b} = \dfrac{ax}{bx}$ (Definition 2)

Theorem 1 tells us, then, that if both the numerator and the denominator of a fraction are multiplied by the same number, the value of the fraction is unchanged. This holds true for dividing both the numerator and denominator of a fraction by the same number since multiplying by $1/x$ is equivalent to dividing by x.

Theorem 2. If $\dfrac{a}{b}$ ($b \neq 0$) is a rational number, then $-\left(\dfrac{a}{b}\right) = \dfrac{-a}{b}$ or $\dfrac{a}{-b}.$

Proof:

1. $-\left(\dfrac{a}{b}\right) = -\left(\dfrac{a}{b}\right)$ (Reflexive relation)

2. $\phantom{-\left(\dfrac{a}{b}\right)} = -1\left(\dfrac{a}{b}\right)$ (Definition 3)

3. $\phantom{-\left(\dfrac{a}{b}\right)} = \dfrac{-1}{1}\left(\dfrac{a}{b}\right)$ (Rule of signs for division)

4. $\phantom{-\left(\dfrac{a}{b}\right)} = \dfrac{-a}{b}$ (Multiplication of signed numbers)

Likewise,

1. $-\left(\dfrac{a}{b}\right) = -\left(\dfrac{a}{b}\right)$ (Reflexive relation)

2. $\phantom{-\left(\dfrac{a}{b}\right)} = -1\left(\dfrac{a}{b}\right)$ (Definition 3)

3. $$= \frac{1}{-1}\left(\frac{a}{b}\right) \qquad \text{(Rule of signs for division)}$$

4. $$= \frac{a}{-b} \qquad \text{(Multiplication of signed numbers)}$$

Every fraction has three signs—the sign of the fraction, the sign of the numerator, and the sign of the denominator. In the fraction a/b the signs of the fraction, of the numerator, and of the denominator are all assumed to be positive since no signs are shown.

In Theorem 2 we have shown that any two of the three signs of a fraction may be changed without changing the value of the fraction. Observing the first part of the proof of Theorem 2 we see that

$$-\frac{a}{b} = \frac{-a}{b}$$

in which case the sign of the fraction and the sign of the numerator were changed.

In the second part of the proof we proved that

$$-\frac{a}{b} = \frac{a}{-b}$$

in which case the sign of the fraction and the sign of the denominator were changed.

Finally, if we have the fraction $+\dfrac{-a}{-b}$, this may be written $+\dfrac{a}{b}$ since in division if the signs are alike the quotient is positive.

As a simple practical application of this concept, we know that

$$+\frac{+12}{+4} = +3$$

since $(+3)(+4) = +12$. Then if we change the sign of the fraction and of the numerator, we have

$$-\frac{-12}{+4} = -(-3)$$

$$= +3$$

Likewise, if we change the original problem such that the signs of both the fraction and the denominator are changed, we have

$$-\frac{+12}{-4} = -(-3)$$

$$= +3$$

In each of the above cases we changed two of the three signs of the fraction and each time obtained the same quotient $+3$. As we continue with the development of the concepts in this chapter, there will be times when we shall find it necessary to make changes in the signs of a fraction in order to accomplish the task with which we are confronted.

Simplifying a fraction involves changing the given fraction to an equivalent fraction whose numerator and denominator are smaller numbers in the case of numerical fractions or simplified expressions in the case of algebraic representations of numbers.

Simplifying a fraction, especially a more complex one, involves factoring both the numerator and denominator. Consider the simple arithmetic number, $\frac{10}{15}$, which we wish to simplify.

$$\frac{10}{15} = \frac{5 \cdot 2}{5 \cdot 3}$$

$$= \frac{5}{5} \cdot \frac{2}{3}$$

$$= 1 \cdot \frac{2}{3}$$

$$= \frac{2}{3}$$

Hence $\frac{2}{3}$ is a fraction equivalent to the given one, $\frac{10}{15}$, and is in a simplified form.

Example 1. Simplify $\frac{6}{9}$.

$$\frac{6}{9} = \frac{3 \cdot 2}{3 \cdot 3}$$

$$= \frac{3}{3} \cdot \frac{2}{3}$$

$$= 1 \cdot \frac{2}{3}$$

$$= \frac{2}{3}$$

Example 2. Simplify ab^3/b^2.

$$\frac{ab^3}{b^2} = \frac{b^2}{b^2} \cdot \frac{ab}{1}$$

$$= 1 \cdot ab$$
$$= ab$$

It will be observed in Example 2 that the expression was not completely factored. It is our purpose in simplifying fractions to obtain the multiplicative identity, 1, from identical factors in the numerator and denominator. Hence we can divide both the numerator and denominator by b^2 and get as one of our factors b^2/b^2 and from that get the multiplicative identity 1.

Example 3. Simplify $\dfrac{x^4y^2z}{x^3y^3z^2}$.

$$\frac{x^4y^2z}{x^3y^3z^2} = \frac{x^3y^2z}{x^3y^2z} \cdot \frac{x}{yz}$$

$$= 1 \cdot \frac{x}{yz}$$

$$= \frac{x}{yz}$$

Example 4. Simplify $\dfrac{x^2 - y^2}{x - y}$.

$$\frac{x^2 - y^2}{x - y} = \frac{(x - y)(x + y)}{x - y}$$

$$= \frac{(x - y)}{(x - y)} \cdot \frac{(x + y)}{1}$$

$$= 1 \cdot (x + y)$$

$$= (x + y)$$

$$= x + y$$

Example 5. Simplify $\dfrac{mx - my}{x - y}$.

$$\frac{mx - my}{x - y} = \frac{m(x - y)}{(x - y)}$$

$$= \frac{(x - y)}{(x - y)} \cdot m$$

$$= 1 \cdot m$$

$$= m$$

Example 6. Simplify $\dfrac{a^2 - 4a - 21}{ab + 3b}$.

$$\frac{a^2 - 4a - 21}{ab + 3b} = \frac{(a + 3)(a - 7)}{b(a + 3)}$$

$$= \frac{(a + 3)}{(a + 3)} \cdot \frac{(a - 7)}{b}$$

$$= 1 \cdot \frac{a - 7}{b}$$

$$= \frac{a - 7}{b}$$

It can be observed in Examples 4, 5, and 6 that in the original form of the problems each numerator and denominator was made up of two or more terms. Each of these multinomials then was expressed as the implied product of factors rather than as a series of terms. It is most important that this be done when reducing fractions.

The student should visualize now that unless there are identical factors in both the numerator and denominator, the common fraction cannot be simplified. Consider the following examples:

Example 7. Simplify $\dfrac{x^2 + xy}{xy - y^2}$.

$$\frac{x^2 + xy}{xy - y^2} = \frac{x(x + y)}{y(x - y)}$$

We find that when this is factored we have no identical factors in both the numerator and denominator. Hence the only change we can make in the original fraction is to express it in factored form in which there can be made no simplification as was done in the previous examples.

Example 8. Simplify $\dfrac{x^3 + y^3}{x^3 - y^3}$.

$$\frac{x^3 + y^3}{x^3 - y^3} = \frac{(x + y)(x^2 - xy + y^2)}{(x - y)(x^2 + xy + y^2)}$$

Again, there are no identical factors in both the numerator and denominator.

We introduced the three signs of a fraction earlier in this discussion and proved that the changing of any two of the three signs of a fraction gives us an equivalent fraction. Examples 9, 10, and 11 below show the need for such changes in order to simplify certain fractions.

Example 9. Simplify $\dfrac{x - y}{y - x}$.

$$\frac{x - y}{y - x} = \frac{(x - y)}{(y - x)}$$

$$= -\frac{(x - y)}{-(y - x)}$$

$$= -\frac{(x - y)}{(x - y)}$$

$$= -(1)$$
$$= -1$$

Example 10. Simplify $\dfrac{3(m-2n)}{4(2n-m)}$.

$$\frac{3(m-2n)}{4(2n-m)} = \frac{(3m-6n)}{(8n-4m)}$$

$$= -\frac{-(3m-6n)}{(8n-4m)}$$

$$= -\frac{6n-3m}{8n-4m}$$

$$= -\frac{3(2n-m)}{4(2n-m)}$$

$$= -\frac{3}{4}\cdot\frac{(2n-m)}{(2n-m)}$$

$$= -\frac{3}{4}\cdot(1)$$

$$= -\frac{3}{4}$$

Additional insight into the changing of signs would reduce somewhat the work involved in simplifying the fraction in Example 10. We recall from our work with signs when multiplying algebraic signed numbers that the result of multiplying together two negative numbers is a positive number. Then if we multiply two factors by -1, the resulting product is unchanged. Thus

$$(x-1)(x+3) = x^2 + 2x - 3$$

Now if we multiply both factors by -1, we have

$$(-1)(x-1)\cdot(-1)(x+3) = (-1)(-1)(x-1)(x+3)$$
$$= (+1)(x-1)(x+3)$$
$$= x^2 + 2x - 3$$

It can be seen that if we multiply an even number of factors by -1, there is no change in the resulting product. Likewise, multiplying an odd number of factors by -1 will give us the negative of the original expression. If we multiply one factor of the above example by -1, we have

$$(-1)(x-1)\cdot(x+3) = (-1)(x^2 + 2x - 3)$$
$$= -x^2 - 2x + 3$$

which is the negative of the original product. Then the fraction in Example 10 could be simplified in that manner as follows:

$$\frac{3(m - 2n)}{4(2n - m)} = -\frac{3 \cdot (-1)(m - 2n)}{4(2n - m)}$$

$$= -\frac{3(2n - m)}{4(2n - m)}$$

$$= -\frac{3}{4} \cdot 1$$

$$= -\frac{3}{4}$$

Example 11. Simplify $\dfrac{x^2 - 8x + 16}{20 - x - x^2}$.

$$\frac{x^2 - 8x + 16}{20 - x - x^2} = \frac{(x^2 - 8x + 16)}{(20 - x - x^2)}$$

$$= -\frac{(x^2 - 8x + 16)}{-(20 - x - x^2)}$$

$$= -\frac{x^2 - 8x + 16}{x^2 + x - 20}$$

$$= -\frac{(x - 4)(x - 4)}{(x - 4)(x - 5)}$$

$$= -\frac{(x - 4)}{(x - 4)} \cdot \frac{(x - 4)}{(x + 5)}$$

$$= -1 \cdot \frac{x - 4}{x + 5}$$

$$= (+1) \cdot \frac{-(x - 4)}{(x + 5)}$$

$$= \frac{4 - x}{x + 5} \text{ or } \frac{4 - x}{5 + x}$$

This problem may also be solved as follows:

$$\frac{x^2 - 8x + 16}{20 - x - x^2} = \frac{(x - 4)(x - 4)}{(4 - x)(5 + x)}$$

$$= \frac{(4 - x)}{(4 - x)} \cdot \frac{(4 - x)}{(5 + x)}$$

Because the signs of the two factors in the numerator were changed, the value remains the same.

$$= 1 \cdot \frac{(4 - x)}{(5 + x)}$$

$$= \frac{(4 - x)}{(5 + x)}$$

$$= \frac{4 - x}{5 + x}$$

EXERCISE 31

Simplify the following (for any that will not simplify, state the answer as "Will not simplify"):

A

1. $\dfrac{21}{35}$
2. $\dfrac{16}{48}$
3. $\dfrac{24}{42}$

4. $\dfrac{30}{75}$
5. $\dfrac{8}{60}$
6. $\dfrac{12}{72}$

7. $\dfrac{9z^2}{36az}$
8. $\dfrac{28c^2b^3}{7c^3b}$
9. $\dfrac{36r^2t^4}{45st^2}$

10. $\dfrac{26z^2b}{39zb^2}$
11. $\dfrac{45at^3}{9a^2t}$
12. $\dfrac{42mx^3}{56mx^4}$

13. $\dfrac{ab+ax}{am-an}$
14. $\dfrac{rt-r}{t-1}$
15. $\dfrac{3y-6}{6x-3}$

16. $\dfrac{m-n}{n-m}$
17. $\dfrac{3m-n}{m-3n}$
18. $\dfrac{3d-6c}{8c-4d}$

19. $\dfrac{s+r}{s^2-r^2}$
20. $\dfrac{amt-ams}{am}$
21. $\dfrac{z^2-4}{(z-2)^2}$

22. $\dfrac{x^2-y^2}{y-x}$
23. $\dfrac{c^2+c}{c-c^2}$
24. $\dfrac{x^2+xy+y^2}{x^3+y^3}$

25. $\dfrac{ax+bx+cx}{mx-nx}$
26. $\dfrac{ac-cd-ce}{a-d-e}$
27. $\dfrac{y^2-b^2}{3y-3b}$

28. $\dfrac{y^2-8y+12}{y^2-4y+4}$
29. $\dfrac{a^2+7a+10}{a^2+3a-10}$
30. $\dfrac{m^2-3m-18}{m^2+6m+9}$

B

Simplify the following (for any that will not simplify, state the answer as "Will not simplify"):

1. $\dfrac{y^2-7y+12}{y^2+y-12}$
2. $\dfrac{2t^2+11t-6}{t^2+6t}$
3. $\dfrac{6b^2+11b+3}{4b^2+12b+9}$

4. $\dfrac{4x-3y}{3y-4x}$
5. $\dfrac{x^2+2x+1}{x^2-2x+1}$
6. $\dfrac{x^3+y^3}{x^2+y^2}$

7. $\dfrac{16y^2+40y+25}{4y^2+13y+10}$
8. $\dfrac{(a+b)^3}{(a+b)^2}$
9. $\dfrac{m^2-4mn+4n^2}{m^2-4n^2}$

10. $\dfrac{x^2 + x - 2}{2 - x - x^2}$

11. $\dfrac{x^2 + 4x + 4}{x^2 - 4x + 4}$

12. $\dfrac{2x^2 - 2x - 24}{24 + 2x - 2x^2}$

13. $\dfrac{x^2 + x - 6}{4x - x^2 - 4}$

14. $\dfrac{x^4 - 16}{x^2 - 4}$

15. $\dfrac{a^4 - 81}{3a^2 - 27}$

36. MULTIPLYING AND DIVIDING FRACTIONS

Definition 1. If a/b and c/d are any rational numbers, then

$$\frac{a}{b} \cdot \frac{c}{d} = \frac{ac}{bd} \qquad (b \neq 0 \text{ and } d \neq 0)$$

From the above definition we observe that *the product of two or more fractions is a fraction whose numerator is the product of the numerators of the given fractions and whose denominator is the product of the denominators of the given fractions.*

If the product obtained can be simplified, this should be completed for the final answer.

Example 1. Multiply $\dfrac{3xz}{2} \cdot \dfrac{4y}{z}$.

$$\frac{3xz}{2} \cdot \frac{4y}{z} = \frac{12xyz}{2z}$$

$$= \frac{2 \cdot 6 \cdot x \cdot y \cdot z}{2 \cdot z}$$

$$= \frac{2 \cdot z \cdot 6 \cdot x \cdot y}{2 \cdot z}$$

$$= \frac{2}{2} \cdot \frac{z}{z} \cdot 6xy$$

$$= 1 \cdot 1 \cdot 6xy$$

$$= 6xy$$

Example 2. Multiply $\dfrac{5m^2n}{8p^3} \cdot \dfrac{4p^2}{15mn}$.

$$\frac{5m^2n}{8p^3} \cdot \frac{4p^2}{15mn} = \frac{20m^2np^2}{120mnp^3}$$

$$= \frac{20 \cdot m \cdot m \cdot n \cdot p \cdot p}{20 \cdot 6 \cdot m \cdot n \cdot p \cdot p \cdot p}$$

$$= \frac{20}{20} \cdot \frac{m}{m} \cdot \frac{n}{n} \cdot \frac{p^2}{p^2} \cdot \frac{m}{6p}$$

$$= 1 \cdot 1 \cdot 1 \cdot 1 \cdot \frac{m}{6p}$$

$$= \frac{m}{6p}$$

Example 3. Multiply $4t \cdot \dfrac{t}{2t^2}$.

$$4t \cdot \frac{t}{2t^2} = \frac{4t}{1} \cdot \frac{t}{2t^2}$$

$$= \frac{4t^2}{2t^2}$$

$$= \frac{2 \cdot 2 \cdot t^2}{2 \cdot t^2}$$

$$= \frac{2}{2} \cdot \frac{t^2}{t^2} \cdot 2$$

$$= 1 \cdot 1 \cdot 2$$

$$= 2$$

Example 4. Multiply $\dfrac{x+y}{x-y} \cdot \dfrac{x^2-y^2}{x+y}$.

$$\frac{x+y}{x-y} \cdot \frac{x^2-y^2}{x+y} = \frac{x+y}{x-y} \cdot \frac{(x-y)(x+y)}{x+y}$$

$$= \frac{(x+y)(x-y)(x+y)}{(x-y)(x+y)}$$

$$= \frac{(x+y)}{(x+y)} \cdot \frac{(x-y)}{(x-y)} \cdot (x+y)$$

$$= 1 \cdot 1 \cdot (x+y)$$

$$= x+y$$

Example 5. Multiply $\dfrac{x^2+5x+6}{x^2+x-6} \cdot \dfrac{x^2-4x+4}{x^2-4}$.

$$\frac{x^2+5x+6}{x^2+x-6} \cdot \frac{x^2-4x+4}{x^2-4} = \frac{(x+2)(x+3)}{(x+3)(x-2)} \cdot \frac{(x-2)(x-2)}{(x-2)(x+2)}$$

$$= \frac{(x+2)(x+3)(x-2)(x-2)}{(x+3)(x-2)(x-2)(x+2)}$$

$$= \frac{(x+3)(x-2)(x-2)(x+2)}{(x+3)(x-2)(x-2)(x+2)}$$

$$= \frac{(x+3)}{(x+3)} \cdot \frac{(x-2)}{(x-2)} \cdot \frac{(x-2)}{(x-2)} \cdot \frac{(x+2)}{(x+2)}$$
$$= 1 \cdot 1 \cdot 1 \cdot 1$$
$$= 1$$

It was learned in arithmetic that if one fraction is divided by another fraction, the divisor is inverted and the two fractions are then multiplied together. To substantiate this procedure, let us consider the following theorem. Before proving the theorem we must recall that we defined the reciprocal of a number as that number multiplied by the given number such that their product is equal to 1. Thus $1/x$ is the reciprocal of x since $x(1/x) = 1$. Likewise a/b and b/a are reciprocals of each other, as are $3/4$ and $4/3$.

Theorem 1.   If a, b, c, and d are any real numbers (*except $b \neq 0$, $c \neq 0$, and $d \neq 0$*), then

$$\frac{\dfrac{a}{b}}{\dfrac{c}{d}} = \frac{a}{b} \cdot \frac{d}{c}$$

$$\frac{\dfrac{a}{b}}{\dfrac{c}{d}} = \frac{\dfrac{a}{b} \cdot \dfrac{d}{c}}{\dfrac{c}{d} \cdot \dfrac{d}{c}}$$ (If both members of a fraction are multiplied by the same number, the value of the fraction is unchanged.)

$$= \frac{\dfrac{a}{b} \cdot \dfrac{d}{c}}{1}$$ (A number multiplied by its reciprocal is equal to 1.)

$$= \frac{a}{b} \cdot \frac{d}{c}$$ (Any number divided by 1 is equal to the given number.)

Thus we have proved that to divide one fraction by another fraction, we invert the divisor and multiply.

Example 6.   Divide $\dfrac{x^2 - x}{3}$ by $\dfrac{x^2 - 2x + 1}{9}$.

$$\frac{x^2 - x}{3} \div \frac{x^2 - 2x + 1}{9} = \frac{x^2 - x}{3} \cdot \frac{9}{x^2 - 2x + 1}.$$
$$= \frac{x(x-1)}{3} \cdot \frac{9}{(x-1)(x-1)}$$
$$= \frac{3 \cdot (x-1) \cdot 3x}{3 \cdot (x-1) \cdot (x-1)}$$

$$= \frac{3}{3} \cdot \frac{(x-1)}{(x-1)} \cdot \frac{3x}{(x-1)}$$

$$= 1 \cdot 1 \cdot \frac{3x}{x-1}$$

$$= \frac{3x}{x-1}$$

Example 7. Divide $\dfrac{a^2 - b^2}{3a^2 - 2ab - b^2}$ by $\dfrac{a^2 + 2ab + b^2}{3ab + b^2}$.

$$\frac{a^2 - b^2}{3a^2 - 2ab - b^2} \div \frac{a^2 + 2ab + b^2}{3ab + b^2}$$

$$= \frac{a^2 - b^2}{3a^2 - 2ab - b^2} \cdot \frac{3ab + b^2}{a^2 + 2ab + b^2}$$

$$= \frac{(a-b)(a+b)}{(3a+b)(a-b)} \cdot \frac{b(3a+b)}{(a+b)(a+b)}$$

$$= \frac{(a-b)(a+b)(b)(3a+b)}{(3a+b)(a-b)(a+b)(a+b)}$$

$$= \frac{(3a+b)}{(3a+b)} \cdot \frac{(a-b)}{(a-b)} \cdot \frac{(a+b)}{(a+b)} \cdot \frac{b}{(a+b)}$$

$$= 1 \cdot 1 \cdot 1 \cdot \frac{b}{(a+b)} = \frac{b}{a+b}$$

If a problem indicates both multiplication and division, invert those expressions that immediately follow the division symbol, remembering that any part of the problem included within grouping symbols is to be done before the remaining parts are considered.

Example 8. Perform the indicated operations: $\left(\dfrac{3}{4} \cdot \dfrac{2}{3} \right) \div \dfrac{1}{2}$.

$$\left(\frac{3}{4} \cdot \frac{2}{3} \right) \div \frac{1}{2} = \left(\frac{3 \cdot 2}{4 \cdot 3} \right) \div \frac{1}{2}$$

$$= \left(\frac{3}{3} \cdot \frac{2}{4} \right) \div \frac{1}{2}$$

$$= \left(1 \cdot \frac{1}{2} \right) \div \frac{1}{2}$$

$$= \frac{1}{2} \div \frac{1}{2}$$

$$= \frac{1}{2} \cdot \frac{2}{1}$$

$$= \frac{1 \cdot 2}{2 \cdot 1}$$

$$= \frac{1}{1} \cdot \frac{2}{2}$$

$$= 1 \cdot 1$$

$$= 1$$

Example 9. Perform the indicated operations: $\dfrac{3x^2}{y} \div \left(\dfrac{4x}{y^2} \div \dfrac{2x^3}{z} \right)$.

$$\frac{3x^2}{y} \div \left(\frac{4x}{y^2} \div \frac{2x^3}{z} \right) = \frac{3x^2}{y} \div \left(\frac{4x}{y^2} \cdot \frac{z}{2x^3} \right)$$

$$= \frac{3x^2}{y} \div \left(\frac{4xz}{2x^3 y^2} \right)$$

$$= \frac{3x^2}{y} \div \left(\frac{4}{2} \cdot \frac{x}{x} \cdot \frac{z}{x^2 y^2} \right)$$

$$= \frac{3x^2}{y} \div \left(2 \cdot 1 \cdot \frac{z}{x^2 y^2} \right)$$

$$= \frac{3x^2}{y} \div \frac{2z}{x^2 y^2}$$

$$= \frac{3x^2}{y} \cdot \frac{x^2 y^2}{2z}$$

$$= \frac{3x^4 y^2}{2yz}$$

$$= \frac{3}{2} \cdot \frac{y}{y} \cdot \frac{x^4 y}{z}$$

$$= \frac{3}{2} \cdot 1 \cdot \frac{x^4 y}{z}$$

$$= \frac{3x^4 y}{2z}$$

Example 10. Simplify $\left(\dfrac{x^2 - y^2}{x - y} \div \dfrac{x^2 - 2xy + y^2}{x^2 - 5x + 6} \right) \div \dfrac{x^2 - 6x + 9}{x - y}$.

$$\left(\frac{x^2 - y^2}{x + y} \div \frac{x^2 - 2xy + y^2}{x^2 - 5x + 6} \right) \div \frac{x^2 - 6x + 9}{x - y}$$

$$= \left(\frac{x^2 - y^2}{x + y} \cdot \frac{x^2 - 5x + 6}{x^2 - 2xy + y^2} \right) \div \frac{x^2 - 6x + 9}{x - y}$$

$$= \left[\frac{(x + y)(x - y)}{(x + y)} \cdot \frac{(x - 2)(x - 3)}{(x - y)(x - y)} \right] \div \frac{x^2 - 6x + 9}{x - y}$$

$$= \left[\frac{(x+y)(x-y)(x-2)(x-3)}{(x+y)(x-y)(x-y)} \right] \div \frac{x^2 - 6x + 9}{x-y}$$

$$= \left[\frac{(x+y)}{(x+y)} \cdot \frac{(x-y)}{(x-y)} \cdot \frac{(x-2)(x-3)}{(x-y)} \right] \div \frac{x^2 - 6x + 9}{x-y}$$

$$= \left[1 \cdot 1 \cdot \frac{(x-2)(x-3)}{(x-y)} \right] \div \frac{(x-3)(x-3)}{(x-y)}$$

$$= \frac{(x-2)(x-3)}{(x-y)} \cdot \frac{(x-y)}{(x-3)(x-3)}$$

$$= \frac{(x-3)(x-y)(x-2)}{(x-3)(x-y)(x-3)}$$

$$= \frac{(x-3)}{(x-3)} \cdot \frac{(x-y)}{(x-y)} \cdot \frac{(x-2)}{(x-3)}$$

$$= 1 \cdot 1 \cdot \frac{(x-2)}{(x-3)}$$

$$= \frac{x-2}{x-3}$$

EXERCISE 32

A

Multiply:

1. $\dfrac{a}{b} \cdot \dfrac{x}{y}$

2. $\dfrac{cx}{y} \cdot \dfrac{dx}{z}$

3. $\dfrac{m}{n} \cdot b$

4. $\dfrac{4b}{5} \cdot \dfrac{c}{2}$

5. $\dfrac{7t}{3} \cdot \dfrac{9s}{21}$

6. $\dfrac{3p}{5} \cdot \dfrac{10p}{9q}$

7. $\dfrac{y^2}{8b} \cdot \dfrac{3b^2}{y^4}$

8. $\dfrac{t^4 y^2}{2w} \cdot \dfrac{8w^2}{t^3 y^3}$

9. $\dfrac{1}{y} \cdot \dfrac{y^2}{3} \cdot \dfrac{2x^2}{z}$

10. $\dfrac{5w}{z} \cdot \dfrac{3a}{10w} \cdot \dfrac{2z}{a}$

11. $\dfrac{x^2 - x}{x-1} \cdot \dfrac{x+y}{x}$

12. $\dfrac{a^2 - b^2}{a-b} \cdot \dfrac{a+b}{a^2 - b^2}$

13. $\dfrac{b^2 - 1}{b} \cdot \dfrac{3b}{b+1}$

14. $\dfrac{t^2 - 9}{7} \cdot \dfrac{21}{t^2 - t - 6}$

15. $\dfrac{d^2 + 7d + 12}{d+3} \cdot \dfrac{d^2}{d+4}$

Divide:

16. $\dfrac{5x}{3y} \div \dfrac{2x}{6y^2}$

17. $\dfrac{4cd}{a} \div \dfrac{c^2d}{a^2}$

18. $\dfrac{m^2n^3}{4p^2} \div \dfrac{m^2n^2}{2p}$

19. $\dfrac{8c^2d}{mx} \div \dfrac{2cd^2}{mx^2}$

20. $t^2 \div \dfrac{3t^3}{5}$

21. $\dfrac{b^2d^3}{3} \div \dfrac{bd}{6}$

22. $\dfrac{t^2r^4}{x} \div t^2r^2$

23. $\dfrac{mnp^2}{3s} \div \dfrac{m^2n^2p^2}{9s^2}$

24. $\dfrac{ab + b}{b} \div a$

25. $\dfrac{x - y}{3} \div \dfrac{x^2 - y^2}{6x + 6y}$

26. $\dfrac{x^2 + x}{x^2 + 2x + 1} \div \dfrac{x^2 - 1}{x^2 - x - 2}$

27. $\dfrac{x^2 + xy}{x^2} \div \dfrac{x + y}{x^3}$

28. $\dfrac{r^2 + 5r + 6}{rs + 2s} \div \dfrac{r + 3}{3}$

29. $\dfrac{m - p}{3} \div \dfrac{m^2 - mp}{9}$

30. $\dfrac{a^3}{m - 3p} \div \dfrac{a^2}{m - 3p}$

31. $\dfrac{3x^2y}{2a - 2b} \div \dfrac{5xy}{5a - 5b}$

32. $\dfrac{a^2 - 1}{5} \div \dfrac{a + 1}{10}$

Simplify:

33. $\left(\frac{3}{4} \cdot \frac{4}{3}\right) \div \frac{8}{9}$

34. $\left(\frac{7}{8} \div \frac{1}{4}\right) \div \frac{3}{4}$

35. $\left(\dfrac{4x^2}{y} \div \dfrac{2x}{y^2}\right) \cdot \dfrac{y}{3}$

36. $\left(\dfrac{x^2y^3}{3} \div \dfrac{xy}{9}\right) \cdot \dfrac{1}{y^2}$

37. $\left(\dfrac{x^2 - y^2}{x^2 - xy} \cdot \dfrac{2x^2 - 2x}{x - 1}\right) \div \dfrac{x + y}{x^2}$

38. $\left(\dfrac{a^2 - ab}{a^2 - 2ab + b^2} \div \dfrac{a + 2b}{a^2 + ab - 2b^2}\right) \cdot \dfrac{a - b}{a^2 - b^2}$

39. $\left(\dfrac{m^2 - 2m - 3}{m^2 - 1} \div \dfrac{m^2 - 6m + 9}{4m - 4}\right) \div \dfrac{2m - 10}{3m - 9}$

40. $\dfrac{r - rs}{18 - 3s} \cdot \left(\dfrac{4}{1 - 4s + 3s^2} \div \dfrac{3r^2}{6 - 19s + 3s^2}\right)$

B

Multiply:

1. $\dfrac{4q^2 - 16q}{q - 4} \cdot \dfrac{q + 3}{4q^2}$

2. $\dfrac{z^2 - 4z - 21}{z^2 - 9} \cdot \dfrac{z - 3}{z - 7}$

3. $\dfrac{w^2 - 16w + 39}{w^2 - w - 6} \cdot \dfrac{w + 2}{3}$

4. $\dfrac{x^2 - xy}{x^2 - y^2} \cdot \dfrac{x + y}{3x}$

5. $\dfrac{2m^2 - 7mn + 3n^2}{m^2 - 3mn + 2n^2} \cdot \dfrac{m^2 - 4mn + 3n^2}{m^2 - 6mn + 9n^2}$

6. $\dfrac{2a^2 - 2ab}{3a} \cdot \dfrac{a + b}{a^2 - b^2}$

7. $\dfrac{4x^2 - 13x + 3}{16x^2 - 4x} \cdot \dfrac{8x^2}{x^2 - 6x + 9}$

8. $\dfrac{4x^2}{x - 1} \cdot \dfrac{x^2 - 2x + 1}{x + 1} \cdot \dfrac{x^2 - 1}{x^3 - x^2}$

9. $\dfrac{ab - b}{3b} \cdot \dfrac{a^2 + 2a + 1}{a^2 - 1} \cdot \dfrac{b^2}{a + 1}$

10. $\dfrac{rs - r}{s^2 - 2s + 1} \cdot \dfrac{s^2 - 1}{r^2 - r} \cdot \dfrac{3r^2 - 2r - 1}{4s^2 + 13s + 9}$

Divide:

11. $\dfrac{4 - b^2}{12} \div \dfrac{2 - b}{3}$

12. $\dfrac{rt + t}{5} \div \dfrac{r + 1}{t^2}$

13. $\dfrac{16x^2 - 1}{y^2} \div \dfrac{4x + 1}{y^3}$

14. $\dfrac{6x^2 - 7x - 3}{m^2 - 1} \div \dfrac{2x - 3}{m - 1}$

15. $\dfrac{r^2 + 7r + 12}{r^2 + 5r + 6} \div \dfrac{r^2 + 9r + 20}{r^2 + 4r + 4}$

16. $\dfrac{c^2 - d^2}{4c^2 + 13cd + 9d^2} \div \dfrac{2c^2 - cd - d^2}{8c^2 + 22cd + 9d^2}$

17. $\dfrac{ab - a}{b^2 - 2b + 1} \div \dfrac{b + 3}{b^2 - b}$

18. $\dfrac{a^2 + 2a - 15}{a^2 + 3a - 10} \div \dfrac{a^2 - 2a - 3}{a^2 - 4a + 4}$

Perform the indicated operations:

19. $\left(\dfrac{c^2 - d^2}{2c^2 - cd - d^2} \div \dfrac{c^2 - cd}{4c^2 + 4cd + d^2} \right) \cdot \dfrac{3c - 3d}{2c^2 + 3cd + d^2}$

20. $\left(\dfrac{m^2 + m - 12}{2m - 10} \div \dfrac{m^2 - 11m + 24}{m^2 - 9m + 8} \right) \div \dfrac{m^2 + 3m - 4}{3m + 15}$

21. $\dfrac{x^2 - y^2}{a^2 - b^2} \cdot \dfrac{b^2x - a^2x}{y - x}$

22. $\dfrac{mp - np}{n - m} \cdot \dfrac{3}{2p}$

23. $\dfrac{c^2 - c - 12}{d + 3} \div \dfrac{4 - c}{d^2 + 6d + 9}$

24. $\dfrac{x^2 - 7x + 6}{1 - x} \div \dfrac{x^2 - 4x - 12}{x^2 - 4}$

25. $\dfrac{x^2 - 5x + 6}{6 - x - x^2} \cdot \dfrac{x^2 - x - 12}{8x - x^2 - 16}$

37. THE LEAST COMMON MULTIPLE

Multiples of a number are numbers into which that given number will exactly divide. Thus multiples of 3 are 3, 6, 9, 12, 15, 18, 21, 24, 27, and so on, and multiples of 4 are 4, 8, 12, 16, 20, 24, 28, and so on. If we observe these two lists of numbers, we find that 12 is in both lists, as is 24. Both 12 and 24 are multiples of 3 as well as of 4, and 12 is the least of these multiples common to both 3 and 4. Hence we say that 12 is the *least common multiple* of both 3 and 4.

> The *least common multiple* (abbreviated L.C.M.) of a set of numbers is the smallest number that is a multiple of each member in that set of given numbers or algebraic expressions.

It is an easy matter to determine the L.C.M. of a set of small numbers. As an example, we can readily see that 6 is a multiple of both 2 and 3. Then 6 is the L.C.M. of 2 and 3. As the numbers become larger, it is sometimes difficult or even impossible to visualize the least common multiple of them. To enumerate a list of multiples of each of the given numbers as we did the 3 and 4 above becomes tedious and laborious.

If each of the given numbers is factored into its prime factors, these prime factors are factors of the least common multiple of the given set of numbers. Then the product of all the prime factors of each of the given numbers will be a common multiple of the given numbers. However, this may not be the least common multiple. If the same number is a factor in two or more of the given numbers, we need to use it only once if it is a unique factor of each number. If any factor common to the set of numbers is repeated among the prime factors of any one of the set of given numbers, it must be used the greatest number of times it appears as a prime factor in any one of the given set of numbers.

Example 1. Find the L.C.M. of 15 and 6.
$$15 = 5 \cdot 3$$
$$6 = 2 \cdot 3$$
$$\text{L.C.M.} = 2 \cdot 3 \cdot 5$$
$$= 30$$

Example 2. Find the L.C.M. of 8 and 12.
$$8 = 2 \cdot 2 \cdot 2$$
$$12 = 2 \cdot 2 \cdot 3$$
$$\text{L.C.M.} = 2 \cdot 2 \cdot 2 \cdot 3$$
$$= 24$$

Example 3. Find the L.C.M. of 8, 6, and 15.
$$8 = 2 \cdot 2 \cdot 2$$
$$6 = 2 \cdot 3$$
$$15 = 3 \cdot 5$$
$$\text{L.C.M.} = 2 \cdot 2 \cdot 2 \cdot 3 \cdot 5$$
$$= 120$$

Example 4. Find the L.C.M. of m^2n, mnp, and $6p^2n$.

$$m^2n = m \cdot m \cdot n$$
$$mnp = m \cdot n \cdot p$$
$$6p^2n = 3 \cdot 2 \cdot p \cdot p \cdot n$$
$$\text{L.C.M.} = 3 \cdot 2 \cdot m \cdot m \cdot n \cdot p \cdot p = 6m^2np^2$$

Example 5. Find the L.C.M. of $a^2 - b^2$, $a - b$, and $5a + 5b$.

$$a^2 - b^2 = (a + b)(a - b)$$
$$a - b = (a - b)$$
$$5a + 5b = 5(a + b)$$
$$\text{L.C.M.} = 5(a + b)(a - b)$$

Example 6. Find the L.C.M. of $x^2 - 7x + 12$, $x^2 - 2x - 3$, and $x^2 - 8x + 16$.

$$x^2 - 7x + 12 = (x - 3)(x - 4)$$
$$x^2 - 2x - 3 = (x - 3)(x + 1)$$
$$x^2 - 8x + 16 = (x - 4)(x - 4)$$
$$\text{L.C.M.} = (x - 3)(x - 4)(x - 4)(x + 1)$$

It can be observed that the least common multiple for Example 5 and Example 6 are left in factored form. At this time that form is to be used.

EXERCISE 33

Find the L.C.M. of each of the following:

1. 5, 10, 15
2. 6, 9, 12
3. 4, 8, 12
4. 5, 8, 10
5. 12, 15, 18
6. 15, 20, 30
7. 3, 9, 12, 24
8. 4, 10, 16, 20
9. x^2y^3, xyz^2, x^3yz
10. d^3c, $3d^2c^2$, $6dc^3$
11. $12m$, $8mn^2$, $16mnp$
12. $8r$, $12rs$, $4r^2t$
13. $18p^3$, pq^2, $12pq$
14. $3xz$, $15z^3$, $6x^2z$
15. bm, $7b^2n$, $21mn^2$
16. $c + d$, $c^2 - d^2$, $c - d$
17. $t^2 - t$, $t^2 - 1$
18. $a - b$, $a^2 - 2ab + b^2$
19. $y^2 + y$, $y^2 + 2y + 1$, $y^2 - 1$
20. $m - 2p$, $m^2 - 4p^2$, $m^2 - 4mp + 4p^2$
21. $d^2 - 5d + 6$, $d^2 - 6d + 9$, $d^2 - 4d + 4$
22. $x^2 - 4x$, $x^2 - 7x + 12$, $x^2 - 9x + 20$
23. $y^2 - 4$, $y^2 - 6y + 8$, $y^2 + 4y - 12$
24. $4x^2 - 4x + 1$, $4x^2 + 4x - 3$, $4x^2 - 8x + 3$
25. $6x^2 - 6$, $x^2 - 2x + 1$, $x^2 - 5x + 4$

38. ADDING AND SUBTRACTING FRACTIONS

Definition 1. If a, b, c, and d are real numbers ($b \neq 0$), then $\dfrac{a}{b} + \dfrac{c}{b} = \dfrac{a+c}{b}$.

Theorem 1. If a, b, c, and d are real numbers ($b \neq 0$, $d \neq 0$), then $\dfrac{a}{b} + \dfrac{c}{d}$

$$= \frac{ad + bc}{bd}.$$

Proof:

$$\frac{a}{b} + \frac{c}{d} = \frac{ad}{bd} + \frac{bc}{bd} \qquad \text{(Theorem 1, Section 35)}$$

$$= ad\left(\frac{1}{bd}\right) + bc\left(\frac{1}{bd}\right) \qquad \text{(Definition 1, Section 36)}$$

$$= (ad + bc)\left(\frac{1}{bd}\right) \qquad \text{(Inverse of the distributive law)}$$

$$= \frac{ad + bc}{bd} \qquad \text{(Definition 1, Section 36)}$$

Thus *the sum of two or more fractions that have a common denominator is a single fraction whose denominator is that common denominator and whose numerator is the algebraic sum of the numerators of the given fractions.*

Example 1. Add $\frac{3}{8} + \frac{1}{8} + \frac{5}{8}$.

$$\frac{3}{8} + \frac{1}{8} + \frac{5}{8} = \frac{3 + 1 + 5}{8}$$

$$= \frac{9}{8}$$

Example 2. Add $\frac{1}{3} + \frac{1}{4} + \frac{5}{6}$.

$$3 = 3$$
$$4 = 2 \cdot 2$$
$$6 = 2 \cdot 3$$
$$\text{L.C.M.} = 2 \cdot 2 \cdot 3$$
$$= 12$$

Hence the common denominator is 12. In order to convert each of the original denominators to the common denominator, multiply each by the number that will produce 12. If the numerator of a fraction is multiplied by the same number as the denominator, the value of the fraction is unchanged.

$$\frac{1}{3} + \frac{1}{4} + \frac{5}{6} = \frac{4 \cdot 1}{4 \cdot 3} + \frac{3 \cdot 1}{3 \cdot 4} + \frac{2 \cdot 5}{2 \cdot 6}$$

$$= \frac{4}{12} + \frac{3}{12} + \frac{10}{12}$$

$$= \frac{4 + 3 + 10}{12}$$

$$= \frac{17}{12}$$

Example 3. Add $\dfrac{3x}{2} + \dfrac{4x}{3} + \dfrac{7x}{6}$.

$$2 = 2$$
$$3 = 3$$
$$6 = 2 \cdot 3$$
$$\text{L.C.M.} = 6$$

$$\frac{3x}{2} + \frac{4x}{3} + \frac{7x}{6} = \frac{3 \cdot 3x}{3 \cdot 2} + \frac{2 \cdot 4x}{2 \cdot 3} + \frac{7x}{6}$$

$$= \frac{9x}{6} + \frac{8x}{6} + \frac{7x}{6}$$

$$= \frac{9x + 8x + 7x}{6}$$

$$= \frac{24x}{6}$$

$$= 4x$$

Example 4. Add $\dfrac{x}{3yz} + \dfrac{3}{y^2} + \dfrac{5x}{12y^3}$.

$$3yz = 3 \cdot y \cdot z$$
$$y^2 = y \cdot y$$
$$12y^3 = 2 \cdot 2 \cdot 3 \cdot y \cdot y \cdot y$$
$$\text{L.C.M.} = 2 \cdot 2 \cdot 3 \cdot y \cdot y \cdot y \cdot z = 12y^3z$$

$$\frac{x}{3yz} + \frac{3}{y^2} + \frac{5x}{12y^3} = \frac{(x)(4y^2)}{12y^3z} + \frac{(3)(12yz)}{12y^2z} + \frac{(5x)(z)}{12y^3z}$$

$$= \frac{4xy^2 + 36yz + 5xz}{12y^3z}$$

Example 5. Add $\dfrac{1}{x-y} + \dfrac{3}{x+y} + \dfrac{5}{x^2-y^2}$.

$$x - y = (x - y)$$
$$x + y = (x + y)$$
$$x^2 - y^2 = (x + y)(x - y)$$
$$\text{L.C.M.} = (x + y)(x - y)$$

$$\dfrac{1}{x-y} + \dfrac{3}{x+y} + \dfrac{5}{x^2-y^2}$$

$$= \dfrac{1(x+y)}{(x+y)(x-y)} + \dfrac{3(x-y)}{(x+y)(x-y)} + \dfrac{5}{(x+y)(x-y)}$$

$$= \dfrac{x + y + 3x - 3y + 5}{(x+y)(x-y)}$$

$$= \dfrac{4x - 2y + 5}{(x+y)(x-y)}$$

Example 6. Add $\dfrac{x-5}{x^2-7x+10} + \dfrac{x-2}{x^2-10x+25}$.

$$x^2 - 7x + 10 = (x - 5)(x - 2)$$
$$x^2 - 10x + 25 = (x - 5)(x - 5)$$
$$\text{L.C.M.} = (x - 2)(x - 5)(x - 5)$$

$$\dfrac{x-5}{x^2-7x+10} + \dfrac{x-2}{x^2-10x+25} = \dfrac{x-5}{(x-5)(x-2)} + \dfrac{x-2}{(x-5)(x-5)}$$

$$= \dfrac{(x-5)(x-5)}{(x-2)(x-5)(x-5)} + \dfrac{(x-2)(x-2)}{(x-2)(x-5)(x-5)}$$

$$= \dfrac{x^2-10x+25}{(x-2)(x-5)(x-5)} + \dfrac{x^2-4x+4}{(x-2)(x-5)(x-5)}$$

$$= \dfrac{x^2-10x+25+x^2-4x+4}{(x-2)(x-5)(x-5)}$$

$$= \dfrac{2x^2-14x+29}{(x-2)(x-5)(x-5)}$$

To subtract one fraction from another fraction, find the common denominator. Then subtract the second numerator from the first numerator and place the result over the common denominator. If all terms in both numerators are placed over one common denominator, change the signs of all terms of the numerator of the fraction that follows a negative sign. This conforms to the rule for changing all signs in the subtrahend when subtracting.

Example 7. Subtract $\frac{3}{8} - \frac{1}{12}$.

$$8 = 2 \cdot 2 \cdot 2$$
$$12 = 2 \cdot 2 \cdot 3$$
$$\text{L.C.M.} = 2 \cdot 2 \cdot 2 \cdot 3$$
$$= 24$$

$$\frac{3}{8} - \frac{1}{12} = \frac{9}{24} - \frac{2}{24}$$
$$= \frac{7}{24}$$

Example 8. Subtract $\dfrac{5}{x} - \dfrac{3}{x^2}$.

$$x = x$$
$$x^2 = x \cdot x$$
$$\text{L.C.M.} = x \cdot x$$
$$= x^2$$

$$\frac{5}{x} - \frac{3}{x^2} = \frac{5x}{x^2} - \frac{3}{x^2}$$
$$= \frac{5x - 3}{x^2}$$

Example 9. Subtract $\dfrac{x}{x-1} - \dfrac{2}{x^2-1}$.

$$x - 1 = (x - 1)$$
$$x^2 - 1 = (x - 1)(x + 1)$$
$$\text{L.C.M.} = (x - 1)(x + 1)$$

$$\frac{x}{x-1} - \frac{2}{x^2-1} = \frac{x(x+1)}{(x-1)(x+1)} - \frac{2}{(x-1)(x+1)}$$
$$= \frac{x^2 + x - 2}{(x-1)(x+1)}$$
$$= \frac{(x-1)(x+2)}{(x-1)(x+1)}$$
$$= \frac{(x-1)}{(x-1)} \cdot \frac{(x+2)}{(x+1)}$$
$$= 1 \cdot \frac{x+2}{x+1}$$
$$= \frac{x+2}{x+1}$$

Both addition and subtraction may occur in the same problem. In such cases convert all denominators to a common denominator and then place all terms in the numerators over one denominator. As this is done, be sure to change the signs of all terms in any numerator of a fraction that follows a negative sign.

Example 10. Simplify $\frac{5}{8} + \frac{1}{6} - \frac{1}{3}$.

$$8 = 2 \cdot 2 \cdot 2$$
$$6 = 3 \cdot 2$$
$$3 = 3$$
$$\text{L.C.M.} = 2 \cdot 2 \cdot 2 \cdot 3 = 24$$

$$\frac{5}{8} + \frac{1}{6} - \frac{1}{3} = \frac{15}{24} + \frac{4}{24} - \frac{8}{24}$$
$$= \frac{15 + 4 - 8}{24}$$
$$= \frac{11}{24}$$

Example 11. Simplify $\dfrac{2}{3} - \dfrac{1}{x-2} + \dfrac{3x}{x+3}$.

$$3 = 3$$
$$x - 2 = (x - 2)$$
$$x + 3 = (x + 3)$$
$$\text{L.C.M.} = 3(x - 2)(x + 3)$$

$$\frac{2}{3} - \frac{1}{x-2} + \frac{3x}{x+3}$$

$$= \frac{2(x-2)(x+3)}{3(x-2)(x+3)} - \frac{1(3)(x+3)}{3(x-2)(x+3)} + \frac{3x(3)(x-2)}{3(x-2)(x+3)}$$

$$= \frac{2x^2 + 2x - 12}{3(x-2)(x+3)} - \frac{3x+9}{3(x-2)(x+3)} + \frac{9x^2 - 18x}{3(x-2)(x+3)}$$

$$= \frac{2x^2 + 2x - 12 - 3x - 9 + 9x^2 - 18x}{3(x-2)(x+3)}$$

$$= \frac{11x^2 - 19x - 21}{3(x-2)(x+3)}$$

A

Perform the indicated operations:

1. $\dfrac{3x}{2} + \dfrac{2y}{5}$

2. $\dfrac{b}{3} + \dfrac{c}{12}$

3. $\dfrac{5}{a} - \dfrac{3}{b}$

4. $\dfrac{3}{4m} + \dfrac{7}{6m}$

5. $\dfrac{6t}{5} + \dfrac{t}{3}$

6. $\dfrac{b^2}{2a} - \dfrac{b}{4}$

7. $\dfrac{1}{a} + \dfrac{1}{b} + \dfrac{1}{c}$

8. $\dfrac{1}{3a^2} - \dfrac{5}{12a}$

9. $\dfrac{5b}{a - b} + \dfrac{3a}{a + b}$

10. $\dfrac{4}{x^2 - x} - \dfrac{3}{x - 1}$

11. $\dfrac{m + n}{3} - \dfrac{m - n}{2}$

12. $\dfrac{1}{ab} - \dfrac{1}{cd}$

13. $\dfrac{z^2 - 3z}{2} + \dfrac{5z - 1}{3}$

14. $\dfrac{5}{t - 1} + \dfrac{3}{t + 1} - \dfrac{8}{t^2 - 1}$

15. $\dfrac{4a}{a - 3} - \dfrac{a - 3}{a + 3}$

16. $\dfrac{3y - 5}{7y} - \dfrac{2y + 1}{y^2} + \dfrac{y + 6}{3y}$

17. $\dfrac{9}{2b - c} - \dfrac{5}{b - c}$

18. $\dfrac{4}{x^2 - xy} + \dfrac{3}{x - y} - \dfrac{5}{x + y}$

B

Perform the indicated operations:

1. $\dfrac{4x}{x^2 - 5x + 6} - \dfrac{3x}{x - 3} + \dfrac{4x}{x - 2}$

2. $\dfrac{5x}{2x^2 - x - 1} - \dfrac{7x}{2x^2 + 3x + 1} + \dfrac{3x}{x^2 - 1}$

3. $\dfrac{2}{x^2 - y^2} + \dfrac{5}{x^2 - 2xy + y^2} - \dfrac{3}{x^2 + 2xy + y^2}$

4. $\dfrac{3}{x + 3} + \dfrac{3x}{x^2 - x - 12} - \dfrac{x}{(x - 4)^2}$

5. $\dfrac{m + n}{m^2 + 2mn + n^2} - \dfrac{m - n}{m^2 - 2mn + n^2} + \dfrac{m + n}{m^2 - n^2}$

6. $\dfrac{1}{x^2 - 4x} - \dfrac{6}{x} + 1$

7. $3 - x^2 + \dfrac{x^3 - 8}{x + 2}$

8. $\dfrac{4a}{a^2 - a - 6} - \dfrac{3a}{12 - a - a^2}$

9. $\dfrac{3}{x^2 - 3x - 4} + \dfrac{2}{3 + 2x - x^2}$

10. $\dfrac{x}{x^2 - 3x - 10} + \dfrac{3}{6 + x - x^2}$

39. SUBSTITUTION IN FRACTIONAL EXPRESSIONS

Certain problems in algebra require that we substitute given values in a fractional expression. The following examples illustrate that substitution.

Example 1. Find the value of $\dfrac{a + b - c}{3}$ if $a = 3$, $b = 4$, and $c = 1$.

$$\frac{a + b - c}{3} = \frac{3 + 4 - 1}{3}$$
$$= \frac{6}{3}$$
$$= 2$$

Example 2. Find the value of $\dfrac{x^2}{y + z}$ if $x = 4$, $y = 3$, and $z = 5$.

$$\frac{x^2}{y + z} = \frac{4^2}{3 + 5}$$
$$= \frac{16}{8}$$
$$= 2$$

Example 3. Find the value of $\dfrac{m^2 - 1}{n}$ if $m = 2$ and $n = 4$.

$$\frac{m^2 - 1}{n} = \frac{2^2 - 1}{4}$$
$$= \frac{4 - 1}{4} = \frac{3}{4}$$

Example 4. Find the value of $\dfrac{b^2 - c^2}{b}$ if $b = 3$ and $c = 2$.

$$\frac{b^2 - c^2}{b} = \frac{3^2 - 2^2}{3}$$

$$= \frac{9 - 4}{3}$$

$$= \frac{5}{3}$$

Example 5. Find the value of $\dfrac{[3x - 2y]^2}{3x}$, if $x = 3$ and $y = -1$.

$$\frac{[3x - 2y]^2}{3x} = \frac{[3(3) - 2(-1)]^2}{3(3)}$$

$$= \frac{[9 + 2]^2}{9}$$

$$= \frac{[11]^2}{9}$$

$$= \frac{121}{9}$$

EXERCISE 35

A

Find the value of the following if $a = 1$, $b = 2$, $x = 5$, and $y = -2$.

1. $\dfrac{a + b}{x}$ 2. $\dfrac{b - a}{b}$ 3. $\dfrac{x - y^2}{b}$

4. $\dfrac{a^2 + b^2}{y^2}$ 5. $ab - \dfrac{y}{x}$ 6. $\dfrac{ab^2}{x}$

7. $\dfrac{ab}{a} - \dfrac{xy}{x}$ 8. $\dfrac{xy^2}{b}$ 9. $\dfrac{b - a^2}{a}$

10. $\dfrac{b^2a - a}{b}$ 11. $\dfrac{x}{a - y}$ 12. $\dfrac{y^2 - a}{b}$

13. $\dfrac{ab}{b} + \dfrac{xy}{x}$ 14. $\dfrac{xy^2}{a} + \dfrac{b}{a}$ 15. $\dfrac{1}{b} - \dfrac{2}{a}$

16. $\dfrac{b}{3} + \dfrac{a}{3}$ 17. $\dfrac{a}{a + b} - \dfrac{1}{b}$ 18. $\dfrac{y^2 + 1}{x}$

162   FRACTIONS

19. $\dfrac{b^2x + 4}{y^2}$ 20. $\dfrac{1 - b^2}{b^2 - 1}$ 21. $\dfrac{1}{a^2} + \dfrac{1}{b^2}$

22. $\dfrac{x - b^2}{b}$ 23. $\dfrac{ax - by}{3}$ 24. $\dfrac{x^2}{5} - \dfrac{b^3}{8}$

25. $\dfrac{3x}{5} - \dfrac{ab}{a}$

B

Evaluate the following if $x = 2$, $y = 1$, and $z = -2$.

1. $\dfrac{x^2 + y^2 + z^2}{3y + z}$ 2. $\dfrac{z - (x + y)^2}{2x - 3y}$ 3. $\dfrac{3x^2 + y}{3z^2}$

4. $\dfrac{3(y^2 + 4z)}{2x}$ 5. $\dfrac{z^2}{2x - 3y}$ 6. $\dfrac{2x^2 + z^3}{y - z}$

7. $\dfrac{z(y^2 - x)}{z^2}$ 8. $\dfrac{(x - z)^2}{(z - 1)^2}$ 9. $\dfrac{xyz^3}{y - x}$

10. $\dfrac{y^3 - z^3}{(y - z)^3}$

40. COMPLEX FRACTIONS

A *complex fraction* is a fractional expression in which either the numerator or denominator, or both, is fractional. The expression $\dfrac{\frac{1}{4}}{\frac{1}{2}}$ is a complex fraction.

If the fractions in the numerator and denominator are relatively simple, they may be solved by dividing the numerator by the denominator.

Example 1. Simplify $\dfrac{\frac{2}{3}}{\frac{1}{3}}$.

$$\dfrac{\frac{2}{3}}{\frac{1}{3}} = \dfrac{2}{3} \div \dfrac{1}{3}$$

$$= \dfrac{2}{3} \cdot \dfrac{3}{1}$$

$$= \dfrac{6}{3}$$

$$= 2$$

Example 2. Simplify $\dfrac{3}{\frac{1}{2}}$.

$$\frac{3}{\frac{1}{2}} = 3 \div \frac{1}{2}$$

$$= 3 \cdot \frac{2}{1}$$

$$= 6$$

Example 3. Simplify $\dfrac{\frac{1}{4}}{5}$.

$$\frac{\frac{1}{4}}{5} = \frac{1}{4} \div 5$$

$$= \frac{1}{4} \cdot \frac{1}{5} = \frac{1}{20}$$

If more than one fraction appears in the numerator or denominator or in both, convert each of them into a single fraction before setting it up as a division problem. It may be necessary to get a common denominator before they can be simplified into a single fraction.

Example 4. Simplify $\dfrac{\frac{1}{2} + \frac{1}{3}}{\frac{1}{4}}$.

$$\frac{\frac{1}{2} + \frac{1}{3}}{\frac{1}{4}} = \frac{\frac{3}{6} + \frac{2}{6}}{\frac{1}{4}}$$

$$= \frac{\frac{5}{6}}{\frac{1}{4}}$$

$$= \frac{5}{6} \div \frac{1}{4}$$

$$= \frac{5}{6} \cdot \frac{4}{1}$$

$$= \frac{20}{6}$$

$$= \frac{10}{3}$$

Example 5. Simplify $\dfrac{\frac{a}{b} + a}{\frac{a}{b}}$.

$$\frac{\frac{a}{b} + a}{\frac{a}{b}} = \frac{\frac{a}{b} + \frac{ab}{b}}{\frac{a}{b}}$$

$$= \frac{\frac{a + ab}{b}}{\frac{a}{b}}$$

$$= \frac{a+ab}{b} \div \frac{a}{b}$$

$$= \frac{a+ab}{b} \cdot \frac{b}{a}$$

$$= \frac{a(1+b)}{b} \cdot \frac{b}{a}$$

$$= \frac{b}{b} \cdot \frac{a}{a} \cdot (1+b)$$

$$= 1 \cdot 1 \cdot (1+b)$$

$$= 1+b$$

Example 6. Simplify $\dfrac{x - \dfrac{y^2}{x}}{1 - \dfrac{y}{x}}$.

$$\frac{x - \dfrac{y^2}{x}}{1 - \dfrac{y}{x}} = \frac{\dfrac{x^2}{x} - \dfrac{y^2}{x}}{\dfrac{x}{x} - \dfrac{y}{x}}$$

$$= \frac{\dfrac{x^2 - y^2}{x}}{\dfrac{x - y}{x}}$$

$$= \frac{x^2 - y^2}{x} \div \frac{x - y}{x}$$

$$= \frac{(x-y)(x+y)}{x} \cdot \frac{x}{(x-y)}$$

$$= \frac{x(x-y)(x+y)}{x(x-y)}$$

$$= \frac{x}{x} \cdot \frac{(x-y)}{(x-y)} (x+y)$$

$$= 1 \cdot 1 \cdot (x+y)$$

$$= x+y$$

An alternate method for simplifying complex fractions is that of multiplying both the numerator and denominator of the complex fraction by the least common multiple of the denominators of the two fractions that make up the complex fraction. This method is illustrated in the following examples:

Example 7. Simplify $\dfrac{\frac{2}{3}}{\frac{1}{4}}$.

The least common multiple of 3 and 4 is 12. Hence we multiply both the numerator and denominator of the complex fraction by 12. Then

$$\frac{\frac{2}{3}}{\frac{1}{4}} = \frac{12 \cdot \frac{2}{3}}{12 \cdot \frac{1}{4}}$$

$$= \frac{\frac{12}{3} \cdot 2}{\frac{12}{4} \cdot 1}$$

$$= \frac{4 \cdot 2}{3 \cdot 1}$$

$$= \frac{8}{3}$$

Example 8. Simplify $\dfrac{\dfrac{x}{x-y}}{\dfrac{y}{x^2-y^2}}$.

The least common multiple of $x - y$ and $x^2 - y^2$ is $(x - y)(x + y)$. Then we multiply both the numerator and denominator of the complex fraction by $(x - y)(x + y)$.

$$\frac{\dfrac{x}{x-y}}{\dfrac{y}{x^2-y^2}} = \frac{(x-y)(x+y)\left(\dfrac{x}{x-y}\right)}{(x-y)(x+y)\left(\dfrac{y}{x^2-y^2}\right)}$$

$$= \frac{(x-y)(x+y)\left(\dfrac{x}{x-y}\right)}{(x-y)(x+y)\left(\dfrac{y}{(x-y)(x+y)}\right)}$$

$$= \frac{\dfrac{(x-y)}{(x-y)} \cdot x(x+y)}{\dfrac{(x-y)}{(x-y)} \cdot \dfrac{(x+y)}{(x+y)} \cdot y}$$

$$= \frac{1 \cdot x(x+y)}{1 \cdot 1 \cdot y}$$

$$= \frac{x(x+y)}{y}$$

Example 9. Simplify $\dfrac{a - 1 - \dfrac{b}{a}}{b - 1 - \dfrac{a}{b}}$.

The student may find this problem to be solved more readily if the numerator and denominator of the complex fraction are each expressed as a single fraction. Then

$$\frac{a - 1 - \dfrac{b}{a}}{b - 1 - \dfrac{a}{b}} = \frac{\dfrac{a^2}{a} - \dfrac{a}{a} - \dfrac{b}{a}}{\dfrac{b^2}{b} - \dfrac{b}{b} - \dfrac{a}{b}}$$

$$= \frac{\dfrac{a^2 - a - b}{a}}{\dfrac{b^2 - b - a}{b}}$$

Now the least common multiple of the two denominators of the complex fraction is ab. Then

$$\frac{\dfrac{a^2 - a - b}{a}}{\dfrac{b^2 - b - a}{b}} = \frac{ab \cdot \dfrac{a^2 - a - b}{a}}{ab \cdot \dfrac{b^2 - b - a}{b}}$$

$$= \frac{\dfrac{a}{a} \cdot b(a^2 - a - b)}{\dfrac{b}{b} \cdot a(b^2 - b - a)}$$

$$= \frac{1 \cdot b(a^2 - a - b)}{1 \cdot a(b^2 - b - a)}$$

$$= \frac{b(a^2 - a - b)}{a(b^2 - b - a)}$$

EXERCISE 36

A

Simplify:

1. $\dfrac{\dfrac{c}{d}}{\dfrac{b}{d}}$ 2. $\dfrac{\dfrac{2}{3a}}{\dfrac{2}{a}}$ 3. $\dfrac{\dfrac{x^2y}{z}}{\dfrac{xy^2}{z}}$ 4. $\dfrac{\dfrac{3}{5m}}{\dfrac{n}{10m}}$

5. $\dfrac{\dfrac{t^2}{y}}{\dfrac{y}{t}}$ 6. $\dfrac{\dfrac{3p^2}{8}}{\dfrac{q}{2}}$ 7. $\dfrac{\dfrac{6w^2}{5x}}{\dfrac{2w}{10x^2}}$ 8. $\dfrac{\dfrac{ab^2}{c}}{\dfrac{2b}{c^2}}$

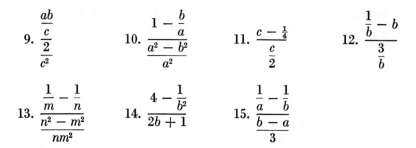

9. $\dfrac{\dfrac{ab}{c}}{\dfrac{2}{c^2}}$

10. $\dfrac{1 - \dfrac{b}{a}}{\dfrac{a^2 - b^2}{a^2}}$

11. $\dfrac{c - \frac{1}{4}}{\dfrac{c}{2}}$

12. $\dfrac{\dfrac{1}{b} - b}{\dfrac{3}{b}}$

13. $\dfrac{\dfrac{1}{m} - \dfrac{1}{n}}{\dfrac{n^2 - m^2}{nm^2}}$

14. $\dfrac{4 - \dfrac{1}{b^2}}{2b + 1}$

15. $\dfrac{\dfrac{1}{a} - \dfrac{1}{b}}{\dfrac{b - a}{3}}$

B

Simplify:

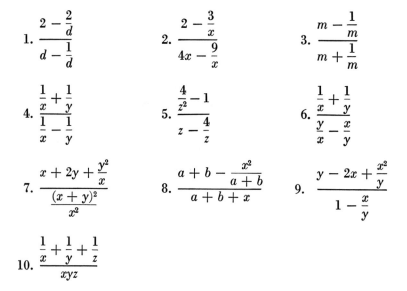

1. $\dfrac{2 - \dfrac{2}{d}}{d - \dfrac{1}{d}}$

2. $\dfrac{2 - \dfrac{3}{x}}{4x - \dfrac{9}{x}}$

3. $\dfrac{m - \dfrac{1}{m}}{m + \dfrac{1}{m}}$

4. $\dfrac{\dfrac{1}{x} + \dfrac{1}{y}}{\dfrac{1}{x} - \dfrac{1}{y}}$

5. $\dfrac{\dfrac{4}{z^2} - 1}{z - \dfrac{4}{z}}$

6. $\dfrac{\dfrac{1}{x} + \dfrac{1}{y}}{\dfrac{y}{x} - \dfrac{x}{y}}$

7. $\dfrac{x + 2y + \dfrac{y^2}{x}}{\dfrac{(x + y)^2}{x^2}}$

8. $\dfrac{a + b - \dfrac{x^2}{a + b}}{a + b + x}$

9. $\dfrac{y - 2x + \dfrac{x^2}{y}}{1 - \dfrac{x}{y}}$

10. $\dfrac{\dfrac{1}{x} + \dfrac{1}{y} + \dfrac{1}{z}}{xyz}$

41. FRACTIONAL EQUATIONS

To solve an equation containing fractions, multiply each term by the least common denominator. Then if each denominator is divided into that multiplier (the least common denominator), the problem is cleared of fractions and becomes an equation similar to those found in Chapter 4.

Example 1. Solve the equation $\frac{x}{3} = \frac{1}{6}$.

$$\frac{x}{3} = \frac{1}{6}$$

$$(6)\frac{x}{3} = (6)\frac{1}{6}$$

$$\frac{6}{3} \cdot x = \frac{6}{6} \cdot 1$$

$$2 \cdot x = 1 \cdot 1$$

$$2x = 1$$

$$x = \tfrac{1}{2}$$

Check: $\frac{x}{3} = \frac{1}{6}$

$$\frac{\frac{1}{2}}{3} = \frac{1}{6}$$

$$\frac{1}{2} \div 3 = \frac{1}{6}$$

$$\frac{1}{2} \cdot \frac{1}{3} = \frac{1}{6}$$

$$\frac{1}{6} = \frac{1}{6}$$

Example 2. Solve the equation $\frac{2x}{3} + 1 = 7$.

$$\frac{2x}{3} + 1 = 7$$

$$\frac{2x}{3} = 6$$

$$(3)\frac{2x}{3} = (3)(6)$$

$$\frac{3}{3} \cdot 2x = 18$$

$$1 \cdot 2x = 18$$

$$2x = 18$$

$$x = 9$$

Check: $\frac{2x}{3} + 1 = 7$

$$\frac{(2)(9)}{3} + 1 = 7$$

$$\frac{18}{3} + 1 = 7$$

$$6 + 1 = 7$$

$$7 = 7$$

Example 3. Solve the equation $\frac{3y + 1}{4} = \frac{5}{2}$.

$$\frac{3y + 1}{4} = \frac{5}{2}$$

$$(4)\frac{3y + 1}{4} = (4)\frac{5}{2}$$

$$\frac{4}{4} \cdot (3y + 1) = \frac{4}{2} \cdot 5$$

$$1 \cdot (3y + 1) = 2 \cdot 5$$

$$3y + 1 = 10$$

$$3y = 9$$

$$y = 3$$

Check: $\frac{3y + 1}{4} = \frac{5}{2}$

$$\frac{3(3) + 1}{4} = \frac{5}{2}$$

$$\frac{9 + 1}{4} = \frac{5}{2}$$

$$\frac{10}{4} = \frac{5}{2}$$

$$\frac{5}{2} = \frac{5}{2}$$

Example 4. Solve the equation $\dfrac{a^2 + 4}{3} = \dfrac{2a^2 + a}{6}$.

$$\dfrac{a^2 + 4}{3} = \dfrac{2a^2 + a}{6}$$

$$(6)\,\dfrac{a^2 + 4}{3} = (6)\,\dfrac{2a^2 + a}{6}$$

$$\dfrac{6}{3} \cdot (a^2 + 4) = \dfrac{6}{6}\,(2a^2 + a)$$

$$2(a^2 + 4) = 1 \cdot (2a^2 + a)$$
$$2a^2 + 8 = 2a^2 + a$$
$$8 = a$$
$$a = 8$$

Check:
$$\dfrac{a^2 + 4}{3} = \dfrac{2a^2 + a}{6}$$

$$\dfrac{(8)^2 + 4}{3} = \dfrac{2(8)^2 + 8}{6}$$

$$\dfrac{64 + 4}{3} = \dfrac{128 + 8}{6}$$

$$\dfrac{68}{3} = \dfrac{136}{6}$$

$$\dfrac{68}{3} = \dfrac{68}{3}$$

EXERCISE 37

A

Solve the following equations:

1. $\dfrac{y}{3} = \dfrac{1}{3}$

2. $\dfrac{b}{4} = \dfrac{1}{2}$

3. $\dfrac{m}{2} = \dfrac{1}{8}$

4. $\dfrac{2t}{5} = \dfrac{4}{5}$

5. $\dfrac{3x}{2} = \dfrac{5}{8}$

6. $\dfrac{4c}{15} = \dfrac{4}{5}$

7. $\dfrac{t}{3} + \dfrac{t}{2} = \dfrac{25}{12}$

8. $\dfrac{z}{4} + \dfrac{z}{2} = \dfrac{3}{4}$

9. $\dfrac{a}{5} - \dfrac{a}{6} = \dfrac{4}{5}$

10. $\dfrac{d}{3} + \dfrac{d}{4} = 28$

11. $\dfrac{m}{5} + \dfrac{m}{3} = 8$

12. $\dfrac{p}{2} - \dfrac{p}{8} = \dfrac{3}{2}$

13. $\dfrac{x}{3} - \dfrac{2x}{9} = \dfrac{1}{18}$

14. $\dfrac{4y}{3} - \dfrac{y}{4} = \dfrac{13}{3}$

15. $\dfrac{4b}{6} - \dfrac{b}{18} = 22$

16. $\dfrac{8t}{3} - \dfrac{2t}{5} = \dfrac{17}{5}$

17. $\dfrac{1}{x} + \dfrac{2}{3} = 1$

18. $\dfrac{2}{y} + \dfrac{1}{2} = \dfrac{7}{6}$

19. $\dfrac{x + 1}{3} + \dfrac{2x + 3}{4} = \dfrac{5}{4}$

20. $\dfrac{x - 1}{3} - \dfrac{x + 1}{4} = \dfrac{1}{6}$

B

Solve the following equations:

1. $\dfrac{5x + 2}{6} = \dfrac{2x + 4}{3}$

2. $\dfrac{y + 8}{4} = \dfrac{5y - 2}{6}$

3. $\dfrac{2a + 6}{5} - \dfrac{a + 4}{4} = -1$

4. $\dfrac{m + 1}{8} + \dfrac{3}{4} = \dfrac{3}{16}$

5. $\dfrac{z-5}{3} + \dfrac{3z-1}{2} = \dfrac{z-5}{12}$

6. $\dfrac{3x+4}{4} - \dfrac{5x-6}{2} = \dfrac{2x+8}{8}$

7. $\dfrac{y-1}{3} + \dfrac{2y+5}{9} = \dfrac{5+4y}{12}$

8. $\dfrac{x-1}{4} + \dfrac{3}{4} + \dfrac{3x+1}{12} = \dfrac{5}{6}$

9. $\dfrac{4b+1}{5} - \dfrac{b+7}{10} = \dfrac{b+2}{15}$

10. $\dfrac{c^2-1}{2} - \dfrac{c^2+c+1}{3} = \dfrac{c^2-3c-1}{6}$

11. $\dfrac{3x-2}{3} + \dfrac{2x-1}{2} = \dfrac{4x+1}{6} - \dfrac{2x-2}{12}$

12. $\dfrac{d+3}{6} - \dfrac{2d-1}{8} = \dfrac{4-3d}{4} + \dfrac{d-1}{12}$

EXERCISE 38

Perform the indicated operations

1. $\dfrac{x-3}{5} \cdot \dfrac{5x+5}{x^2-6x+9}$

2. $\dfrac{xy+x}{y-1} \cdot \dfrac{y^2-1}{2xy+2x}$

3. $\dfrac{a^2-7a+10}{a^2-4a+4} \cdot \dfrac{a^2+2a-3}{a^2-2a-15}$

4. $\dfrac{t^2-t-6}{t^2+t-2} \div \dfrac{t^2-6t+9}{t^2-t-6}$

5. $\dfrac{b^2-4b-5}{b^2-b-12} \div \dfrac{b^2-1}{b^2+2b-3}$

6. $\dfrac{c^2-7c-18}{c^2-10c+9} \cdot \dfrac{c^2+4c-5}{5ac+10a}$

7. $\dfrac{p^2-3p+2}{p^2-p-12} \cdot \dfrac{p^2+4p+3}{p^2-2p+1} \cdot \dfrac{p^2-1}{p^2-p-2}$

8. $\dfrac{s^2-3s+2}{s^2+2s-3} \cdot \dfrac{s^2+2s-3}{s^2-1} \cdot \dfrac{s^2+6s+5}{s^2-7s+10}$

9. $\dfrac{x^2-13x+40}{x^2-5x-24} \div \dfrac{x^2-10x+25}{x^2-8x+15}$

10. $\dfrac{6b^2+b-1}{12b^2-13b+3} \div \dfrac{6b^2+5b+1}{8b^2-2b-3}$

11. $\dfrac{4x^2+11x-3}{16x^2-1} \cdot \dfrac{16x^2+8x+1}{4x^2+13x+3}$

12. $\dfrac{8t^2+6t-9}{8t^2-26t+15} \cdot \dfrac{16t^2+18t-9}{4t^2+12t+9}$

13. $\left(\dfrac{6x^2-13x+6}{4x^2+5x+1} \cdot \dfrac{8x^2-2x-1}{18x^2+3x-10} \right) \div \dfrac{4x^2-8x+3}{12x^2-8x-15}$

14. $\left(\dfrac{4x^2 - 3x - 1}{x^3 - x^2} \div \dfrac{4x^2 + 13x + 3}{x^2 - x} \right) \div \dfrac{x^2 - 2x + 1}{x^2 + 2x - 3}$

15. $\left(\dfrac{x^2 + xy - 2y^2}{x^2 + 3xy + 2y^2} \cdot \dfrac{6x^2 - 5xy - 4y^2}{3x^2 - 7xy + 4y^2} \right) \div \dfrac{8x^2 + 10xy + 3y^2}{4x^2 - 5xy - 6y^2}$

16. $\dfrac{7x + 3y}{2} + \dfrac{5x - 4y}{3}$

17. $\dfrac{2x^2 + x - 4}{2} - \dfrac{4x^2 - 7x + 5}{4}$

18. $\dfrac{x + 3}{2} + \dfrac{2x - 5}{3} - \dfrac{x - 7}{6}$

19. $\dfrac{t - 5}{3} - \dfrac{3t + 7}{4} + \dfrac{5t - 1}{2}$

20. $\dfrac{p^2 - 3p}{5} - \dfrac{2p^2 - 3}{10} + \dfrac{p^2 + p - 1}{3}$

21. $\dfrac{3(a - 2b)}{2} + \dfrac{5a - b}{3} - \dfrac{2(2a + b)}{9}$

22. $\dfrac{2c - 5d}{8} + \dfrac{c - 2d}{3} - \dfrac{2c - 9d}{6}$

23. $\dfrac{m - 2n}{2} - \dfrac{3n + 1}{8} - \dfrac{3m - 6}{12}$

24. $\dfrac{r - 2t}{6} + \dfrac{2r + t}{5} - \dfrac{2r - t}{12}$

25. $\dfrac{x - y - z}{18} + \dfrac{x + y + z}{6} - \dfrac{x - y + z}{9}$

42. STATED PROBLEMS

Sometimes stated problems involve fractional expressions. The following examples illustrate such problems:

Example 1. If one number is two-thirds of another number and their sum is 30, what are the numbers?

Let x = the larger number and $\dfrac{2x}{3}$ = the smaller number. Then

$$x + \frac{2x}{3} = 30$$

$$(3)x + (3)\frac{2x}{3} = (3)30$$

$$3x + \frac{3}{3} \cdot 2x = 90$$

$$3x + 1 \cdot 2x = 90$$
$$3x + 2x = 90$$
$$5x = 90$$
$$x = 18$$

$$\frac{2x}{3} = 12$$

Check: $\qquad 18 + 12 = 30$

Example 2. If one-fourth of a certain number is subtracted from that number, the remainder is 48. What is the number?

Let x = the number. Then

$$x - \frac{1}{4}x = 48$$

$$\frac{3x}{4} = 48$$

$$(4)\frac{3x}{4} = (4)48$$

$$\frac{4}{4} \cdot 3x = 192$$

$$1 \cdot 3x = 192$$
$$3x = 192$$
$$x = 64$$

Check: $\qquad 64 - \frac{1}{4}(64) = 48$
$$64 - 16 = 48$$
$$48 = 48$$

Example 3. John has one-third as much money as Fred and Melvin has three-fourths as much as Fred. If the three boys have a total of $50, how much has each?

Let x = the amount Fred has, $x/3$ = the amount John has, and $3x/4$ = the amount Melvin has. Then

$$x + \frac{x}{3} + \frac{3x}{4} = \$50$$

$$(12)x + (12)\frac{x}{3} + (12)\frac{3x}{4} = \$50(12)$$

$$(12)x + \frac{3}{3}(4)x + \frac{4}{4}(3)3x = \$50(12)$$

$$12x + 1 \cdot 4x + 1 \cdot 9x = \$50(12)$$
$$12x + 4x + 9x = \$50(12)$$
$$25x = \$600$$
$$x = \$24$$

$$\frac{x}{3} = \$8$$

$$\frac{3x}{4} = \$18$$

Check: $\$24 + \$8 + \$18 = \$50$

EXERCISE 39

Solve the following problems: $2\left(\frac{2x}{3}\right) + 2x = 110$ $x = 33$

1. The width of a rectangle is two-thirds its length. If the perimeter is 110 feet, what are the dimensions of the rectangle?

2. Beverly is two-thirds as old as Gwen, and Margaret is one-half as old as Gwen. If the sum of their ages is 39 years, how old is each?

3. One-sixth of the length of a telephone pole is in the ground. If the pole extends 25 feet above the ground, how long is the pole?

$\frac{1}{6}x + 25 = x$

4. Three brothers inherited their deceased father's estate. The will directed that the oldest receive one-third of the estate, the second son one-half of it, and the youngest the remaining $4000. How much did the oldest and second sons receive? (*Hint:* Find the fractional part that the youngest received.)

5. A man bought two properties for which he paid $21,000. If one of them cost him $1500 more than one-half as much as the other one, how much did he pay for each property? $13 - 8$

$\frac{1}{2}x + x + 1500 = 21,000$

6. An insurance agent quoted a certain rate for fire insurance on household goods. He then stated that a four-year policy would cost only two and one-half times as much as a one-year policy. If his client paid $27.50 for the four-year policy, how much would the one-year policy cost him?

7. A man bought a new automobile and a new trailer. The automobile cost him one and one-half times as much as the trailer. If the cost of both was $4000, how much did he pay for each?

$X + \frac{3x}{2} = 4000$

174   FRACTIONS

$2x + 3x = 8000$
$5x = 8000$
$x = 1600$

8. A man and his son worked together on a certain job. The father's weekly wage was $10 more than one and one-half times that the son received. If their combined weekly wages was $110, what was the weekly wage of each?

$x + 56 = x$

9. David had a package of football schedules. He gave one-third of them to James and 18 of them to Bob. If he had 38 schedules left, how many did he have before he distributed them to the other two ushers?

10. A man had withheld from his monthly pay check one-fourth of his salary for federal income tax and one-twelfth of it for retirement. If his check was $320, what was his monthly salary before the deductions?

$$2\left(\tfrac{2}{3}x+4\right) +2(x) \qquad \text{B.}$$

1. The width of a rectangular garden plot is 4 feet more than two-thirds its length. If the perimeter is 228 feet, what are the dimensions of the garden?

2. On an examination one-half of the class received a grade of C, one-fourth a grade of B, and one-sixth a grade of D. If the two remaining students received grades of A, how many received a grade of B, of C, and of D?

3. Admission prices for a basketball game were $1 for adults, 75 cents for students, and 50 cents for those under 12 years of age. Three-fourths as many adult tickets were sold as were student tickets. The number of 50-cent tickets sold was one-sixth the number of student tickets. If a total of 322 tickets were sold, how many were there of each priced ticket?

4. If a certain number is added to the numerator of the fraction $\tfrac{7}{8}$ and 4 is added to the denominator, the fraction becomes, after it is reduced, $\tfrac{2}{3}$. How much was added to the numerator?

5. If to the numerator of the fraction $\tfrac{2}{5}$ is added a certain number and from the denominator is subtracted the same number, the result is 6. What is that number?

$$\frac{2+x}{5-x} = 6 \qquad = 2+x=6$$
$$x=4$$

REVIEW TEST 18

In the left-hand column are listed groups of numbers or algebraic expressions. The least common multiple for each group will be found in the right-hand column. On a sheet of paper write the numbers 1 through 20 to correspond to the numbered groups in the left-hand column. After each number place a letter to correctly match

$(24)\tfrac{3}{4}x + \tfrac{1}{6}x + x = 322$

$18x + 4x + 24x = 7728$
$46x = 7728$

$x = 168$ student

126 Ad.

28 kids

a least common multiple with each group of expressions. Some of the expressions in the right-hand column do not match any of the groups in the left-hand column.

1. $x^2 - xy; x - y$ a. $12xy$

2. $x^2 - y^2; x + y$ b. $m(n - 1)(n - 1)$

3. $6x^3y; 3x^2y^2; 2xy^3$ c. $2(b - 2)(b + 2)$

4. $ab + b; a^2 - 1$ d. $x(x - y)$

5. $a^2 - 4a; a^2 - a - 12$ e. $(t + 1)(t + 1)(t - 9)$

6. $mn - m; n^2 - 2n + 1$ f. $xyzvw$

7. $vwx; wxy; xyz$ g. $2(b - 2)(b - 2)(b + 2)(b + 2)$

8. $m^2n - mn^2; m^2 - 2mn + n^2$ h. $a(a + 3)(a - 4)$

9. $12x^2y^2; 2x^3y; 3xy^3$ i. $m^2n^2(m - n)(m - n)$

10. $2b^2 - 8b + 8; 2b + 4$ j. $b(a + 1)(a - 1)$

11. $t^2 + 2t + 1; t^2 - 8t - 9$ k. $4(b + 2)(b - 2)(b - 2)$

12. $v^2wx; vw^2x; vwx^2$ l. $6x^3y^3$

13. $m^2 - n^2; m^3 - 2m^2n + mn^2$ m. $mn(m - n)$

14. $2b - 4; b^2 - 4$ n. $(m + n)(m - n)(m - 2n)(m - 2n)$

15. $t^2 - 12t + 27; t^2 - 9$ o. $(x + y)(x - y)$

16. $4b^2 - 16; 2b^2 - 8b + 8$ p. $v^2w^2x^2$

17. $x^2 - 2xy + y^2; x^2 + 2xy + y^2$ q. $a(a + 3)(a - 4)(a - 4)$

18. $m^2 - mn - 2n^2;$ r. $(m + n)(m - n)(m + 2n)$
$\quad\quad m^2 - 3mn + 2n^2$ s. $mn(m - n)(m - n)$

19. $m^2 - 4mn + 4n^2; m^2 - n^2$ t. $2(b - 2)(b - 2)(b + 2)$

20. $m^2 + 3mn + 2n^2;$ u. $(x - y)(x - y)(x + y)(x + y)$
$\quad\quad m^2 + mn - 2n^2$ v. $12x^3y^3$

w. $(m - n)(m + n)(m - 2n)$

x. $8(b + 2)(b - 2)(b - 2)$

y. $(t - 3)(t + 3)(t - 9)$

z. $m(m - n)(m - n)(m + n)$

REVIEW TEST 19

In the following problems $x = 2$, $y = -2$, and $z = 1$. Each problem has four answers following it. On a sheet of paper write the numbers 1 through 20 to correspond to the numbered problems and after each number place the letter a, b, c, or d to indicate which is the correct answer.

1. x^2yz a. 5   b. 8   c. -8 d. None of these

2. $x^2 + y^2$ a. 0   b. 8   c. 4   d. -4

3. $x^2 + y - z$ a. 3   b. -1 c. 1   d. None of these

4. $\dfrac{x + y + 2z}{y}$ a. 1   b. 2   c. -2 d. None of these

5. $\dfrac{xy^2}{x^2}$ a. 2   b. -2 c. 4   d. -4

6. $\dfrac{x^2 + z^2}{z^2}$ a. 3   b. $\dfrac{3}{2}$ c. 5   d. $\dfrac{5}{2}$

7. $\dfrac{x^2 - xy + 2z}{y^2}$ a. $\dfrac{1}{2}$ b. $-\dfrac{5}{2}$ c. $-\dfrac{1}{2}$ d. $\dfrac{5}{2}$

8. $\dfrac{z^2 - y^2 + x^2}{z}$ a. 2   b. 1   c. 9   d. -9

9. $\dfrac{y^2 - 2y + 1}{y^2}$ a. $\dfrac{9}{4}$ b. $-\dfrac{9}{4}$ c. $\dfrac{1}{4}$ d. None of these

10. $\dfrac{y^2 + 2xy + x^2}{y^2 - z^2}$ a. 16   b. -8 c. 0   d. None of these

11. $\dfrac{3xyz}{y}$ a. 12   b. -6 c. -4 d. 6

12. $-9xyz - \dfrac{y}{2}$ a. 35   b. -37 c. 37   d. -35

13. $\dfrac{y - z}{3} - \dfrac{y - x}{2}$ a. 1   b. 3   c. -7 d. None of these

14. $\dfrac{x}{y} + \dfrac{x}{z}$ a. 3   b. 4   c. -1 d. 1

15. $\dfrac{zy^2}{y} - z$ a. 1   b. -3 c. -2 d. -1

16. $\dfrac{x + y}{3} + \dfrac{x}{z}$ a. $\dfrac{13}{3}$ b. 0   c. 2   d. $\dfrac{3}{13}$

17. $\dfrac{x^2 - z}{z^2}$ a. 3   b. $\dfrac{3}{2}$ c. 2   d. 0

18. $\dfrac{z - y^2}{x + z}$ a. $-\dfrac{2}{3}$ b. 1   c. $\dfrac{2}{3}$ d. -1

19. $\dfrac{xyz}{y}$ a. -2 b. 2   c. $\dfrac{5}{2}$ d. 0

20. $\dfrac{x}{y} - \dfrac{y}{z} + \dfrac{x}{z}$ a. 3   b. -3 c. 1   d. None of these

8

Changing the Subject
of a Formula

The subject of a formula is that part of the formula in the left member of the equation. Each time we use a formula for solving a problem, the unknown quantity for which we are solving is the subject of the formula.

In the formula $p = 4s$, p is the subject. If we wrote the formula in a statement, it would read as follows: "The perimeter (of a square) equals four times one side," where the word *perimeter* is the subject of the statement.

In the formula $A = \frac{1}{2}bh$, A is the subject. This formula could be written: "The area of a triangle equals one-half the product of the base and the height," where the word *area* is the subject of the statement and also the subject of the formula.

Sometimes we are asked to find the value of an unknown quantity that appears in the right-hand member of the equation. This is especially true in the study of physics and chemistry. To change the subject of a formula, we use Laws 10 and 11, the additive inverse and the multiplicative inverse as was done in Chapter 4. The following examples illustrate the method for changing the subject of a formula:

Example 1. The formula for finding *distance* in terms of *rate* and *time* is $d = rt$. (Rate and time must be expressed in the same unit of measurement. For example, rate may be in terms of miles per hour and time in terms of hours, or rate may be in feet per second and time in seconds.) In the above formula, solve for r.

$$d = rt \quad \text{(Given)}$$
$$rt = d \quad \text{(Law of symmetry)}$$
$$r = \frac{d}{t} \quad \text{(Division)}$$

Example 2. The equation expressing the volume of a rectangular solid in terms of the dimensions of the solid is $V = lwh$. In this case l represents the length, w the width, and h the height of the solid. Using the given equation, solve for h.

$$V = lwh \quad \text{(Given)}$$
$$lwh = V \quad \text{(Law of symmetry)}$$
$$h = \frac{V}{lw} \quad \text{(Division)}$$

Example 3. The scientist uses the term *density*, which is defined as *mass* per *volume*. The equation for this concept is written $D = m/V$. Solve this equation for V.

$$D = \frac{m}{V} \quad \text{(Given)}$$

$$V \cdot D = V \cdot \frac{m}{V} \quad \text{(Multiplication)}$$

$$VD = m \quad \text{(Simplification of the right member of the equation by dividing out identical factors)}$$

$$V = \frac{m}{D} \quad \text{(Division)}$$

Example 4. The physicist defines *acceleration* as the rate of change of *velocity* with *time*. If the velocity is uniform, the acceleration is determined by the formula $a = \dfrac{(v - v_0)}{t}$, in which case a is the acceleration, v the velocity at the end of the time lapse period, v_0 the initial velocity, and t the lapse of time between the instants when velocity was v and v_0. (It should be noted that v_0 is not always zero, as in the case of determining the acceleration from the time an automobile travels 35 miles per hour to the time it reaches a speed of 50 miles per hour.) In the above example solve for v_0.

$$a = \frac{(v - v_0)}{t} \qquad \text{(Given)}$$

$$at = v - v_0 \qquad \text{(Multiplication)}$$
$$v_0 + at = v \qquad \text{(Addition)}$$
$$v_0 = v - at \qquad \text{(Subtraction)}$$

When the above formula is used in its original form to find acceleration, the answer may be either positive or negative. If speed is increasing over the time lapse period, the acceleration would be positive. If the initial velocity is greater than the final velocity, in which case the speed is decreasing, then the acceleration would be decreasing and represented by a negative number.

Example 5. A trapezoid is defined as a polygon of four sides in which two and only two sides are parallel to each other. The two parallel sides are called the bases of the trapezoid and may be designated by the letters b and b'. The formula for finding the area of a trapezoid is $A = \frac{(b + b')h}{2}$. The h in this formula represents the perpendicular height between the bases. In the above equation solve for b.

$$A = \frac{(b + b')h}{2} \qquad \text{(Given)}$$

$$2A = (b + b')h \qquad \text{(Multiplication axiom)}$$
$$(b + b')h = 2A \qquad \text{(Reflexive relation)}$$
$$bh + b'h = 2A \qquad \text{(Distributive law)}$$
$$bh = 2A - b'h \qquad \text{(Subtraction axiom)}$$

$$b = \frac{2A - b'h}{h} \qquad \text{(Division axiom)}$$

EXERCISE 40

A

Solve each of the following for the indicated letter:

1. $I = Prt$. Solve for P.
2. $C = \pi d$. Solve for d.
3. $y = mx + b$. Solve for b.
4. $A = lw$. Solve for w.
5. $C = 2\pi r$. Solve for r.
6. $y = mx + b$. Solve for m.

7. $I = Prt$. Solve for t.

8. $P = 2l + 2w$. Solve for l.

9. $V = \pi r^2 h$. Solve for h.

10. $d = rt$. Solve for t.

11. $I = Prt$. Solve for r.

12. $V = lwh$. Solve for l.

13. $y = mx + b$. Solve for x.

14. $V = lwh$. Solve for w.

15. $A = lw$. Solve for l.

16. $P = 2l + 2w$. Solve for w.

17. $V = \dfrac{\pi r^2 h}{3}$. Solve for r^2.

18. $V = \pi r^2 h$. Solve for r^2.

19. $V = \dfrac{\pi r^2 h}{3}$. Solve for h.

20. $V = \dfrac{Bh}{3}$. Solve for B.

21. $E = RI$. Solve for R.

22. $A = P + Prt$. Solve for t.

23. $V = \dfrac{\pi r^2 h}{3}$. Solve for r.

24. $E = RI$. Solve for I.

25. $V = \dfrac{Bh}{3}$. Solve for h.

26. $A = P + Prt$. Solve for r.

27. $c^2 = a^2 + b^2$. Solve for b^2.

28. $c^2 = a^2 + b^2$. Solve for a^2.

29. $c^2 = a^2 + b^2$. Solve for c.

30. $A = P + Prt$. Solve for P.

31. $c^2 = a^2 + b^2$. Solve for b.

32. $c^2 = a^2 + b^2$. Solve for a.

33. $s = 16t^2$. Solve for t^2.

34. $2c^2 = a^2 + b^2$. Solve for a^2.

35. $x^2 = y + c$. Solve for y.

36. $m = p^2 - c$. Solve for c.

B

Solve each of the following for the indicated letter:

1. $A = \dfrac{(b + b')h}{2}$. Solve for h.

2. $s = 16t^2$. Solve for t.

3. $C = \tfrac{5}{9}(F - 32)$. Solve for F.

4. $A = \dfrac{(b + b')h}{2}$. Solve for b'.

5. $m = p^2 - c$. Solve for p.

6. $F = \tfrac{9}{5}C + 32$. Solve for C.

7. $l = a + (n - 1)d$. Solve for a.

8. $S = \dfrac{n(a + l)}{2}$. Solve for n.

9. $S = \dfrac{n(a + l)}{2}$. Solve for a.

10. $l = a + (n - 1)d$. Solve for d.

11. $K = \dfrac{mv^2}{2g}$. Solve for g.

12. $S = \dfrac{n(a + l)}{2}$. Solve for l.

13. $l = a + (n - 1)d$. Solve for n.

14. $K = \dfrac{mv^2}{2g}$. Solve for m.

43. STATED PROBLEMS

A great many applied problems make use of common formulas. Sometimes it is desirable to change the subject of a known formula before it can be used to solve these problems. The following examples are representative of such problems:

Example 1. The perimeter of a rectangle is 138 feet. If the width is 22 feet, what is the length?

The formula to be used is $P = 2l + 2w$. Solve for l.

$$P = 2l + 2w$$
$$2l + 2w = P$$

Subtract $2w$ from both members of the equation.

$$2l = P - 2w$$

Divide both members of the equation by 2.

$$l = \frac{P - 2w}{2}$$

Now substitute the given values in that formula.

$$l = \frac{P - 2w}{2}$$

$$l = \frac{138 - 2(22)}{2}$$

$$l = \frac{138 - 44}{2}$$

$$l = \frac{94}{2}$$

$$l = 47 \text{ feet}$$

Example 2. If the circumference of a circle is 44 inches, what is its radius?

Use the formula $C = 2\pi r$, and solve for r.

$$C = 2\pi r$$
$$2\pi r = C$$

$$r = \frac{C}{2\pi}$$

Substitute the given value of the circumference in the formula and let $\pi \approx \frac{22}{7}$ ($\approx$ means "approximately equal to").

$$r = \frac{C}{2\pi}$$

$$r = \frac{44}{2 \cdot \frac{22}{7}}$$

$$r = \frac{44}{\frac{44}{7}}$$

$$r = \frac{44}{1} \div \frac{44}{7}$$

$$r = \frac{44}{1} \cdot \frac{7}{44}$$

$$r = 7 \text{ inches}$$

Example 3.   A man borrowed $475.00 and paid it back at the end of two years, at which time he was required to pay $522.50. What rate of interest did he pay?

The amount required to pay the principal and interest is found by using the following formula: $A = P + Prt$. Solve for r and substitute the known values in that formula.

$$A = P + Prt$$
$$P + Prt = A$$
$$Prt = A - P$$
$$r = \frac{A - P}{Pt}$$
$$r = \frac{\$522.50 - \$475.00}{(\$475)(2)}$$
$$r = \frac{\$47.50}{\$950.00}$$
$$r = 0.05, \text{ or } 5\%$$

Example 4.   The area of a triangle is 42 square inches. If the altitude of the triangle is 12 inches, what is the length of its base?

Use the formula $A = bh/2$, and solve for b.

$$A = \frac{bh}{2}$$
$$2A = bh$$
$$bh = 2A$$
$$b = \frac{2A}{h}$$

Substitute the given values in the new formula, and solve for b.

$$b = \frac{2A}{h}$$

$$b = \frac{2(42)}{12}$$

$$b = \frac{84}{12}$$

$$b = 7 \text{ inches}$$

Example 5. The area of a trapezoid is 38 square inches. If the shorter base is 6 inches and the height is 4 inches, what is the length of the longer base?

Use the formula $A = \frac{(b + b')h}{2}$, and solve for b.

$$A = \frac{(b + b')h}{2}$$

$$2A = (b + b')h$$
$$(b + b')h = 2A$$
$$bh + b'h = 2A$$
$$bh = 2A - b'h$$

$$b = \frac{2A - b'h}{h}$$

Substitute the given values in the new formula, and solve for b.

$$b = \frac{2A - b'h}{h}$$

$$b = \frac{(2)(38) - (6)(4)}{4}$$

$$b = \frac{76 - 24}{4}$$

$$b = \frac{52}{4}$$

$$b = 13 \text{ inches}$$

1. If the perimeter of a square is 62 inches, what is the length of each side?

2. The circumference of a circle is 66 inches. What is the diameter of the circle? (Use $\frac{22}{7}$ for π.)

3. A man borrowed $800 at 6 percent interest. He was required to pay $920 when the loan became due. For how long did he borrow the money?

4. An automobile traveled at an average speed of 45 miles per hour to go a distance of 315 miles. How long did it take to make the trip?

5. The area of a triangle whose base is 7 inches is 14 square inches. What is the altitude of the triangle?

6. The perimeter of a rectangle is 64 inches. If the width of the rectangle is 13 inches, what is its length?

7. If the area of a circle is 154 square inches, what is the radius of that circle?

8. A rectangular garden contains 777 square yards. If the length of the garden is 37 yards, what is its width?

9. A ball is dropped from the top of a building to the ground. If the building is 144 feet high, how long did it take for the ball to reach the ground? (Use the formula $s = 16t^2$.)

10. A man borrowed $1200 for 3 years. When the loan was due, he paid the lender $1344. What rate of interest did he pay?

11. The two bases of a trapezoid whose area is 55 square inches are 9 inches and 13 inches. What is the height of the trapezoid?

12. A business firm borrowed a sum of money from a bank for 6 months at 6 percent interest. At the end of the 6 months the firm was required to pay the bank $2317.50. How much did they borrow from the bank?

13. The volume of a pyramid is 243 cubic inches. If the area of the base is 54 square inches, what is the height of the pyramid?

14. The radius of the base of a cylinder is 4 inches. If the volume of the cylinder is 352 cubic inches, what is its height?

15. A centigrade thermometer registers a temperature of 35°. What would be the corresponding reading on the Fahrenheit thermometer?

16. The circumference of a circle is 121 inches. What is the diameter of the circle?

17. A pyramid rests on a square base whose sides are 6 feet. If the volume of the pyramid is 162 cubic feet, what is its height?

18. The volume of a cone is 66 cubic inches. If the diameter of the base is 6 inches, what is the altitude of the cone?

19. The volume of a pyramid whose height is 9 feet is 243 cubic feet. What is the area of the base of the pyramid?

20. The perimeter of a rectangle is 134 inches. If it is 2 feet wide, what is its length?

B

1. The volume of a cylinder whose height is 7 inches is 792 cubic inches. What is the diameter of the base of the cylinder?

2. A Fahrenheit thermometer registers a temperature of 77°. What would be the corresponding reading on a centigrade thermometer?

3. The volume of a rectangular prism is 24 cubic feet. If the prism is 2 feet wide and 1 foot high, how long is it?

4. An electrical current of 120 volts has a resistance of 15 ohms. How many amperes are there in the current? (Use Ohm's Law found in the Appendix.)

5. How much will be required to repay a loan of $1500 at 7 percent for a period of 8 months?

6. The longer base of a trapezoid is twice as long as the shorter base. If the altitude is 9 inches and the area 108 square inches, what are the lengths of the two bases?

7. A borrower paid $877.25 to pay off a loan of $725. If he kept the money for 3 years, what rate of interest did he pay?

8. A dealer sold a piece of farm machinery that cost him $175 for $227.50. What was his percentage of profit on the cost of the machinery?

9. If the diameter of a circle is 7 inches, what is its area?

10. The base of a pyramid 8 inches high is a triangle whose longest side is 10 inches. If the altitude of the triangle drawn to the longest side is 7 inches, what is the volume of the pyramid?

11. What is the resistance to an electrical current of 110 volts with an intensity of 20 amperes?

12. How much interest must be paid on a loan of $400 at 7 percent for a period of 3 months?

13. What is the area of a rectangle 4 feet long and 9 inches wide?

14. A farmer had 140 feet of wire fence. He constructed a long narrow pen at one side of his barn, using the barn as one of the shorter sides

of the pen. If the length of the pen was three times its width, what were the dimensions of the pen?

15. A farmer tied his horse at one corner of a barn 54 feet long and 24 feet wide. If the rope by which the horse was tied was 12 feet long, over how many square feet of surface could the horse move?

$A = lw$

$24 = \dfrac{A}{w}$

$24 = \dfrac{12 \cdot 16}{w} \cdot w$

$\overline{12 \cdot 16}$

$\dfrac{12 \cdot 16}{24} = w$

9

Relations, Functions, and Graphs

44. ORDERED PAIRS

Let us assume we are going to the school cafeteria for a lunch consisting of a beverage and a sandwich. There are four sandwiches from which to choose—beef, ham, chicken, and tuna. The beverages that are available are milk, coffee, and Coca-Cola. There are thus 12 possible combinations of lunch consisting of a sandwich and a beverage.

If we specify these items in the lunch as the set S representing the various sandwiches and set D representing the available beverages, we select one element from each set and combine them to form a pair of elements.

Let us arbitrarily list the sandwich first and then the beverage and enclose each combination in parentheses. These 12 pairs form a new set of 12 elements, each an ordered pair. This relationship of pairs can be graphically represented as in Figure 32.

Each dot in the graph represents one of the lunch combinations, or an ordered pair. We have labeled them here for emphasis. However, this is not necessary. We must label the elements of each set along the intersecting perpendicular lines which we call the *axes*. It is usual practice to list the elements from the set that form the first members of the ordered pairs along the horizontal axis and the elements from the set that form the second members of the ordered pairs along the vertical axis. These pairs are called *ordered pairs* because the order in which the elements are listed is important and they *cannot* be interchanged.

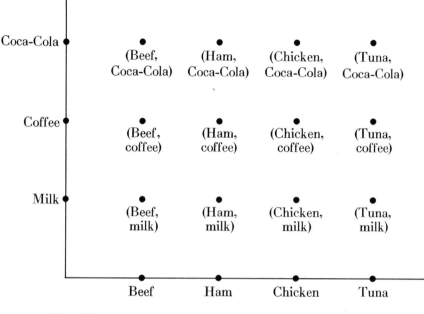

Figure 32

This new set consisting of ordered pairs from sets S and D is usually referred to as $S \times D$, read: "S cross D." In the set builder this is written $S \times D = \{(x, y) \mid x \in S \text{ and } y \in D\}$, read: "$S$ cross D is the set of ordered pairs in (x, y) such that x is an element of S and y is an element of D." The x and y are used here because the horizontal axis is usually called the X-axis and the vertical axis the Y-axis.

Let us now consider two sets X and Y such that $X = \{1, 2, 3\}$ and $Y = \{1, 2, 3, 4\}$. $X \times Y$ then means that each element in X is paired with each element in Y. These ordered pairs obtained from $X \times Y$ are shown in Figure 33.

Again, we have shown the ordered pairs with the dots they represent only for the sake of emphasis. We shall subsequently omit the ordered pairs in the figures and read them from the elements in X and Y as shown along the axes.

45. RELATIONS

A *relation* is defined as a set of ordered pairs. Figures 32 and 33 are relations since they represent a set of ordered pairs.

We may use negative numbers and zero as well as positive numbers for the elements in the two sets. However, this requires the extension of

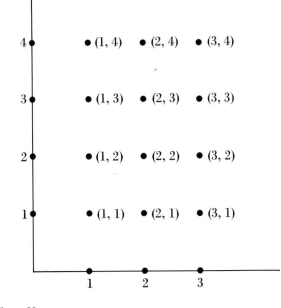

Figure 33

the axes as shown in Figure 34. The two axes are perpendicular to each other and could be thought of as two number lines. We locate the 0 on the number lines at the intersection of the lines. This point of intersection is called the *origin*. It can be observed in Figure 34 that the plane is divided into four parts by the intersecting axes. Each of these four parts is called a *quadrant* and is designated as the first, second, third, or fourth quadrant as shown in Figure 34.

Positive values from set X are located to the right of the origin, and negative values are found to the left of the origin. This is consistent with our previous use of the number line. Positive values of Y are located above the origin and negative values of Y below the origin. We could think of the Y-axis as the original number line rotated counterclockwise 90°.

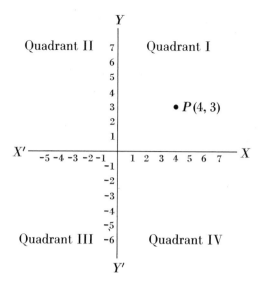

Figure 34

If $X = \{-2, -1, 0, 1\}$ and $Y = \{-1, 0, 2\}$, the graph of $X \times Y$ is as shown in Figure 35. With each element from set X we pair all the elements found in set Y and obtain the following ordered pairs: $(-2, -1)$, $(-2, 0)$, $(-2, 2)$, $(-1, -1)$, $(-1, 0)$, $(-1, 2)$, $(0, -1)$, $(0, 0)$, $(0, 2)$, $(1, -1)$, $(1, 0)$, and $(1, 2)$.

We may use a universal set from which to select the elements for both X and Y. Thus if we state that $U = \{1, 2, 3\}$, this means that the 1, 2, and 3 are all to be used as elements for the first members of the ordered pairs as well as for the second members of those ordered pairs.

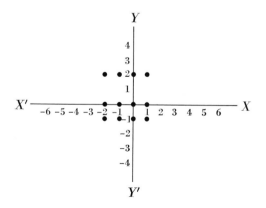

Figure 35

The possible ordered pairs for $X \times Y$, then, are (1, 1), (1, 2), (1, 3), (2, 1), (2, 2), (2, 3), (3, 1), (3, 2), and (3, 3).

Example 1. If $U = \{1, 2, 3\}$, graph the relation $y = x$.

In the set builder this would read $\{(x, y) \mid y = x\}$. The condition placed upon (x, y) is, of course, $y = x$. The possible ordered pairs representing $X \times Y$ from the given universal set are (1, 1), (1, 2), (1, 3), (2, 1), (2, 2), (2, 3), (3, 1), (3, 2), and (3, 3). However, because of the condition imposed on (x, y), we may select only the ordered pairs from the above list that satisfy that given condition; these are (1, 1), (2, 2), and (3, 3). This relation is shown graphically in Figure 36.

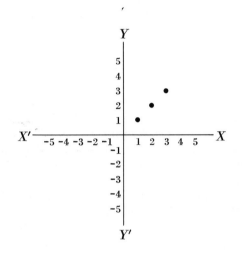

Figure 36

Example 2. If U is the set of all positive real numbers, graph the relation $y = x$.

It will be observed that this problem has the same condition imposed on (x, y) as does the problem in Example 1. Furthermore, we can see that the universe differs in the two examples. In Example 2 the number of ordered pairs will be infinite, consisting of all positive rational numbers, and all positive irrational numbers. The location of all the points represented by all these ordered pairs will give us a line of infinite length, as shown in Figure 37. This graph is represented by a ray which bisects the first quadrant.

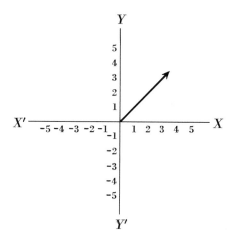

Figure 37

Example 3. If $U = \{1, 2, 3, 4\}$, graph the relation $y > x$.

The possible ordered pairs obtained from $X \times Y$ are $(1, 1)$, $(1, 2)$, $(1, 3)$, $(1, 4)$, $(2, 1)$, $(2, 2)$, $(2, 3)$, $(2, 4)$, $(3, 1)$, $(3, 2)$, $(3, 3)$, $(3, 4)$, $(4, 1)$, $(4, 2)$, $(4, 3)$, and $(4, 4)$. Again, it is necessary that we select from this list only those ordered pairs that satisfy the condition $y > x$. This is easily done if we remember that y represents the second member of the ordered pair. Thus we shall select for our solution set only those ordered pairs in which the second member is larger than the first member. The graphical solution is shown in Figure 38.

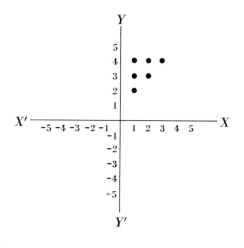

Figure 38

A

Graph the following relations if $U = \{-2, -1, 0, 1, 2\}$:

1. $\{(x, y) \mid y = x + 1\}$ 2. $\{(x, y) \mid y > x + 1\}$
3. $\{(x, y) \mid y < x + 1\}$ 4. $\{(x, y) \mid y = 2x\}$
5. $\{(x, y) \mid y > 2x - 1\}$ 6. $\{(x, y) \mid y < 2x\}$

Graph the following relations if U is the set of nonnegative real numbers:

7. $\{(x, y) \mid y = x + 1\}$ 8. $\{(x, y) \mid y = 2x\}$
9. $\{(x, y) \mid y = 2x - 1\}$ 10. $\{(x, y) \mid y = 1 - x\}$

B

Graph the following relations if U is the set of all real numbers:

1. $\{(x, y) \mid y = x\}$ 2. $\{(x, y) \mid y = x + 1\}$
3. $\{(x, y) \mid y = 1 - x\}$ 4. $\{(x, y) \mid y = 2x\}$
5. $\{(x, y) \mid y - 1 = x\}$

46. FUNCTIONS

From any set of ordered pairs we may formulate two additional sets—the set of all first members and the set of all second members of the given set of ordered pairs.

Let $A = \{(-2, 1), (-2, 2), (-1, 1), (-1, 2), (-1, 3), (0, 1), (0, 2),$ $(0, 3), (0, 4), (1, 1), (1, 2), (1, 3), (2, 1),$ and $(2, 2)\}$, and then let D equal the set of all first members and R equal the set of all second members of the ordered pairs in A. We observe that the first members are $-2, -1, 0, 1,$ and 2 (keeping in mind that we do not list repeated elements in a set). Thus $D = \{-2, -1, 0, 1, 2\}$. In a similar manner, we discover that $R = \{1, 2, 3, 4\}$. We call D the *domain* of the relation associated with set A and we call R the *range* of that relation.

> The *domain* of a relation is the set of all first members of the ordered pairs associated with that relation.

The *range* of a relation is the set of all second members of the ordered pairs associated with that relation.

Example. If U is the set of all one-digit natural numbers and $y = 2x$, find the domain and range of this relation.

The ordered pairs associated with this relation are (1, 2), (2, 4), (3, 6), and (4, 8). Thus the range and domain are

$$\text{domain} = \{1, 2, 3, 4\}$$
$$\text{range} = \{2, 4, 6, 8\}$$

We shall now turn our attention to a special type of relation. Observe in the example above that among the ordered pairs obtained from that relation there is only one second member listed with each first member. Such a relation we call a *function*.

A *function* is a relation in which to every element in set D (the domain) there corresponds exactly one element from set R (the range). (An alternate definition is: A *function* is a relation in which no first component appears more than once.)

In our previous discussion of relations some of the listed ordered pairs associated with a given relation included more than one ordered pair with the same first member. Observe Example 1 in Section 45. The ordered pairs that satisfied the condition that $y = x$ were (1, 1), (2, 2), and (3, 3). In this case for each first member in the ordered pairs there was exactly one second member. Thus this *is* a function. It can be seen from Figure 36 that no dot is directly above any other dot. If in a graph we construct a vertical line (parallel to the Y-axis) at any position in the plane, that vertical line will never intersect more than one dot. If such is the case, the relation represented by that graph is a function. This is called the *vertical line test* for determining whether or not the relation is a function.

In comparison, observe Example 3 in Section 45. From the list of possible ordered pairs it will be seen that in several cases there are more than one second member for a given first member of the ordered pairs. This means that the given relation is *not* a function. Application of the vertical line test in Figure 38 will verify this.

We must be careful that we do not confuse the domain of a function with the domain of a variable. Consider the set M where $M = \{(x, y) \mid y = 2 + x\}$ and $U = \{0, 2, 4, 6, 8, 10\}$. Here, of course, there are 6 values that *may* replace x and 6 numbers that *may* replace y. Both of these replacements would be permissible if the condition

$y = 2 + x$ had not been imposed on the ordered pairs (x, y) that represent the solution set. However, with that condition, we may use for a replacement for x only those values chosen from U which will also give a value of y which is found in U. Observe that if we use 10 as a replacement for x in the condition $y = 2 + x$, we obtain a value for y that is not found in U. Thus we may not use the 10 as a replacement for x and so the domain of the function has 5 replacements whereas all 6 elements found in U constitute the range of the variable.

47. FUNCTIONAL NOTATION

The first member of an ordered pair (x, y) implies the use of any permissible member of the given universal set. The second member represents the *value of the function*. Consider the set A where $A = \{(x, y) \mid y = x + 1\}$ and where U is the set of all one-digit natural numbers. Again, we may use any member of U as a replacement for x if $x + 1$ is also an element found in U. The y is the value of the function $x + 1$, and y must also be an element of U. Again, we may not use 9 as a replacement for x since y, or $x + 1$, would be 10 (a two-digit natural number not found in U).

When we say the function of x is equal to $x + 1$, we mean $y = x + 1$. This is consistent with the above statement that the second member of (x, y) is the value of the function. We might write this in the form

$$\text{the function of } x = x + 1$$

which for the sake of brevity is usually written

$$f(x) = x + 1$$

The symbol $f(x)$ is read "the function of x" or, again for brevity, "f of x." Care must be exercised that we do not confuse this with a product. Previously we used the parentheses to indicate multiplication. Such is not the case with $f(x)$, which is only a symbol encompassing the entire expression $f(x)$. Since both y and $f(x)$ refer to the value of the function, we may use either to denote the value of the function.

If $f(x)$ denotes a given function, then $f(a)$ means the value of the given function when x is replaced with a, or sometimes we say "the value of the function at a."

Example 1. If $f(x) = x + 3$, find $f(a)$, $f(2)$, $f(0)$, and $f(-1)$.

$$f(x) = x + 3$$
$$f(a) = a + 3$$

$$f(2) = 2 + 3$$
$$= 5$$
$$f(0) = 0 + 3$$
$$= 3$$
$$f(-1) = -1 + 3$$
$$= 2$$

Example 2.   If $y = x^2 - 2x + 3$, find $f(2)$ and $f(-2)$.

$$f(x) = x^2 - 2x + 3$$
$$f(2) = (2)^2 - 2(2) + 3$$
$$= 4 - 4 + 3$$
$$= 3$$
$$f(-2) = (-2)^2 - 2(-2) + 3$$
$$= 4 + 4 + 3$$
$$= 11$$

or

$$y = x^2 - 2x + 3$$
$$y = (2)^2 - 2(2) + 3 \qquad (\text{if } x = 2)$$
$$= 4 - 4 + 3$$
$$= 3$$
$$y = x^2 - 2x + 3 \qquad (\text{if } x = -2)$$
$$y = (-2)^2 - 2(-2) + 3$$
$$= 4 + 4 + 3$$
$$= 11$$

EXERCISE 43

Find the values of $f(2)$, $f(1)$, $f(0)$, $f(-1)$, and $f(-2)$ in each of the following:

1. $f(x) = 5x$

2. $f(x) = x - 1$

3. $f(x) = 2x + 3$

4. $f(x) = 3 - 2x$

5. $f(x) = x^2$

6. $f(x) = x^2 + x$

7. $f(x) = x^2 + 3x - 4$

8. $f(x) = x^3 - 3$

9. $f(x) = 2x - x^2$

10. $f(x) = x^2 - 3x + 6$

State the domain and range for each of the following (when no universal set is given, it is assumed to include all real numbers):

11. $f(x) = x + 1$

12. $f(x) = 3 - x$

13. $f(x) = x^2$

14. $f(x) = 3$

15. $f(x) = 2 - x^2$

16. $f(x) = x^2 + x^4$

17. $f(x) = \dfrac{1}{x}$

18. $f(x) = x^2 + \dfrac{1}{x}$

19. $f(x) = x^3 - x^2 - x.$

20. $f(x) = \dfrac{x^2}{x - 2}$

48. GRAPHS OF LINEAR EQUATIONS

To graph a linear equation means to draw its graph. A *linear equation* is an equation in which the variables are to the first degree or first power. This type of equation, in one variable, was developed in Chapter 4. In the present discussion we shall be working with two variables where one is a function of the other in the form $y = ax + c$. In an equation of this form we arbitrarily assign permissible values of x to x. For this reason we call x the *independent* variable. As a value is assigned to x, the value of y is determined, and we call y the *dependent* variable since its value depends upon the value assigned to x.

To graph a linear equation, we assign a set of values to the independent variable and find the corresponding values of the dependent variable. If a table of these values is constructed, numerous points on the line representing the equation [ordered pairs in (x, y)] are evident.

Example 1. In the equation $y = x + 3$, assign values to x and find the corresponding values of y. Set up a table of values, plot the points represented by the established ordered pairs, and construct the line passing through these points. (It will be assumed that $U =$ the set of all real numbers.)

If we let $x = 1$, then
$$y = x + 3$$
$$y = 1 + 3$$
$$y = 4$$

If we let $x = -2$, then
$$y = x + 3$$
$$y = -2 + 3$$
$$y = 1$$

If we let $x = 4$, then
$$y = x + 3$$
$$y = 4 + 3$$
$$y = 7$$

x	1	-2	4
y	4	1	7

Hence three ordered pairs of the relation are $(-1, 2)$, $(-2, 1)$, and $(4, 7)$. The graph of the equation is shown in Figure 39.

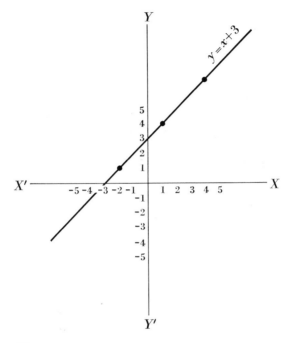

Figure 39

Two points (or ordered pairs) determine a straight line. Because of the possibility of an arithmetic error, it is best to locate three points. If the three points lie in a straight line, it is assumed that no error has been made. If they do not, the computations must be checked to find the error. The three points found are, of course, only three of many such points that lie on this line. When no universal set is given, it is assumed that it consists of all real numbers. Hence there are an infinite number of points between those found as well as beyond either end of the line shown in Figure 39.

Example 2. Graph the following: $\{(x, y) \mid x + y - 5 = 0\}$.

From our previous discussion, the given condition imposed on the variables in the ordered pair can be stated as $x + y = 5$ if we add 5 to both members of the given equation. Then

$$\{(x, y) \mid x + y - 5 = 0\} = \{(x, y) \mid x + y = 5\}$$

When selecting ordered pairs to determine points associated with the graph of an equation, it is usually desirable to assign the value 0 to each of the two variables. This value of 0 is assigned to one variable and then to the other as shown below.

$$x + y - 5 = 0$$
$$x + y = 5$$

If we let $y = 0$, then

$$x + y = 5$$
$$x + 0 = 5$$
$$x = 5$$

If we let $x = 0$, then

$$x + y = 5$$
$$0 + y = 5$$
$$y = 5$$

If we let $y = 1$, then

$$x + y = 5$$
$$x + 1 = 5$$
$$x = 5 - 1$$
$$x = 4$$

x	5	0	4
y	0	5	1

Hence three ordered pairs associated with this relation are (5, 0), (0, 5), and (4, 1). The graph is shown in Figure 40.

A comparison of Figure 40 with Figure 39 and Figure 41 reveals a difference in the direction of the slope of the line. Considerable emphasis will be given the slope of a line in subsequent courses in mathematics after sufficient background has been developed to enable the student to use the concept in sketching graphs.

Example 3.   Construct the graph for the relation $3y = 2x - 1$.

If we let $x = 2$, then

$$3y = 2x - 1$$
$$3y = 2(2) - 1$$
$$3y = 4 - 1$$
$$3y = 3$$
$$y = 1$$

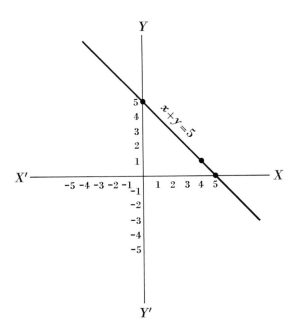

Figure 40

If we let $x = 5$, then

$$3y = 2x - 1$$
$$3y = 2(5) - 1$$
$$3y = 10 - 1$$
$$3y = 9$$
$$y = 3$$

If we let $x = -7$, then

$$3y = 2x - 1$$
$$3y = 2(-7) - 1$$
$$3y = -14 - 1$$
$$3y = -15$$
$$y = -5$$

x	2	5	-7
y	1	3	-5

Hence three ordered pairs associated with the relation are $(2, 1)$, $(5, 3)$, and $(-7, -5)$. The graph is shown in Figure 41.

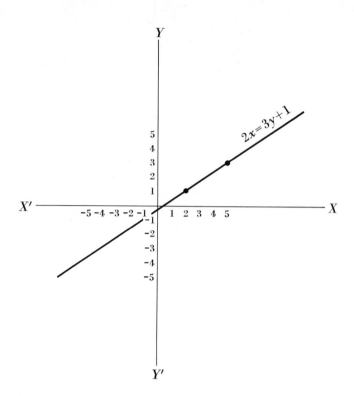

Figure 41

Example 4. Graph the equation $x = 3$.

We observe here that only one variable is used. If we graph this in the plane, we can readily visualize the graphical representation if we use the following format:

$$x + 0y = 3$$

Since the coefficient of y is 0, this term will be 0 for any value we assign to y and x will equal 3 for any value of y.

If we let $y = 4$, then

$$x + 0(y) = 3$$
$$x + 0(4) = 3$$
$$x + 0 = 3$$
$$x = 3$$

If we let $y = 1$, then

$$x + 0(y) = 3$$
$$x + 0(1) = 3$$
$$x + 0 = 3$$
$$x = 3$$

If we let $y = -5$, then

$$x + 0(y) = 3$$
$$x + 0(-5) = 3$$
$$x + 0 = 3$$
$$x = 3$$

x	3	3	3
y	4	1	-5

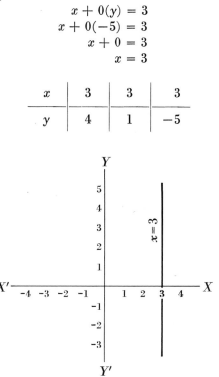

Figure 42

Thus the graph, which is shown in Figure 42, is a line parallel to the Y-axis and three units to the right of the Y-axis. In a similar manner, the equation $x = -3$ would be a line parallel to and three units to the left of the Y-axis.

Example 5. Graph the following: $\{(x,y) \mid y = -4\}$.

In a manner similar to that shown in Example 4, this equation may be written

$$0x + y = -4$$

If we let $x = -2$, then

$$0(x) + y = -4$$
$$0(-2) + y = -4$$
$$0 + y = -4$$
$$y = -4$$

If we let $x = 2$, then

$$0(x) + y = -4$$
$$0(2) + y = -4$$
$$0 + y = -4$$
$$y = -4$$

If we let $x = 6$, then

$$0(x) + y = -4$$
$$0(6) + y = -4$$
$$0 + y = -4$$
$$y = -4$$

x	-2	2	6
y	-4	-4	-4

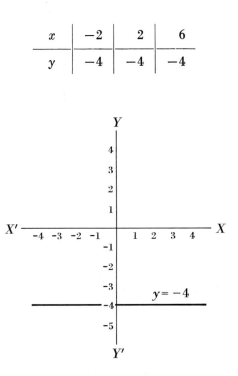

Figure 43

Thus three ordered pairs associated with the relation are $(-2, -4)$, $(2, -4)$, and $(6, -4)$.

We observe that $y = -4$ for any and all values of x. Thus our graph, which is shown in Figure 43, is a line parallel to and four units below the X-axis. If $y = 4$, then the line would be parallel to and four units above the X-axis.

A

Graph the following equations:

1. $x + y = 4$	2. $y = x - 4$	3. $y = 3 - x$
4. $y = 4 - x$	5. $y = x - 2$	6. $y = 2x + 1$
7. $y = 3 - 2x$	8. $y = x$	9. $y = 3x$
10. $3y = x$	11. $3y = 2x$	12. $2y = x$
13. $y = x - 1$	14. $y = 1 - 3x$	15. $y = 8 + x$
16. $x + y = 6$	17. $x - y = 2$	18. $3y = 2x - 2$
19. $x = 5$	20. $y = -2$	

B

Graph the following:

1. $\{(x, y) \mid y = 3\}$ 2. $\{(x, y) \mid x = -4\}$
3. $\{(x, y) \mid y = 5 - x\}$ 4. $\{(x, y) \mid y = x - 5\}$
5. $\{(x, y) \mid 2y = 1 - x\}$ 6. $\{(x, y) \mid y = \frac{1}{2}x + 1\}$
7. $\{(x, y) \mid y = -\frac{1}{2}x - 3\}$ 8. $\{(x, y) \mid y = \frac{1}{4}x + 3\}$
9. $\{(x, y) \mid y = 2 - \frac{1}{3}x\}$ 10. $\{(x, y) \mid y = 4 - \frac{2}{3}x\}$

49. APPLICATIONS OF GRAPHS OF LINEAR EQUATIONS

Formulas or equations involving two variables raised to the first power may be set up in graphic form, as was shown in Section 48. The axes, rather than being called X and Y, will be designated by the two variables used in the formula or equation. The advantage in this is that by extending the straight line indefinitely one can observe the value of either variable at specific values of the other.

Example 1. Graph the equation $C = \pi d$.

This is the formula for finding the circumference of a circle when the diameter is known. The graph will be constructed only in the first quadrant, as both the circumference and diameter must be positive values if a circle is to be formed. (We shall use $\frac{22}{7}$ as the value of π, keeping in mind that this is only an approximate value.)

If we let $d = 0$, then

$$C = \pi d$$
$$C = \pi(0)$$
$$C = 0$$

If we let $d = 7$, then

$$C = \pi d$$
$$C = \left(\tfrac{22}{7}\right)(7)$$
$$C = 22$$

If we let $d = \tfrac{7}{2}$, then

$$C = \pi d$$
$$C = \left(\tfrac{22}{7}\right)\left(\tfrac{7}{2}\right)$$
$$C = 11$$

d	0	7	$\tfrac{7}{2}$
C	0	22	11

The graph of the equation is shown in Figure 44.

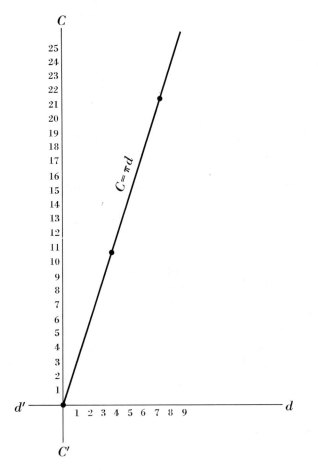

Figure 44

The circumference of a circle can easily be estimated by counting to the right of the origin as many units as are contained in the diameter and then moving upward on the graph to the point where the line of the graph crosses the line representing that diameter. The circumference will be as many units as the number of lines above the d-axis to the point where the straight line formed by the equation crosses the vertical line representing the diameter. Thus if the diameter is 10 units, we count 10 units to the right of the origin and move upward. At a point approximately midway between the thirty-first and thirty-second lines above the d-axis, the line of the equation crosses the line (10 units to the right of the origin) representing the diameter of the circle. Hence the circumference is approximately $31\frac{1}{2}$ units.

Example 2. Graph the equation $C = \frac{5}{9}(F - 32°)$.

This is the equation for converting Fahrenheit temperature readings to equivalent readings on the centigrade thermometer. On the graph let each space represent 10°.

If we let $F = 32°$, then

$$C = \frac{5}{9}(F - 32°)$$
$$C = \frac{5}{9}(32° - 32°)$$
$$C = \frac{5}{9}(0)$$
$$C = 0$$

If we let $F = 41°$, then

$$C = \frac{5}{9}(F - 32°)$$
$$C = \frac{5}{9}(41° - 32°)$$
$$C = \frac{5}{9}(9°)$$
$$C = 5°$$

If we let $F = 50°$, then

$$C = \frac{5}{9}(F - 32°)$$
$$C = \frac{5}{9}(50° - 32°)$$
$$C = \frac{5}{9}(18°)$$
$$C = 10°$$

F	32°	41°	50°
C	0°	5°	10°

The graph of the equation is shown in Figure 45.

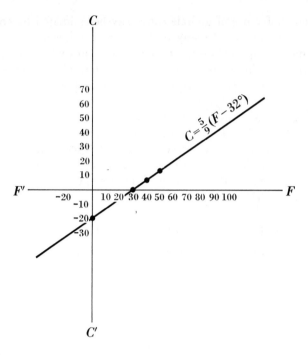

Figure 45

EXERCISE 45

Graph the following as suggested by each problem:

1. If the base of a rectangle remains constant at 3 feet, plot the graph showing the rectangle's area in relation to its altitude. Use the formula $A = bh$, and substitute 3 for b. Then the equation to be graphed is

$$A = 3h$$

2. The circumference of a circle is found by the formula $C = 2\pi r$. Plot the graph showing the circumference in relation to its radius.

3. The perimeter of a square is found by the formula $P = 4s$. Plot the graph showing the relationship between the perimeter and the length of one side of the square.

4. A salesman's weekly pay is $50 plus 2 percent of his total sales. The formula for determining his weekly wage, where W represents his wage and s the total amount of his sales, is expressed by

$$W = \$50 + .02s$$

Plot the graph to show his weekly wage in relationship to the amount of his sales.

5. The monthly retirement income provided by a certain business firm for persons with a minimum of 10 years' service with the firm is $60 plus an additional $4 for each year after 10 years' service. If I equals the monthly income and y the years' service beyond 10 years, the formula for computing the retirement pay is

$$I = \$60 + \$4y$$

Plot the graph to show the monthly income in relationship to the years' service with the firm.

6. A truck driver has a 400-mile trip to make. The time required to make the trip, where t equals time and r the average speed, is determined by the formula

$$t = \frac{400}{r}$$

Plot the graph to show the relationship between the time and his average speed.

7. A farmer has 240 yards of fencing with which to surround a rectangular garden plot. The formula for finding the possible dimensions of the garden is

$$2l = 240 - 2w$$

Plot the graph to show the relationship between the length and width of the garden plot. (*Hint:* Divide both members of the equation by 2 and use the formula $l = 120 - w$.)

8. A laborer gets $60.00 per week for a 40-hour week and time-and-a-half for overtime. The formula for his weekly pay, where W equals his weekly pay and h the number of hours overtime, is expressed as

$$W = \$60.00 + \$2.25h$$

Plot the graph showing the relationship between his weekly wage and the number of hours overtime he works.

9. The selling price of a college annual is $5.00. The annual staff announced that for each annual a student sold, he would be given a reduction of 20 cents on the cost of his own copy of the book. The formula for computing the cost to the student, where C equals the cost and n the number of books sold, is

$$C = \$5.00 - \$0.20n$$

Plot the graph showing the relationship between the cost of the annual to the student and the number of copies he sold for the staff.

10. If $100 is invested at 6 percent simple interest for a period of y years, it will amount to A dollars by using the formula

$$A = 100(1 + .06y)$$

Plot the graph showing the relationship between the amount and the number of years the $100 was invested.

50. GRAPHS OF INEQUALITIES

The expression $\{(x, y) \mid y > x + 3\}$ is read: "The set of all ordered pairs (x, y) such that y is greater than $x + 3$." To graph this expression, we first graph the linear equation $y = x + 3$ in order to get a working line from which to work. This will be a broken line since y is not equal to $x + 3$. In a problem of this type there will be a shaded area either above or below that broken line and it is our task to determine which part is shaded. To accomplish this, we take one of the ordered pairs that deter-

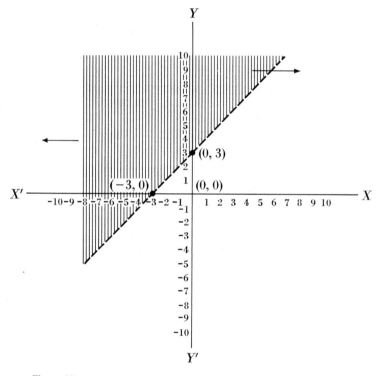

Figure 46

mined the working line. It is well to use two ordered pairs to check our results. Among the ordered pairs associated with the equation we have $(-3, 0)$ and $(0, 3)$. Using the first one, we substitute -3 for x in the expression $y > x + 3$ and find that when x is -3, $y > 0$. This means that when x is -3, y may assume any and all values above 0. In the second ordered pair, $(0, 3)$, we substitute 0 for x in the expression $y > x + 3$ and find that when $x = 0$, $y > 3$ and, of course, this means that when $x = 0$, y may assume any and all values above 3. Both of these tests show that all values of y are above the working line. Thus the graph of the inequality is as shown in Figure 46. Since no universal set was listed, we assume that all real numbers may be used. The arrows used in Figure 46 mean that the working line could be extended indefinitely in both directions; as this is done, the shaded area continues indefinitely with that line and also indefinitely upward.

Example 1. Graph the relation $\{(x, y) \mid y \leq 2x - 1\}$.

First we graph the linear equation $y = 2x - 1$ and obtain a segment of the line as shown in Figure 47. This time the line is continuous since

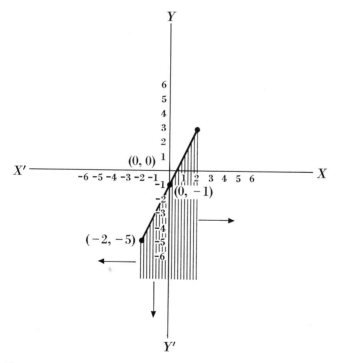

Figure 47

"y is less than *or* equal to $2x - 1$." Two ordered pairs associated with the relation $y = 2x - 1$ are $(2, 3)$ and $(-2, -5)$. To determine on which side the shaded area is found, we substitute 2 for x in the expression $y < 2x - 1$ and obtain $y < 3$. This means that at $x = 2$, y is below the line. Likewise, substituting -2 for x in the relation $y < 2x - 1$, we find that $y < -5$, and values of y at $x = -2$ fall below the line. Thus both checks indicate that the shaded area lies below the line. Again the arrows show that the graph continues in the directions indicated.

Example 2. Graph the relation $\{(x, y) \mid y \leq x + 1, \text{ when } -2 < x < 5\}$.

It can be seen in this problem that an additional restriction or condition has been imposed on the ordered pairs. Although the universal set is the set of all real numbers as they apply to y, x must be greater than -2 and less than 5.

We proceed as before by establishing the working line and, again, since y is less than *or* equal to $x + 1$, the line will be a continuous one. Two ordered pairs that satisfy the relation $y = x + 1$ are $(0, 1)$ and $(2, 3)$. In the relation $y < x + 1$, if we substitute 0 for x, we have $y < 1$, and if we substitute 2 for x, we get $y < 3$. In both cases values of y fall below

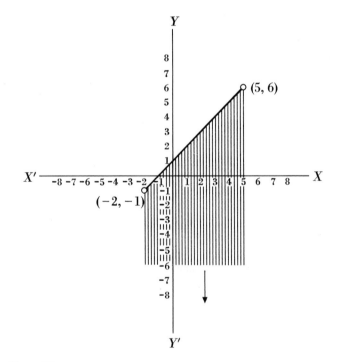

Figure 48

212   RELATIONS, FUNCTIONS, AND GRAPHS

the line. No arrows will be used in this graph except one pointing downward to indicate that the shaded area goes indefinitely downward. There are no arrows to either side because x lies between -2 and 5 but does not reach either of these values. For that reason we circle each end of the line. Figure 48 is the graph of this problem.

A

Graph the following:

1. $\{(x, y) \mid y < x + 1\}$ 2. $\{(x, y) \mid y > 2 - x\}$
3. $\{(x, y) \mid y \leq x - 4\}$ 4. $\{(x, y) \mid y < x - 3\}$
5. $\{(x, y) \mid y \geq 2 + x\}$ 6. $\{(x, y) \mid y \leq 3 - 2x\}$
7. $\{(x, y) \mid y \geq 4 + 3x\}$ 8. $\{(x, y) \mid y < 5 - 3x\}$
9. $\{(x, y) \mid y < 2x + 1,$ when $3 < x < 8\}$
10. $\{(x, y) \mid y \leq 2 - 2x,$ when $-4 < x < 1\}$

B

Graph the following:

1. $\{(x, y) \mid y \leq 3x - 1,$ when $-3 < x < 5\}$
2. $\{(x, y) \mid y \geq x + 2,$ when $-5 < x < -1\}$
3. $\{(x, y) \mid y \leq 1 - x,$ when $-4 \leq x < 3\}$
4. $\{(x, y) \mid y > 4 - 2x,$ when $-6 < x \leq 8\}$
5. $\{(x, y) \mid y \geq 2x + 1,$ when $3 \leq x \leq 7\}$

A

1. If $U = \{-2, -1, 0, 1, 2\}$ and $A = \{(x, y) \mid y = x - 1\}$, list the domain and range of the relation.
2. If $X = \{3, 4, 5, 6\}$ and Y is the set of all real numbers, list the domain and range of $\{(x, y) \mid y = 1 - 3x\}$.
3. If $f(x) = 1 - 4x$, find $f(0)$ and $f(-1)$.

4. If $f(x) = 1 - x^2$, find $f(3)$ and $f(-3)$.

5. Graph the following: $\left\{ (x, y) \mid y = \dfrac{x}{2} - 1 \right\}$.

6. Graph the following: $\left\{ (x, y) \mid y = 1 - \dfrac{x}{2} \right\}$.

B

1. Find the domain and range of
$$\left\{ (x, y) \mid y = \frac{3x - 1}{x^2 - 4} \right\} \text{ if } U = \{-2, -1, 0, 1, 2\}.$$

2. If U is the set of integers, find the domain and range of the set $\{(x, y) \mid y = x^2 - 4x + 1 \text{ and } -1 < x < 3\}$.

3. If $U = \{-1, 0, 1\}$, graph the following: $\{(x, y) \mid x = 3y\}$.

4. Graph the following: $\{(x, y) \mid y = 1 - x^2 \text{ and } -3 < x < 5\}$.

REVIEW TEST 20

On a sheet of paper write the numbers 1 through 15 to correspond to the statements listed below. After each number place T or F to indicate if the corresponding statement is true or false. (Assume the statement to be false unless always true.)

1. $\{3, 4\}$ is an ordered pair.
2. $\{(x, y) \mid y = 3x + 1\}$ is a function.
3. A set of ordered pairs is a function.
4. A relation is a function.
5. $(-3, 0)$ is a function.
6. If $f(x) = 3 - 2x^2$, $f(-1) = 1$.
7. If $f(x) = \dfrac{1 + x}{1 - x^2}$, $f(-1)$ is undefined.
8. The domain of a function is a subset of that function.
9. If $A = \{(1, 1), (1, 2), (1, 3), (2, 1), (2, 2), (2, 3), (3, 1), (3, 2), (3, 3)\}$, then A is a function.
10. $(-3, 0)$ is an ordered pair.
11. The range of a function represents values of y in the plane if Y is the vertical axis.
12. If $B = \{(x, y) \mid y = x^2 \text{ and } -3 < x < 3\}$, then B is a function.
13. If $M = \{(2, 5), (3, 7), (4, 9), (5, 11)\}$, then M is a function.
14. The first members of ordered pairs represent values of the function for specified second members of the corresponding ordered pairs.
15. $(0, 0)$ represents the null set.

10

Systems of Equations

51. THE INTERSECTION OF SETS

In Chapter 1 we defined the intersection of two sets as the set whose elements are common to the two given sets. If we are given two sets X and Y, the $X \cap Y$ is called "the intersection of X and Y" or "X intersection Y."

Any two sets have an intersection. If there are no elements common to both sets, the intersection of the two sets is the empty set $\emptyset$.

Example 1. If $X = \{1, 3, 5\}$ and $Y = \{2, 4, 6\}$, then $X \cap Y = \emptyset$.

Sometimes the set of elements may be one of the given sets from which the intersection was made.

Example 2. If $X = \{1, 2, 3, 4, 5\}$ and $Y = \{2, 5\}$, then $X \cap Y = \{2, 5\}$.

In general, we shall be more concerned with problems in which a unique set evolves from the intersection of two given sets.

Example 3. If $X = \{7, 8, 9, 10\}$ and $Y = \{3, 4, 8, 10, 11\}$, then $X \cap Y = \{8, 10\}$.

Ordered pairs also have intersections. In the previous chapter we graphed sets of ordered pairs and found that a set of ordered pairs derived from a linear equation produced a straight line. In this discussion we shall be primarily concerned with two sets of ordered pairs. Our first consideration will be that of the algebraic solution for finding the new set that represents the intersection of the two given sets.

If $A = \{(x, y) \mid x + y = 3\}$ and $B = \{(x, y) \mid x - y = 1\}$, the intersection of A and B, or $A \cap B = \{(x, y) \mid x + y = 3 \text{ and } x - y = 1\}$. This form is called the *description of the intersection of set A and set B.*

EXERCISE 48

A

In each of the following pairs of sets find the intersection of each pair, writing your answer in the form $X \cap Y = \{\quad\}$.

1. $X = \{2, 7, 9, 11\}$
   $Y = \{1, 3, 5, 7\}$

2. $X = \{1, 2, 3, 4, 5\}$
   $Y = \{2, 4, 6, 8, 10\}$

3. $X = \{-1, 4, 7\}$
   $Y = \{-3, -1, 3, 7, 9\}$

4. $X = \{2, 4, 6, 8\}$
   $Y = \{1, 3, 5, 7\}$

5. $X = \{17, 18, 20\}$
   $Y = \{15, 17, 19, 21\}$

6. $X = \{2, 3, 5\}$
   $Y = \{3, 5\}$

7. $X = \{7, 8, 9, 10\}$
   $Y = \{9, 10, 11, 12\}$

8. $X = \{5, 6, 7, 8, 9\}$
   $Y = \{1, 2, 3, 4, 5\}$

9. $X = \{7, 8, 9, 10\}$
   $Y = \{1, 2, 3, 4, 5\}$

10. $X = \{1, 2, 3, 4, 5\}$
    $Y = \{3, 4\}$

B

Describe each of the following intersections in the form $A \cap B = \{\quad\}$:

1. $A = \{(x, y) \mid 2x + y = 5\}$
   $B = \{(x, y) \mid x - y = 1\}$

2. $A = \{(x, y) \mid x + 2y = 1\}$
   $B = \{(x, y) \mid 3x + 2y = 7\}$

3. $A = \{(x, y) \mid x + y = 3\}$
   $B = \{(x, y) \mid x - y = -3\}$

4. $A = \{(x, y) \mid x + y = 2\}$
   $B = \{(x, y) \mid x - y = 2\}$

5. $A = \{(x, y) \mid x + y = 0\}$
   $B = \{(x, y\} \mid x - y = 2\}$

6. $A = \{(x, y) \mid 2x + y = 5\}$
   $B = \{(x, y) \mid x - y = 4\}$

7. $A = \{(x, y) \mid x + 2y = 4\}$
   $B = \{(x, y) \mid x - 2y = -8\}$

8. $A = \{(x, y) \mid x - 3y = -2\}$
   $B = \{(x, y) \mid 2x - y = 6\}$

9. $A = \{(x, y) \mid x + y = 4\}$
   $B = \{(x, y) \mid x - y = 0\}$

10. $A = \{(x, y) \mid x - y = 3\}$
    $B = \{(x, y) \mid 2x - 3y = 4\}$

A pair of linear equations is referred to as a *system of linear equations.* Sometimes in a problem involving two variables, two conditions concerning those variables will be given. In such cases it is necessary to find what value for each variable will satisfy both equations. From the given conditions we form two equations consisting of terms made up of those two variables, and by one of several methods we solve for the values of those variables.

The equations

$$x + y = 5$$

$$x - y = 1$$

form a system of equations. If in each equation we substitute 3 for x and 2 for y, we find that the left member of each equation is equal to the right member of that equation. Such equations are referred to as *simultaneous equations* if they have *one and only one* ordered pair common to both equations. The above pair of equations would represent the given data in the following problem: "Find two numbers whose sum is 5 and whose difference is 1."

In the above system of equations we write the first one as $A = \{(x, y) \mid x + y = 5\}$ and the second one as $B = \{(x, y) \mid x - y = 1\}$. The intersection of these two sets, then, would be written as follows: $A \cap B = \{(x, y) \mid x + y = 5 \text{ and } x - y = 1\}$. The solution set for this intersection would be $\{(3, 2)\}$.

Sometimes there is no pair of values that will satisfy both equations. In such cases we say that the equations are *inconsistent* and their intersection would be the empty set $\emptyset$.

When more than one set of values for x and y are common to both equations, the equations are identical or equivalent. Such a system of equations is called a *dependent system of equations.* In a pair of equations if one equation can be obtained from the other, the pair forms a dependent system of equations. The following pair is illustrative of such a system:

$$x + 3y = 12$$

$$2x + 6y = 24$$

If each member of the second equation were divided by 2 or the members of the first equation were multiplied by 2, the two equations would be identical. In this case the intersection of the two sets describes the same set and their intersection is that set.

Later in this chapter we shall graph certain systems of equations. When graphing a system of linear equations, we place both straight lines on the same graph. If the lines intersect, the equations have a common solution and thus are a pair of simultaneous equations. If the lines are parallel, the equations are inconsistent and have no common solution. If there is an infinite number of solutions, the lines will be identical and the equations are a pair of dependent equations.

52. SOLVING SYSTEMS OF EQUATIONS BY ADDITION AND SUBTRACTION

If $A \cap B = \{(x, y) \mid x + y = 6$ and $x - y = 2\}$, we take the two equations, $x + y = 6$ and $x - y = 2$, and solve them by any one of several methods. The solution for this pair of equations is shown in Example 1 below.

To solve a pair of linear equations in two variables, we try to obtain an equivalent equation that contains only one of the variables. That equation, then, can be solved as a linear equation in one variable. This process is known as *solving by elimination.*

As linear equations are solved by addition or subtraction, we make use of **Law 11**:

> If equals are added to equals, the sums are equal. If equals are subtracted from equals, the remainders are equal.

Example 1. Find the solution set for the following:

$$\{(x, y) \mid x + y = 6 \text{ and } x - y = 2\}$$

If we add the corresponding members of these equations, we get

$$
\begin{aligned}
x + y &= 6 \qquad (1) \\
\underline{x - y} &= \underline{2} \qquad (2) \\
2x &= 8 \\
x &= 4 \qquad (3)
\end{aligned}
$$

(The numbers in parentheses are used to identify each equation and enable one to follow the solution more easily.)

Substitute in equation (1) the value of x as found in equation (3) and solve for y.

$$
\begin{aligned}
x + y &= 6 \qquad (1) \\
4 + y &= 6 \\
y &= 6 - 4 \\
y &= 2 \qquad (4)
\end{aligned}
$$

Hence the solution set is $\{(4, 2)\}$.

$$
\begin{array}{llll}
\textit{Check:} & x + y = 6 \quad (1) & \qquad & x - y = 2 \quad (2) \\
& 4 + 2 = 6 & & 4 - 2 = 2 \\
& 6 = 6 & & 2 = 2
\end{array}
$$

Example 2. Find the solution set for the following:

$$\{(x, y) \mid 2x + y = 7 \text{ and } x + y = 4\}$$

$$2x + y = 7$$
$$x + y = 4$$

If we add the corresponding members of the two equations, we do not eliminate either variable. If we subtract, the variable y is eliminated.

$$
\begin{array}{ll}
2x + y = 7 & (1) \\
\underline{x + y = 4} & (2) \\
x = 3 & (3)
\end{array}
$$

Substitute in equation (2) the value obtained for x in equation (3)

$$
\begin{array}{ll}
x + y = 4 & (2) \\
3 + y = 4 & \\
y = 1 & (4)
\end{array}
$$

Hence the solution set is $\{(3, 1)\}$.

Check:

$$
\begin{array}{ll}
2x + y = 7 & (1) \\
2(3) + 1 = 7 & \\
6 + 1 = 7 & \\
7 = 7 &
\end{array}
\qquad
\begin{array}{ll}
x + y = 4 & (2) \\
3 + 1 = 4 & \\
4 = 4 &
\end{array}
$$

Example 3. Find the solution set for the following:

$$\{(x, y) \mid 2x + y = 4 \quad \text{and} \quad 3x + 2y = 5\}$$

$$
\begin{array}{ll}
2x + y = 4 & (1) \\
3x + 2y = 5 & (2)
\end{array}
$$

Neither variable in this system of linear equations can be eliminated, in their present form, by addition or subtraction as was done in Examples 1 and 2. In this case if we multiply both members of equation (1) by 2, then by subtraction the y will be eliminated. When this change has been made, identify equation (1) by the symbol (1a), which means that it is equation (1) in a different form.

$$
\begin{array}{ll}
4x + 2y = 8 & (1a) \\
\underline{3x + 2y = 5} & (2) \\
x = 3 & (3)
\end{array}
$$

Substitute in equation (1) the value of x obtained in equation (3).

$$
\begin{array}{ll}
2x + y = 4 & (1) \\
2(3) + y = 4 & \\
6 + y = 4 & \\
y = -2 &
\end{array}
$$

Hence the solution set is $\{(3, -2)\}$.

Check: $2x + y = 4$ (1) $3x + 2y = 5$ (2)

$$2(3) + (-2) = 4 \qquad\qquad 3(3) + 2(-2) = 5$$
$$6 - 2 = 4 \qquad\qquad\qquad 9 - 4 = 5$$
$$4 = 4 \qquad\qquad\qquad\qquad 5 = 5$$

There are times when both equations have to be multiplied by different numbers in order to eliminate one of the variables. The system of linear equations in the following example illustrates such a case.

Example 4. Find the solution set for the following:

$$\{(x, y) \mid 2x + 3y = 8 \quad \text{and} \quad 3x - 4y = -22\}$$
$$2x + 3y = \quad 8 \qquad (1)$$
$$3x - 4y = -22 \qquad (2)$$

Equation (1) can be multiplied by 3 and equation (2) by 2; then by subtraction the x would be eliminated. Also, we could multiply equation (1) by 4 and equation (2) by 3, and by addition eliminate the y.

$$8x + 12y = \quad 32 \qquad (1a)$$
$$\underline{9x - 12y = -66} \qquad (2a)$$
$$17x \qquad\quad = -34$$
$$x = -2 \qquad (3)$$

Substitute in equation (1) the value of x as found in equation (3) and solve for y.

$$2x + 3y = 8 \qquad (1)$$
$$2(-2) + 3y = 8$$
$$-4 + 3y = 8$$
$$3y = 12$$
$$y = 4 \qquad (4)$$

Hence the solution set is $\{(-2, 4)\}$.

Check:

$$2x + 3y = 8 \qquad (1) \qquad\qquad 3x - 4y = -22 \qquad (2)$$
$$2(-2) + 3(4) = 8 \qquad\qquad 3(-2) - 4(4) = -22$$
$$-4 + 12 = 8 \qquad\qquad\qquad -6 - 16 = -22$$
$$8 = 8 \qquad\qquad\qquad\qquad -22 = -22$$

A

Find the solution set for each of the following:

1. $\{(x, y) \mid x + y = 5 \text{ and } 2x + y = 6\}$
2. $\{(x, y) \mid -x + y = 4 \text{ and } x + 3y = 8\}$
3. $\{(x, y) \mid x - y = -3 \text{ and } 2x - y = -1\}$
4. $\{(x, y) \mid x - y = 9 \text{ and } x + y = 3\}$
5. $\{(x, y) \mid x - y = 0 \text{ and } 3x + y = 16\}$
6. $\{(x, y) \mid x + y = 1 \text{ and } 2x + y = 4\}$
7. $\{(x, y) \mid -x - y = 4 \text{ and } -2x + y = 5\}$
8. $\{(x, y) \mid x - y = 3 \text{ and } 3x + y = -3\}$
9. $\{(x, y) \mid 4x + y = 4 \text{ and } 5x + y = 5\}$
10. $\{(x, y) \mid y - x = 4 \text{ and } y + 2x = 7\}$
11. $\{(x, y) \mid y + x = 1 \text{ and } 3y - x = 11\}$
12. $\{(x, y) \mid x - y = 0 \text{ and } x + 2y = 9\}$
13. $\{(x, y) \mid x + 3y = 7 \text{ and } 2x + 2y = 6\}$
14. $\{(x, y) \mid x + 2y = 4 \text{ and } 3x + 5y = 12\}$
15. $\{(x, y) \mid x + 2y = -8 \text{ and } 3x - 4y = 6\}$
16. $\{(x, y) \mid 2x - y = 8 \text{ and } 3x + 5y = -1\}$
17. $\{(x, y) \mid x + y = 6 \text{ and } 2x - 2y = 20\}$
18. $\{(x, y) \mid 3x - y = 18 \text{ and } x + 2y = -8\}$
19. $\{(x, y) \mid 2x - y = 4 \text{ and } 3x + 4y = -16\}$
20. $\{(x, y) \mid 2x + y = 9 \text{ and } x + 2y = 3\}$

B

Find the solution set for each of the following:

1. $\{(x, y) \mid 6x - 2y = -3 \text{ and } 10x + 3y = 14\}$
2. $\{(x, y) \mid 4x - 6y = -16 \text{ and } 5x + 18y = -3\}$
3. $\{(x, y) \mid 8x + 3y = 4 \text{ and } 14x - 5y = 7\}$
4. $\{(x, y) \mid 2x + 3y = -15 \text{ and } 5x + 2y = 1\}$
5. $\{(x, y) \mid \frac{1}{2}x + 2y = 9 \text{ and } 2x - 3y = 14\}$
6. $\{(x, y) \mid \frac{2}{3}x + 3y = 3 \text{ and } 4x - y = -1\}$
7. $\{(x, y) \mid \frac{1}{4}x + \frac{1}{3}y = 3 \text{ and } 3x + 2y = 24\}$

8. $\{(x, y) \mid 0.1x + 0.2y = 2 \text{ and } 3x - 2y = 20\}$
9. $\{(x, y) \mid 0.3x - y = 4 \text{ and } 0.7x + 3y = 12\}$
10. $\{(x, y) \mid 0.5x + 0.9y = 11 \text{ and } 1.5x + 0.3y = 9\}$

53. SOLVING SYSTEMS OF EQUATIONS BY SUBSTITUTION

Another method of solving simultaneous equations is known as *elimination by substitution*. When using this method, we solve one of the equations for one of the variables in terms of the other variable. The following problem illustrates this process:

Solve the equation $x + y = 6$ for x in terms of y.

$$x + y = 6$$
$$x = 6 - y$$

The same equation may be solved for y in terms of x. The result of this procedure is

$$y = 6 - x$$

When an equation has been solved for one variable in terms of the other variable, that value for the variable is then substituted in the other equation. This gives us a linear equation in one variable that can easily be solved as any simple linear equation in one variable. The following examples illustrate such solutions.

In the remaining examples in this chapter we shall omit the set builder. However, it must be kept in mind that a system of two equations in two variables implies the intersection of the two sets of ordered pairs associated with those equations, and the solution set is the ordered pair common to both equations if they are a pair of simultaneous equations or the empty set if they are a pair of inconsistent equations.

Example 1. Find the values of x and y that satisfy both of the following equations by use of the substitution method:

$$x + y = 1 \qquad (1)$$
$$2x - 3y = 7 \qquad (2)$$

Solve equation (1) for x in terms of y.

$$x + y = 1 \qquad (1)$$
$$x = 1 - y \qquad (1a)$$

Substitute the $1 - y$ for x in equation (2).

$$2x - 3y = 7 \qquad (2)$$
$$2(1 - y) - 3y = 7$$
$$2 - 2y - 3y = 7$$
$$2 - 5y = 7$$
$$-5y = 5$$
$$y = -1 \qquad (3)$$

Substitute in equation (1a) the value of y as found in equation (3).

$$x = 1 - y \qquad (1a)$$
$$x = 1 - (-1)$$
$$x = 1 + 1$$
$$x = 2$$

Hence the set of values that satisfies both equations is $x = 2$ and $y = -1$. In other words, the solution set is the ordered pair $\{(2, -1)\}$.

Check: $x + y = 1 \qquad (1)$

$$2 + (-1) = 1$$
$$2 - 1 = 1$$
$$1 = 1$$

$$2x - 3y = 7 \qquad (2)$$
$$2(2) - 3(-1) = 7$$
$$4 + 3 = 7$$
$$7 = 7$$

Example 2. Solve for x and y by substitution:

$$2x + 3y = 11 \qquad (1)$$
$$y = 1 - 2x \qquad (2)$$

This problem already has the value of y given in terms of x. Hence substitute equation (2) in equation (1).

$$2x + 3y = 11 \qquad (1)$$
$$2x + 3(1 - 2x) = 11$$
$$2x + 3 - 6x = 11$$
$$-4x = 8$$
$$x = -2 \qquad (3)$$

Substitute in equation (2) the value of x in equation (3).

$$y = 1 - 2x \qquad (2)$$
$$y = 1 - 2(-2)$$
$$y = 1 + 4$$
$$y = 5$$

Hence the set of values that satisfies both equations is $x = -2$ and $y = 5$.

Check: $2x + 3y = 11 \qquad (1)$

$$2(-2) + 3(5) = 11$$
$$-4 + 15 = 11$$
$$11 = 11$$

$$y = 1 - 2x \qquad (2)$$
$$5 = 1 - 2(-2)$$
$$5 = 1 + 4$$
$$5 = 5$$

Example 3. Solve for x and y by substitution:

$$3x - 4y = 10 \quad (1)$$
$$x - 6y = 1 \quad (2)$$

Solve equation (2) for x in terms of y.

$$x - 6y = 1 \quad (2)$$
$$x = 6y + 1 \quad (2a)$$

Substitute equation (2a) in equation (1).

$$3x - 4y = 10 \quad (1)$$
$$3(6y + 1) - 4y = 10$$
$$18y + 3 - 4y = 10$$
$$14y = 7$$
$$y = \tfrac{1}{2} \quad (3)$$

To find the value of x, substitute in equation (2a) the value of y from equation (3).

$$x = 6y + 1 \quad (2a)$$
$$x = 6(\tfrac{1}{2}) + 1$$
$$x = 3 + 1$$
$$x = 4$$

Hence the set of values that satisfies both equations is $x = 4$ and $y = \tfrac{1}{2}$.

Check:

$$3x - 4y = 10 \quad (1) \qquad\qquad x - 6y = 1 \quad (2)$$
$$3(4) - 4(\tfrac{1}{2}) = 10 \qquad\qquad 4 - 6(\tfrac{1}{2}) = 1$$
$$12 - 2 = 10 \qquad\qquad 4 - 3 = 1$$
$$10 = 10 \qquad\qquad 1 = 1$$

If all coefficients of x and y are greater than 1, it is usually easier to use either addition or subtraction to solve the system of equations. The following example, however, shows the solution for such a problem by the method of substitution:

Example 4. Solve for x and y by substitution:

$$3x + 4y = 17 \quad (1)$$
$$5x - 6y = 3 \quad (2)$$

Solve equation (1) for x in terms of y.

$$3x + 4y = 17 \quad (1)$$
$$3x = 17 - 4y$$
$$x = \frac{17 - 4y}{3} \quad (1a)$$

Substitute equation (1a) in equation (2).

$$5x - 6y = 3 \qquad (2)$$

$$5\left(\frac{17 - 4y}{3}\right) - 6y = 3$$

$$\frac{85 - 20y}{3} - 6y = 3$$

Find a common denominator for all terms in both members of the equation and then eliminate that common denominator, as was explained in Section 41.

$$\frac{85 - 20y}{3} - \frac{3(6y)}{3} = \frac{3(3)}{3}$$

$$85 - 20y - 18y = 9$$

$$-38y = -76$$

$$y = 2 \qquad (3)$$

Substitute equation (3) in equation (1a) to find the value of x.

$$x = \frac{17 - 4y}{3} \qquad (1a)$$

$$x = \frac{17 - 4(2)}{3}$$

$$x = \frac{17 - 8}{3}$$

$$x = \frac{9}{3}$$

$$= 3$$

Hence the set of values that satisfies both equations is $x = 3$ and $y = 2$.

Check: $3x + 4y = 17 \qquad (1)$ $5x - 6y = 3 \qquad (2)$
$3(3) + 4(2) = 17$ $5(3) - 6(2) = 3$
$9 + 8 = 17$ $15 - 12 = 3$
$17 = 17$ $3 = 3$

Example 5.   Solve for x and y by substitution:

$$x + 2y = 5 \qquad (1)$$
$$2x + 4y = 10 \qquad (2)$$

Solve equation (1) for x in terms of y.

$$x = 5 - 2y \qquad (1a)$$

Substitute equation (1a) in equation (2).

$$2x + 4y = 10 \qquad (2)$$
$$2(5 - 2y) + 4y = 10$$
$$10 - 4y + 4y = 10$$

It can be observed that the y terms are eliminated and no solution is forth-coming. If we compare equations (1) and (2), we can see that they are equivalent equations and have an infinite number of solutions.

Example 6.   Solve for x and y by substitution:

$$2x + y = 12 \qquad (1)$$
$$4x + 2y = 16 \qquad (2)$$

Solve equation (1) for y in terms of x.

$$2x + y = 12 \qquad (1)$$
$$y = 12 - 2x \qquad (1a)$$

Substitute in equation (2) the value of y in equation (1a).

$$4x + 2y = 16 \qquad (2)$$
$$4x + 2(12 - 2x) = 16$$
$$4x + 24 - 4x = 16$$

Again, the x terms would be eliminated and there is no solution. It can be observed that equation (2) could be reduced to $2x + y = 8$ by dividing both members of the equation by 2. Then the left members of both equations would be identical. Such is not the case with the right members of the equations. Certainly if $2x + y = 12$, then $2x + y$ cannot equal 8. Hence the equations are inconsistent and there is no common solution.

EXERCISE 50

A

Find the solution set (if there is one) for each of the following:

1. $\{(x, y) \mid x + 3y = 7 \text{ and } x = 5y - 1\}$
2. $\{(x, y) \mid 2x + 5y = 15 \text{ and } x = y - 3\}$
3. $\{(x, y) \mid x = y - 9 \text{ and } y = 3 - 2x\}$
4. $\{(x, y) \mid 3 = 2x + y \text{ and } 3x - 5y = -2\}$
5. $\{(x, y) \mid 2x + 5y = 10 \text{ and } y = 3x - 15\}$
6. $\{(x, y) \mid y = x - 5 \text{ and } 3x = 2y + 8\}$
7. $\{(x, y) \mid 2x + y = 5 \text{ and } 4x + 3y = 14\}$
8. $\{(x, y) \mid x + 3y = -9 \text{ and } 3x - 2y = 17\}$
9. $\{(x, y) \mid x + 3y = 2 \text{ and } 5x - 9y = 2\}$
10. $\{(x, y) \mid x - y = 0 \text{ and } 7x - 3y = 24\}$
11. $\{(x, y) \mid x = y - 2 \text{ and } 2y - 3x = 7\}$

12. $\{(x, y) \mid 3x + 8y = 4 \text{ and } x = 2y - 1\}$
13. $\{(x, y) \mid 2x + y = -2 \text{ and } 4x - 5y = -46\}$
14. $\{(x, y) \mid 7x - y = 16 \text{ and } 3x + 2y = 2\}$
15. $\{(x, y) \mid x + y = 1 \text{ and } 6x - 3y = 0\}$
16. $\{(x, y) \mid x - 4y = 1 \text{ and } 3x + 4y = 7\}$
17. $\{(x, y) \mid 3x - y = 12 \text{ and } 2x + 3y = 8\}$
18. $\{(x, y) \mid y - 2x = 14 \text{ and } 3y + x = 14\}$
19. $\{(x, y) \mid x - 2y = 11 \text{ and } 2x - 3y = 17\}$
20. $\{(x, y) \mid x + y = 0 \text{ and } 4x - 2y = 3\}$

B

Find the solution (if there is one) for each of the following:

1. $\{(x, y) \mid 2x - y = 17 \text{ and } 2x - 7y = -1\}$
2. $\{(x, y) \mid 2x + 3y = -5 \text{ and } 3x - y = 20\}$
3. $\{(x, y) \mid 4x - y = -4 \text{ and } 10x - 2y = -7\}$
4. $\{(x, y) \mid x - 3y = 4 \text{ and } 2x + 9y = 3\}$
5. $\{(x, y) \mid 3x - 8y = 10 \text{ and } x - 4y = 3\}$
6. $\{(x, y) \mid 6x - 5y = 9 \text{ and } 3x - y = 3\}$
7. $\{(x, y) \mid \frac{1}{4}x - y = 5 \text{ and } 2x + 5y = 1\}$
8. $\{(x, y) \mid x + \frac{1}{2}y = 1 \text{ and } 2x + 2y = 1\}$
9. $\{(x, y) \mid 0.2x - 0.1y = 0 \text{ and } y = x + 10\}$
10. $\{(x, y) \mid 0.1x + 0.3y = 5 \text{ and } 3x - y = 0\}$

54. SYSTEMS OF EQUATIONS INVOLVING FRACTIONS

Sometimes one or more of the terms in a system of equations is in fractional form. When this is the case, we clear each equation of fractions by the method developed in Section 41.

Example 1. Solve for x and y:

$$\frac{x}{2} + y = 4 \qquad (1)$$

$$\frac{3x}{4} + \frac{y}{2} = 4 \qquad (2)$$

$$x + 2y = 8 \qquad (1a)$$
$$3x + 2y = 16 \qquad (2a)$$

Subtract the members of equation (1a) from the corresponding members of equation (2a).

$$3x + 2y = 16 \quad \text{(2a)}$$
$$\underline{x + 2y = 8} \quad \text{(1a)}$$
$$2x = 8$$
$$x = 4 \quad \text{(3)}$$

Substitute in equation (1a) the value of x in equation (3).

$$x + 2y = 8 \quad \text{(1a)}$$
$$4 + 2y = 8$$
$$2y = 4$$
$$y = 2$$

Hence the set of values that satisfies both equations is $x = 4$ and $y = 2$. In other words, the solution set is $\{(4, 2)\}$.

Check: $\dfrac{x}{2} + y = 4 \quad$ (1) $\qquad\qquad \dfrac{3x}{4} + \dfrac{y}{2} = 4 \quad$ (2)

$$\dfrac{4}{2} + 2 = 4 \qquad\qquad\qquad \dfrac{3(4)}{4} + \dfrac{2}{2} = 4$$

$$2 + 2 = 4 \qquad\qquad\qquad\qquad 3 + 1 = 4$$
$$4 = 4 \qquad\qquad\qquad\qquad\quad 4 = 4$$

Example 2. Solve for x and y:

$$\frac{2x}{3} - \frac{5y}{2} = \frac{17}{3} \quad \text{(1)}$$

$$\frac{3x}{2} + \frac{y}{8} = \frac{5}{4} \quad \text{(2)}$$

$$4x - 15y = 34 \quad \text{(1a)}$$
$$12x + y = 10 \quad \text{(2a)}$$

Multiply both members of (1a) by 3 to form equation (1b) and subtract equation (2a) from equation (1b).

$$12x - 45y = 102 \quad \text{(1b)}$$
$$\underline{12x + y = 10} \quad \text{(2a)}$$
$$-46y = 92$$
$$y = -2 \quad \text{(3)}$$

Substitute the results of equation (3) in equation (2a).

$$12x + y = 10 \quad \text{(2a)}$$
$$12x + (-2) = 10$$
$$12x - 2 = 10$$
$$12x = 12$$
$$x = 1$$

Hence the set of values that satisfies both equations is $x = 1$ and $y = -2$.

Check: $\dfrac{2x}{3} - \dfrac{5y}{2} = \dfrac{17}{3}$ (1) $\dfrac{3x}{2} + \dfrac{y}{8} = \dfrac{5}{4}$ (2)

$\dfrac{2(1)}{3} - \dfrac{5(-2)}{2} = \dfrac{17}{3}$ $\dfrac{3(1)}{2} + \dfrac{-2}{8} = \dfrac{5}{4}$

$\dfrac{2}{3} + \dfrac{10}{2} = \dfrac{17}{3}$ $\dfrac{3}{2} - \dfrac{1}{4} = \dfrac{5}{4}$

$\dfrac{2}{3} + 5 = \dfrac{17}{3}$ $\dfrac{6}{4} - \dfrac{1}{4} = \dfrac{5}{4}$

$\dfrac{2}{3} + \dfrac{15}{3} = \dfrac{17}{3}$ $\dfrac{5}{4} = \dfrac{5}{4}$

$\dfrac{17}{3} = \dfrac{17}{3}$

EXERCISE 51

A

Solve for x and y:

1. $\dfrac{3x}{2} + y = \dfrac{11}{2}$

$x + \dfrac{y}{4} = \dfrac{13}{4}$

2. $\dfrac{2x}{3} + \dfrac{3y}{2} = 3$

$\dfrac{5x}{3} + \dfrac{3y}{4} = \dfrac{3}{2}$

3. $\dfrac{2x}{3} - \dfrac{y}{2} = \dfrac{25}{6}$

$x + \dfrac{2y}{3} = 2$

4. $\dfrac{x}{6} + \dfrac{y}{2} = \dfrac{7}{3}$

$-x + \dfrac{3y}{4} = \dfrac{19}{4}$

5. $\dfrac{3x}{2} - y = 0$

$\dfrac{x}{4} + \dfrac{y}{6} = 2$

6. $\dfrac{3x}{8} - \dfrac{y}{16} = 1$

$\dfrac{x}{2} + \dfrac{y}{4} = 0$

7. $\dfrac{3x}{8} + \dfrac{y}{6} = \dfrac{23}{24}$

$y = 3x + 4$

8. $x - y = \dfrac{1}{6}$

$2x + \dfrac{2y}{3} = 3$

9. $\dfrac{x}{2} + \dfrac{y}{3} = 7$

$\dfrac{x}{4} - \dfrac{y}{9} = 1$

10. $\dfrac{x}{3} - \dfrac{y}{6} = 5$

$\dfrac{x}{18} + \dfrac{y}{12} = \dfrac{1}{6}$

B

Solve for x and y:

1. $\dfrac{x+2}{3} - \dfrac{y-1}{4} = \dfrac{13}{12}$

$\dfrac{x+3}{5} - \dfrac{y+1}{3} = 0$

2. $\dfrac{x+8}{2} + \dfrac{y-1}{3} = 6\dfrac{2}{3}$

$\dfrac{x-1}{3} - \dfrac{y+4}{7} = 0$

3. $\dfrac{x+5}{4} + \dfrac{y+5}{6} = \dfrac{7}{6}$

$\dfrac{2x-1}{7} + \dfrac{y+7}{3} = 1$

4. $\dfrac{x+2y}{4} - \dfrac{x+y}{5} = 1$

$\dfrac{2x-y}{3} + \dfrac{3x+y}{6} = \dfrac{11}{6}$

5. $\dfrac{2x+5y}{4} - \dfrac{x-y}{6} = \dfrac{3}{4}$

$\dfrac{3x+2y}{8} + \dfrac{2x+4y}{5} = -\dfrac{1}{2}$

55. SOLVING SYSTEMS OF LINEAR EQUATIONS BY THE GRAPHICAL METHOD

The graph of a linear equation in x and y was shown to be a straight line in Chapter 9.

When we have a pair of linear equations in x and y, their solution can be determined by locating on the same graph the two straight lines represented by the two equations. As we solved systems of equations algebraically earlier in this chapter, it was our aim to find the single values of x and y that satisfied both equations. The point of intersection of the two lines will be the solution, the *abscissa* representing the value of x and the *ordinate* the value of y. That point of intersection is the only point common to both lines.

If the lines are parallel, it is evident that there is no common solution and the equations are inconsistent.

When more than one set of values for x and y are common to both lines, the two lines are identical and the equations are equivalent. This represents a dependent system of equations as defined earlier in this chapter.

Example 1. Solve for x and y graphically:

$$y - x = 3 \qquad (1)$$
$$y - 2x = 2 \qquad (2)$$

If we solve both of these equations for y, we have

$$y = x + 3 \qquad (1a)$$
$$y = 2x + 2 \qquad (2a)$$

where (1a) and (2a) signify different forms of equations (1) and (2).

By assigning the values -2, 1, and 3 to x in equation (1a), we obtain the following table of values:

x	-2	1	3
y	1	4	6

and using the values -3, 1, and 3 for x in equation (2a), we have

x	-3	1	3
y	-4	4	8

Observing these two tables, we see that both of them include the values $x = 1$ and $y = 4$. Thus the ordered pair (1, 4) is the common solution and represents the intersection of the sets whose ordered pairs represent the two straight lines.

Example 2. Solve for x and y graphically:

$$3x + y = 18 \qquad (1)$$
$$2x - y = 2 \qquad (2)$$

By assigning the values 2, 3, and 4 to x, we find that the following ordered pairs form the straight line for equation (1):

x	2	3	4
y	12	9	6

The following ordered pairs form the straight line for equation (2):

x	1	3	5	4
y	0	4	8	6

It can be observed in both tables above that when $x = 4$, $y = 6$. Thus the only ordered pair in common is (4, 6) and this represents their point of intersection (see Figure 49). In other words, $x = 4$ and $y = 6$ are the only values that satisfy both equations.

Check: $3x + y = 18$ (1) $2x - y = 2$ (2)

$3(4) + 6 = 18$ $2(4) - 6 = 2$

$12 + 6 = 18$ $8 - 6 = 2$

$18 = 18$ $2 = 2$

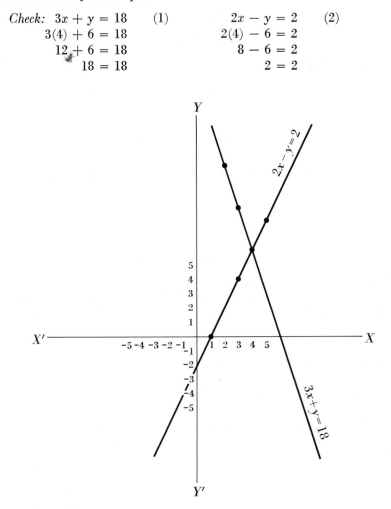

Figure 49

Example 3. Solve for x and y graphically:

$$x - y = 4 \qquad (1)$$
$$5x - 3y = 8 \qquad (2)$$

The following coordinates form the straight line for equation (1):

x	5	2	0
y	1	-2	-4

The following coordinates form the straight line for equation (2):

x	1	-2	4
y	-1	-6	4

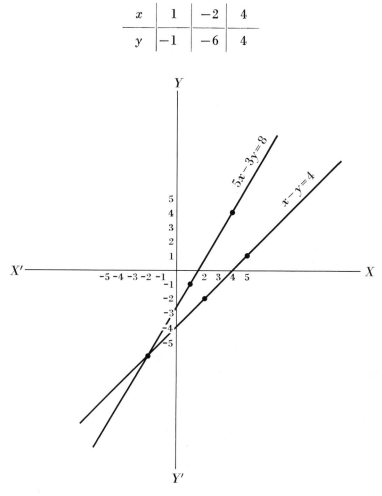

Figure 50

The coordinates of the point of intersection of the two lines are $(-2, -6)$. Hence the values for x and y that satisfy both equations are $x = -2$ and $y = -6$.

Check:
$$
\begin{array}{ll}
x - y = 4 \quad (1) & 5x - 3y = 8 \quad (2) \\
-2 - (-6) = 4 & 5(-2) - 3(-6) = 8 \\
-2 + 6 = 4 & -10 + 18 = 8 \\
4 = 4 & 8 = 8
\end{array}
$$

Example 4. Solve for x and y graphically:

$$
\begin{array}{ll}
x + 3y = 9 & (1) \\
2x + 6y = 14 & (2)
\end{array}
$$

The following table of values forms the coordinates for equation (1):

x	0	9	-9
y	3	0	6

The following table of values forms the coordinates for equation (2):

x	7	13	-8
y	0	-2	5

These lines are everywhere equidistant and thus are parallel lines. Consequently there is no common solution, and they are a pair of inconsistent equations. When the ratio between the coefficients of the two x terms is the same as the ratio between the coefficients of the two y terms, the lines are either parallel or identical. They are identical if the ratio between the two constants, taken in the same order, is the same as the ratio between the x terms and the y terms. When the ratio between the constants is not the same as that ratio between the x terms and the y terms, the lines are parallel.

Consider the coefficients of the above problem. The ratio between the coefficients of the x terms is 1 to 2, or $\frac{1}{2}$. The ratio between the coefficients of the y terms is 3 to 6, or $\frac{3}{6}$, which will reduce to $\frac{1}{2}$. The ratio between the constants is $\frac{9}{14}$, which will not reduce to $\frac{1}{2}$.

Solving equations (1) and (2) for y, we get

$$
y = -\frac{1}{3}x + 3
$$

and

$$
y = -\frac{1}{3}x + \frac{7}{3}
$$

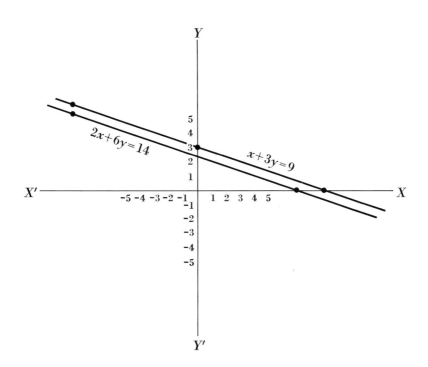

Figure 51

The lines are parallel and intersect the Y-axis at 3 and $\frac{7}{3}$ respectively.

Example 5.   Solve for x and y graphically:

$$x - 2y = 4 \qquad (1)$$
$$3x - 6y = 12 \qquad (2)$$

The following table of values forms the coordinates for equation (1):

x	0	4	-4	10	14	-8
y	-2	0	-4	3	5	-6

The following table of values forms the coordinates for equation (1):

x	0	4	6	-2	12	14
y	-2	0	1	-3	4	5

It can be observed that several of the pairs of coordinates appear in both tables of values. Any pair used for equation (1) could also be used for

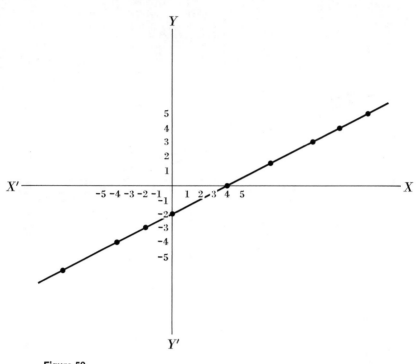

Figure 52

equation (2). Two points determine a straight line; then, since two or more sets of coordinates are common to both equations, the lines represented by the two equations are identical. This is the case when the ratio between the coefficients of the x terms, the y terms, and the constants in the right members of the equations are all equal. The respective ratios are $\frac{1}{3}$, $\frac{2}{6}$, and $\frac{4}{12}$, all of which are equal to $\frac{1}{3}$.

Hence there is an infinite number of solutions, and the lines are identical.

EXERCISE 52

A

Graph the following equations and check your answers by solving algebraically:

1. $x + y = 8$
   $x - y = 4$

2. $x + y = 1$
   $y = 1 - x$

3. $x = 4 - y$
   $y = 10 - x$

4. $x - y = 5$
   $x = 2y$

5. $x + 2y = 18$
   $2x - y = 11$

6. $x + 2y = 1$
   $2y = x$

7. $x - y = 4$
   $3x - 2y = 7$

8. $3x + y = 9$
   $x - 5y = 3$

9. $2x - y = 1$
   $x - 2y = 11$

10. $x = 3y$
    $x + y = 16$

B

Graph the following equations and check your answers by solving algebraically:

1. $x + y = 9$
   $5x - y = -9$

2. $2x + 3y = -10$
   $3x + 2y = 0$

3. $x - y = 0$
   $3x - 2y = 6$

4. $x - y = 6$
   $3x - 2y = 15$

5. $x + y = 1$
   $y - 2x = 0$

6. $x + y = -3$
   $2x - y = 18$

7. $\frac{1}{2}x + \frac{1}{3}y = 11$
   $\frac{1}{3}x + \frac{2}{3}y = 14$

8. $x - 3y = -36$
   $\frac{1}{3}x + \frac{1}{4}y = 13$

9. $y = \frac{2}{3}x$
   $2y - x = 3$

10. $2x - y = 12$
    $x + 3y = 6$

56. GRAPHICAL INTERSECTION OF INEQUALITIES

It is possible to find a set that is the intersection of two or more sets. If $A = \{1, 2, 3, 4\}$, $B = \{2, 3, 4, 5\}$, and $C = \{1, 3, 5, 7\}$, then $A \cap B \cap C = \{1, 2, 3, 4\} \cap \{2, 3, 4, 5\} \cap \{1, 3, 5, 7\}$.

Because the associative law holds true for the intersection of sets, the solution may be accomplished by the intersection of C with the intersection of A and B $[(A \cap B) \cap C]$ or by the intersection of A with the intersection of B and C $[A \cap (B \cap C)]$. Both methods are shown in the following:

$$(A \cap B) \cap C = \{2, 3, 4\} \cap \{1, 3, 5, 7\}$$
$$= \{3\}$$
$$A \cap (B \cap C) = \{1, 2, 3, 4\} \cap \{3, 5\}$$
$$= \{3\}$$

Example 1. Graph $A \cap B \cap C$ in the following: $A = \{(x, y) \mid x + y \leq 5\}$, $B = \{(x, y) \mid x - y \leq 5\}$, $C = \{(x, y) \mid x \geq 0\}$. (Assume that U is the set of all real numbers since U is not stated.)

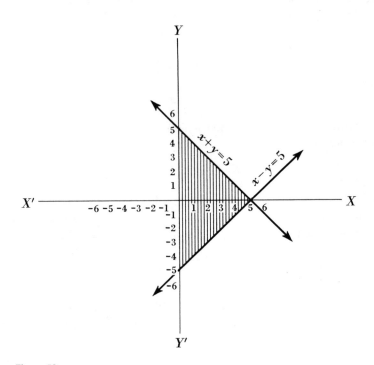

Figure 53

The graphs of A and B are shown in Figure 53. The graph of the equation $x = 0$ is the Y-axis. (This means that, for all values of y, $x = 0$.) Thus the graph of the intersection of A, B, and C is the shaded region in Figure 53.

Example 2. Graph $A \cap B \cap C$ in the following: $A = \{(x, y) \mid x - y \leq 3\}$, $B = \{(x, y) \mid 2x \geq y\}$, $C = \{(x, y) \mid y < 3\}$.

The graphs of A and B are shown in Figure 54 by the continuous lines. Since $y = 3$ is a line three units above, and parallel to, the X-axis, the line must be a broken one to show that $y < 3$.

The graph of $A \cap B \cap C$ is shown in Figure 54.

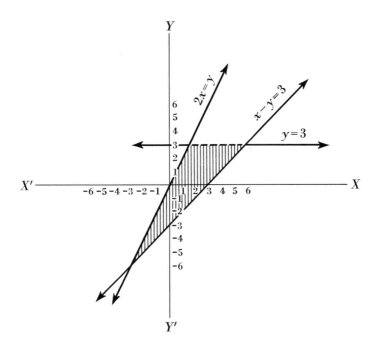

Figure 54

In the following, graph $A \cap B \cap C$:

1. $A = \{(x, y) \mid x + y < 6\}$
   $B = \{(x, y) \mid x - y \leq 4\}$
   $C = \{(x, y) \mid x > 0\}$

2. $A = \{(x, y) \mid 2x - y \leq 0\}$
   $B = \{(x, y) \mid y < 4\}$
   $C = \{(x, y) \mid x \geq 0\}$

3. $A = \{(x, y) \mid 2x + 4y \leq 6\}$
   $B = \{(x, y) \mid y > 0\}$
   $C = \{(x, y) \mid x \geq -5\}$

4. $A = \{(x, y) \mid y > x\}$
   $B = \{(x, y) \mid x \geq 0\}$
   $C = \{(x, y) \mid y < 5\}$

5. $A = \{(x, y) \mid y < -2x + 1\}$
   $B = \{(x, y) \mid y > 0\}$
   $C = \{(x, y) \mid x > -4\}$

6. $A = \{(x, y) \mid y \leq 2x\}$
   $B = \{(x, y \mid x + y > 0\}$
   $C = \{(x, y) \mid x < 4\}$

57. STATED PROBLEMS

A great many stated problems can be solved by setting up two equations
in two variables. This method could have been employed frequently in

solving the linear equations in Chapter 4. The following examples illustrate the application of the principles associated with the solving of simultaneous equations to stated problems.

Example 1. If the length of a rectangle is three times its width and the perimeter is 48 feet, what are the dimensions of the rectangle?

Let $x =$ the number of feet in the length and let $y =$ the number of feet in the width. Then

$$x = 3y \qquad (1)$$
$$2x + 2y = 48 \qquad (2)$$

Divide both members of equation (2) by 2.

$$x + y = 24 \qquad (2a)$$

Substitute in equation $(2a)$ the value of x in equation (1).

$$x + y = 24 \qquad (2a)$$
$$3y + y = 24$$
$$4y = 24$$
$$y = 6 \text{ feet} \qquad (3)$$

Substitute in equation (1) the value of y as found in equation (3).

$$x = 3y$$
$$x = 3(6)$$
$$x = 18 \text{ feet}$$

Hence the length is 18 feet and the width is 6 feet.

Check:

$x = 3y \qquad (1)$		$2x + 2y = 48 \qquad (2)$
$18 = 3(6)$		$2(18) + 2(6) = 48$
$18 = 18$		$36 + 12 = 48$
		$48 = 48$

Example 2. A boy has 15 nickels and dimes with a value of $1.10. How many of each coin does he have?

Let $n =$ the number of nickels whose value is $0.05n$ and let $d =$ the number of dimes whose value is $0.10d$. Then

$$n + d = 15 \qquad (1) \quad \text{(the number equation)}$$
$$0.05n + 0.10d = 1.10 \qquad (2) \quad \text{(the value equation)}$$

Multiply each member of equation (2) by 100.

$$5n + 10d = 110 \qquad (2a)$$

Divide each member of equation (2a) by 5.

$$n + 2d = 22 \qquad (2b)$$

Subtract equation (1) from equation (2b).

$$n + 2d = 22 \qquad (2b)$$
$$\underline{n + \ \ d = 15} \qquad (1)$$
$$d = \ \ 7 \qquad (3)$$

Substitute the value of d from equation (3) in equation (1).

$$n + d = 15 \qquad (1)$$
$$n + 7 = 15$$
$$n = 8$$

Hence he has 8 nickels and 7 dimes.

Check: $n + d = 15$ (1) $\$0.05n + \$0.10d = \$1.10$ (2)
        $8 + 7 = 15$ $\$0.05(8) + \$0.10(7) = \$1.10$
           $15 = 15$ $\$0.40 + \$0.70 = \$1.10$
                                          $\$1.10 = \$1.10$

Example 3. How many pounds each of 80-cent coffee and 95-cent coffee must a grocer mix to give him 100 pounds of coffee that will sell for 86 cents per pound?

Let $x =$ the number of pounds of 80-cent coffee whose value is $\$0.80x$ and let $y =$ the number of pounds of 95-cent coffee whose value is $\$0.95y$. Then

$$x + y = 100 \qquad (1) \quad \text{(the number equation)}$$
$$0.80x + 0.95y = 86.00 \qquad (2) \quad \text{(the value equation)}$$

Multiply equation (2) by 100.

$$80x + 95y = 8600 \qquad (2a)$$

Divide each member of equation (2a) by 5.

$$16x + 19y = 1720 \qquad (2b)$$

Multiply both members of equation (1) by 16 and subtract from equation (2b).

$$16x + 19y = 1720 \qquad (2b)$$
$$\underline{16x + 16y = 1600} \qquad (1a)$$
$$3y = \ \ 120$$
$$y = 40 \text{ pounds} \qquad (3)$$

Substitute the value of y from equation (3) in equation (1).

$$x + y = 100 \qquad (1)$$
$$x + 40 = 100$$
$$x = 60 \text{ pounds}$$

Hence he will have to use 60 pounds of the 80-cent coffee and 40 pounds of the 95-cent coffee.

$x + y = 100$ (1) $\$0.80x + \$0.95y = \$86$ (2)
$$60 + 40 = 100$$
$$100 = 100$$

$$\$0.80(60) + \$0.95(40) = \$86$$
$$\$48 + \$38 = \$86$$
$$\$86 = \$86$$

Example 4.   The sum of the digits in a two-digit number is 12. If the digits are reversed, the number is 36 greater than the original number. What is the original number?

Let u = the number in unit's place and t = the number in ten's place. Consider the number 39. The 9 is in unit's place and the 3 is in ten's place. The 3 in ten's place is the same as 10 times 3, or 30. Then

$$\frac{\begin{array}{r} 9 \\ 30 \end{array}}{39}$$

From the same reasoning, let $u + 10t$ = the original number and $t + 10u$ = the new number with the digits reversed.

From the statement in the problem, the new number is 36 greater than the original number. Then

$$t + 10u - (u + 10t) = 36$$
$$t + 10u - u - 10t = 36$$
$$9u - 9t = 36$$

Divide both members of the equation by 9 and use the result for equation (1). Equation (2) below was taken from a given statement in the problem.

$$
\begin{array}{rl}
u - t = 4 & (1) \\
\underline{u + t = 12} & (2) \\
2u = 16 & \\
u = 8 & (3)
\end{array}
$$

Substitute the value of u from equation (3) in equation (2).

$$
\begin{array}{rl}
u + t = 12 & (2) \\
8 + t = 12 & \\
t = 4 &
\end{array}
$$

Hence the original number, if 8 is the digit in unit's place and 4 the digit in ten's place, is 48.

Check: $u - t = 4$ (1) $u + t = 12$ (2)
$$8 - 4 = 4$$
$$4 = 4$$

$$8 + 4 = 12$$
$$12 = 12$$

A

Solve each of the following problems by setting up two equations involving two unknowns:

1. The sum of two numbers is 44 and their difference is 8. What are the numbers?

2. The sum of two numbers is 78. If the larger one is subtracted from twice the smaller one, the remainder is 15. What are the two numbers?

3. One number is three times as large as a second number. If their sum is 52, what are the numbers?

4. Tom is 8 years older than his brother Curtis. Four years from now Tom will be twice as old as Curtis. How old is each at the present time?

5. The length of a rectangle is 6 feet more than its width. If the perimeter is 52 feet, what are the dimenisons of the rectangle?

6. A boy has 29 coins in his pocket that total $1.31. He has twice as many nickels as dimes. If 11 of the coins are pennies, how many nickels and how many dimes does he have?

7. The perimeter of a rectangle is 80 feet. If the length is four times the width, what are the dimensions of the rectangle?

8. Barbara is twice as old as her sister Jean. In 8 years the sum of their ages will be 40 years. How old is each at the present time?

9. Edwin has 13 coins in his pocket consisting of quarters and nickels. Their value is $1.25. How many of each does he have?

10. The sum of two numbers is 40. The sum of twice the larger one and seven times the smaller number is 160. What are the numbers?

11. A merchant had 23 suits of clothes he wished to sell at once to make room for new merchandise. One lot of the suits he priced at $35 and the other at $45. For the 23 suits he received $945. How many did he sell at each price?

12. The admission prices to a basketball game were $1.00 for adults and 50 cents for students. A total of 295 tickets were sold, for which $235 was received. How many adult and how many student tickets were sold?

13. A realtor sold two houses for $22,000. If one sold for $3,000 more than the other, how much was received for each house?

14. A man made two investments totaling $15,000. From one he received 4 percent and from the other 5 percent interest. If his annual income

from the two investments was $686, how much did he have invested in each?

15. A certain fraction, if reduced, is equal to $\frac{4}{5}$. If 3 is added to the numerator, the fraction is equal to 1. What is the fraction?

B

Solve each of the following problems by setting up two equations involving two unknowns:

1. A city lot is twice as deep as it is wide. If its perimeter is 360 feet, how wide and how deep is the lot?

2. Separate 84 into two parts so that the larger is 12 more than the smaller part.

3. A merchant has a quantity of peanuts and walnuts. The peanuts are priced to sell for 30 cents a pound and the walnuts for 45 cents a pound. How many pounds of each must he use to make a 100-pound mixture that will sell for 40 cents a pound?

4. A mixture of 100 gallons of 50 percent alcohol is to be made from quantities of 30 percent alcohol and 75 percent alcohol. How many gallons of each will be required to make the mixture?

5. The sum of two numbers is 6 and their difference is 38. What are the numbers?

6. The annual income from two investments is $456. If one pays $16 more annually than the other, what is the income from each investment?

7. Two pairs of slacks and one shirt cost $40. Two shirts and one pair of slacks are priced at $26. What is the price of each?

8. The sum of the units' and tens' digits of a two-digit number is 8. If the digits are interchanged, the number is 36 greater than the original number. What is the original number?

9. In a certain two-digit number, the digit in units place is twice the digit in tens place. If the digits are interchanged, the new number is 18 greater than the original number. What is the original number?

10. A basketball team played 26 games during one season, winning 10 more games than it lost. How many games were won and how many lost during the season?

A

Find the solution set for each of the following:

1. $\{(x, y) \mid x - 3y = -6 \text{ and } 3x + 4y = 21\}$
2. $\{(x, y) \mid 2x - y = 7 \text{ and } 5x + 3y = 1\}$
3. $\{(x, y) \mid 2x + 3y = 18 \text{ and } 5x + 2y = 12\}$
4. $\{(x, y) \mid x = y - 12 \text{ and } y = 6 - x\}$
5. $\{(x, y) \mid 4x + 3y = 1 \text{ and } 7x - 2y = 9\}$
6. $\{(x, y) \mid x + 2y = 4 \text{ and } y = 12 - 3x\}$
7. $\{(x, y) \mid 2x - 3y = 4 \text{ and } 3x - 2y = 16\}$
8. $\{(x, y) \mid x = y + 3 \text{ and } 2x - y = 15\}$
9. $\{(x, y) \mid 2x - y = -14 \text{ and } y - 3x = 17\}$
10. $\{(x, y) \mid 4x + 5y = 0 \text{ and } 3x - 2y = 0\}$
11. $\left\{ (x, y) \mid \dfrac{x - y}{2} = 3 \text{ and } \dfrac{x + y}{5} = 1 \right\}$
12. $\{(x, y) \mid y = -2x \text{ and } 2x - 5y = 48\}$

B

Find the solution set for each of the following:

1. $\{(x, y) \mid 2x - 7y = -8 \text{ and } x = y + 6\}$
2. $\{(x, y) \mid 5x + 4y = 7 \text{ and } 3x + 5y = -14\}$
3. $\{(x, y) \mid 6x - 5y = 7 \text{ and } 4x + 3y = -27\}$
4. $\{(x, y) \mid \frac{1}{4}x + \frac{1}{3}y = 9 \text{ and } \frac{2}{3}x + \frac{1}{2}y = 17\}$
5. $\{(x, y) \mid \frac{2}{3}x + y = 20 \text{ and } y = \frac{2}{3}x\}$
6. $\{(x, y) \mid \frac{1}{3}x + \frac{2}{3}y = -2 \text{ and } \frac{2}{3}x + \frac{1}{3}y = 11\}$
7. $\{(x, y) \mid \frac{1}{2}x + \frac{1}{2}y = 8 \text{ and } 3x - 2y = 8\}$
8. $\left\{ (x, y) \mid \dfrac{x + y}{4} = \dfrac{x - y}{12} \text{ and } x - 7 = y + 17 \right\}$

On a sheet of paper write the numbers 1 through 20 to correspond to those below. After each number write one of the words *equivalent, simultaneous,* or *inconsistent* to classify properly each pair of equations.

1. $\ x + 6y = \ 7$ $\ \ \ \ 3x + 2y = 15$	2. $2x - 3y = \ 4$ $\ \ \ \ x + 5y = 15$
3. $\ x + 3y = \ 5$ $\ \ \ 2x + 6y = 10$	4. $\ x + y = \ 2$ $\ \ \ 3x - y = 10$
5. $2x - \ y = \ 6$ $\ \ \ 4x - 2y = 15$	6. $3x + \ y = 10$ $\ \ \ 9x + 3y = 15$
7. $\ 4x - \ 5y = 10$ $\ \ 12x - 15y = 30$	8. $3x + \ y = \ \ 4$ $\ \ \ x - 2y = -8$
9. $\ x - 2y = \ 1$ $\ \ \ 2x + \ y = 17$	10. $4x + \ y = 2$ $\ \ \ \ 8x - 3y = 4$
11. $2x - \ 3y = 1$ $\ \ \ 8x - 12y = 4$	12. $\ x + 3y = 11$ $\ \ \ 3x - 9y = 7$
13. $\ 4x + \ 3y = \ 7$ $\ \ 20x + 15y = 32$	14. $\ x - \ y = -3$ $\ \ 2x - 7y = \ \ 4$
15. $3x + \ y = \ \ 3$ $\ \ \ x - 3y = -9$	16. $\ x - 3y = \ 6$ $\ \ 2x - 6y = 21$
17. $\frac{1}{2}x + \frac{1}{3}y = 10$ $\ \ \ x + \frac{2}{3}y = 20$	18. $x + \ y = \ \ 5$ $\ \ x + 3y = -3$
19. $2x - \ y = \ \ 2$ $\ \ \ 3x - 2y = -2$	20. $\ 3x - \ 4y = \ \ 0$ $\ \ 12x - 16y = 10$

On a sheet of paper write the numbers 1 through 20 to correspond to those in the left-hand column below. After each number write the letter that correctly matches the answer from the right-hand column with the pair of equations in the left-hand column. Do not use any letter more than once. Some of the answers found in the right-hand column do not match any of the problems found in the left-hand column.

1. $2x + 3y = 5$ $\ \ \ 3x + 2y = 5$	a. $x = -3, y = 7$
	b. $x = 1, y = 8$
2. $\ x + \ y = \ \ 4$ $\ \ \ 2x + 7y = -2$	c. $x = 6, y = -2$
3. $4x + \ y = \ \ 3$ $\ \ \ 2x - 3y = -9$	d. $x = 4, y = 3$
	e. $x = 6, y = 0$
4. $\ x + 2y = 0$ $\ \ \ 3x + 6y = 0$	f. $x = 1, y = 1$
	g. No solution

5. $x + y = 4$
$2x + y = 11$

6. $x + y = 0$
$2x + 5y = 3$

7. $x + y = 4$
$2x - y = -13$

8. $x + 3y = 6$
$4x - y = 24$

9. $\frac{1}{2}x + \frac{1}{2}y = 7$
$\frac{1}{4}x + \frac{1}{3}y = 4$

10. $x + y = 0$
$x - 3y = 4$

11. $2x - y = -6$
$5x - 2y = -11$

12. $2x - y = 9$
$x - 2y = -9$

13. $x + y = 3$
$2x + 3y = 2$

14. $3x - y = -2$
$x - 3y = 2$

15. $x + 4y = 10$
$3x - y = 4$

16. $x + 2y = 0$
$6x + 7y = -10$

17. $2x + 3y = 9$
$x - 2y = -27$

18. $2x - 5y = 6$
$x - 3y = 4$

19. $x - 3y = 12$
$3x - y = 12$

20. $5x - 3y = 12$
$2x + 5y = 42$

h. $x = 0, y = 3$

i. $x = -4, y = 2$

j. $x = -1, y = 1$

k. $x = 7, y = -4$

l. $x = 2, y = -2$

m. $x = -2, y = -2$

n. An infinite number of solutions

o. $x = -3, y = -3$

p. $x = 2, y = 2$

q. $x = 1, y = -1$

r. $x = -9, y = 9$

s. $x = 3, y = -3$

t. $x = 7, y = -3$

u. $x = -2, y = 2$

v. $x = 9, y = 9$

w. $x = 6, y = 6$

x. $x = -1, y = -1$

y. $x = -6, y = -6$

z. $x = 8, y = 6$

11

Exponents and Radicals

Some use of exponents has been made throughout the text thus far. In an earlier discussion we defined an *exponent* as the number placed above and to the right of a quantity to indicate how many times that quantity is to be used as a factor. Thus x^5 means that x is to be used as a factor five times.

In this chapter we shall extend the application of exponents and introduce additional laws governing their use.

58. THE LAWS OF EXPONENTS

Law 1. $x^m = x \cdot x \cdot x \cdot \cdots \cdot$ *to m factors (if m is an integer).*

The expression $(x^2)(x^4)$ could be written $(x \cdot x)(x \cdot x \cdot x \cdot x)$ or $x \cdot x \cdot x \cdot x \cdot x \cdot x$ or x^6, since x is used as a factor six times. Hence $(x^2)(x^4) = x^{2+4} = x^6$. Then we have the next law.

Law 2. $x^m \cdot x^n = x^{m+n}$ *(if m and n are positive integers).*

The expression $\dfrac{x^4}{x^2}$ implies division. This expression could be written $\dfrac{x \cdot x \cdot x \cdot x}{x \cdot x}$. Then

$$\frac{x \cdot x \cdot x \cdot x}{x \cdot x} = \frac{x}{x} \cdot \frac{x}{x} \cdot x \cdot x$$

$$= 1 \cdot 1 \cdot x \cdot x$$

$$= x^2$$

Then

$$\frac{x^4}{x^2} = x^{4-2}$$

$$= x^2$$

Likewise,

$$\frac{x^2}{x^4} = \frac{x \cdot x}{x \cdot x \cdot x \cdot x} = \frac{x}{x} \cdot \frac{x}{x} \cdot \frac{1}{x \cdot x} = 1 \cdot 1 \cdot \frac{1}{x^2} = \frac{1}{x^2}$$

Hence

$$\frac{x^2}{x^4} = \frac{1}{x^{4-2}} = \frac{1}{x^2}$$

Then our third law of exponents is as follows:

Law 3. $\dfrac{x^m}{x^n} = x^{m-n}$ *(if* $m > n$ *and* $x \neq 0$*) or* $\dfrac{x^m}{x^n} = \dfrac{1}{x^{n-m}}$ *(if* $n > m$ *and* $x \neq 0$*).*

Law 3 states that, in division, if the bases (x) are the same, the exponent of the divisor is subtracted from the exponent of the dividend (unless the exponent of the divisor is larger than the exponent of the dividend). Consider the following problem:

$$\frac{x^4}{x^4} = x^{4-4}$$

$$= x^0$$

In arithmetic we learned that if a quantity is divided by itself, the quotient is 1. In the above problem x^4 is divided by x^4. Thus the quotient is 1. Then we have Law 4.

Law 4. $x^0 = 1$ *(if* x *is not equal to zero).*

From Law 1, we see that the problem $(x^2)^2$ is solved as follows:

$$(x^2)(x^2) = x^4$$

The problem $(x^2)^2$ is called a *power of a power* and in such problems the exponents are multiplied, giving us the next law.

Law 5. $(x^m)^n = x^{mn}$.

Use Law 1 to solve the expression $(xy)^m$ (x, y, and m positive integers).

$$(xy)^m = xy \cdot xy \cdot xy \cdots \text{ to } m \text{ factors}$$

By use of the commutative law for multiplication, the above may be arranged as follows:

$$= (x \cdot x \cdot x \cdots \text{ to } m \text{ factors})(y \cdot y \cdot y \cdots \text{ to } m \text{ factors})$$

Thus we have the next law.

Law 6. $(xy)^m = x^m y^m$ (*if x, y, and m are positive integers*).

Consider the expression $\left(\dfrac{x}{y}\right)^m$ (x, y, and m positive integers).

$$\left(\frac{x}{y}\right)^m = \frac{x}{y} \cdot \frac{x}{y} \cdot \frac{x}{y} \cdots \text{ to } m \text{ factors}$$

$$= \frac{x \cdot x \cdot x}{y \cdot y \cdot y} \cdots \quad \begin{array}{l} \text{to } m \text{ factors in both the numerator} \\ \text{and denominator} \end{array}$$

$$= \frac{x^m}{y^m}$$

Then we have the final law in this series.

Law 7. $\left(\dfrac{x}{y}\right)^m = \dfrac{x^m}{y^m}$ (*if x, y, and m are positive integers*).

Example 1. Simplify $x^2 \cdot x^6$.

$$x^2 \cdot x^6 = x^{2+6} \qquad \text{(Law 2)}$$
$$= x^8$$

The addition should be done mentally.

Example 2. Simplify $\dfrac{x^5}{x^2}$.

$$\frac{x^5}{x^2} = x^{5-2} \qquad \text{(Law 3)}$$

$$= x^3$$

Example 3. Simplify $\dfrac{x^7}{x^7}$.

$$\frac{x^7}{x^7} = x^{7-7}$$

$$= x^0$$
$$= 1 \qquad \text{(Law 4)}$$

Example 4. Simplify $(x^5)^3$.

$$(x^5)^3 = x^{5 \cdot 3} \qquad \text{(Law 5)}$$
$$= x^{15}$$

Example 5. Simplify $(3x^2y)^2$.

$$(3x^2y)^2 = (3)^2(x^2)^2(y)^2$$
$$= 9x^4y^2 \qquad \text{(Law 6)}$$

Example 6. Simplify $\left(\dfrac{3x}{2y}\right)^2$.

$$\left(\frac{3x}{2y}\right)^2 = \frac{(3x)^2}{(2y)^2} \qquad \text{(Law 7)}$$

$$= \frac{3^2 \cdot x^2}{2^2 \cdot y^2} \qquad \text{(Law 6)}$$

$$= \frac{9x^2}{4y^2}$$

Example 7. Simplify $2x^2y^0$.

Observe that only the factor y is affected by the zero exponent. Then

$$2x^2y^0 = 2x^2 \cdot 1$$
$$= 2x^2$$

Example 8. Simplify $3(xy)^0$.

In this problem the product of x and y represents a number and that number is to the zero power. Then

$$3(xy)^0 = 3 \cdot 1$$
$$= 3$$

This problem could also be worked by using Law 6. Then

$$3(xy)^0 = 3 \cdot x^0 \cdot y^0$$
$$= 3 \cdot 1 \cdot 1$$
$$= 3$$

EXERCISE 56

A

Simplify the following:

1. $a^2 \cdot a^3$ 2. $y^5 \cdot y^2$ 3. $b \cdot b^3$

4. $2^2 \cdot 2$ 5. $4^2 \cdot 4^2$ 6. $3^2 \cdot 3^2$

7. $y^3 \cdot y^2 \cdot y$ 8. $b^4 \cdot b^4 \cdot b$ 9. $2^2 \cdot 2^3 \cdot 2^4$

10. $\dfrac{d^5}{d}$ 11. $\dfrac{x^4}{x^2}$ 12. $\dfrac{y^5}{y^3}$

13. $\dfrac{a^2b^2}{a}$ 14. $\dfrac{x^3y^3}{xy}$ 15. $\dfrac{m^5n^3}{m^2n^2}$

16. x^0 17. $3y^0$ 18. $(5d)^0$

19. $(a^2)^3$ 20. $(x^2)^5$ 21. $(mn)^2$

22. $(ab^2c)^2$ 23. $(2x^2y^2)^3$ 24. $(m^2n^2p^3)^3$

25. $\left(\dfrac{b^2}{c}\right)^2$ 26. $\left(\dfrac{x^2}{y^2}\right)^3$ 27. $\left(\dfrac{2m}{n^2}\right)^2$

B

Simplify the following:

1. $3(a)^0$ 2. xy^0z^2 3. 7^0

4. $(3x^0y^4)^2$ 5. $(c^2d^4)^3$ 6. $3(mn^2)^2$

7. $\left(\dfrac{3a^2}{b^3}\right)^2$ 8. $\left(\dfrac{2r^2s}{3t^2}\right)^2$ 9. $\left(\dfrac{c^2d}{a^3}\right)^4$

10. $\left(\dfrac{m^0n^2}{p}\right)^3$ 11. $\left(\dfrac{2ab^2}{c^2d}\right)^3$ 12. $\left(\dfrac{xy^2z^3}{m^2}\right)^4$

59. NEGATIVE AND FRACTIONAL EXPONENTS

In scientific and technical pursuits we frequently find it either necessary or convenient to work with negative exponents.

Law 3, stating that $x^m/x^n = x^{m-n}$, applies even when n is larger than m ($x \neq 0$, of course). Thus $x/x^2 = x^{1-2} = x^{-1}$. Also $x/x^2 = 1/x$ by dividing both the numerator and denominator by x.

Now we have two expressions, x^{-1} and $1/x$, both equal to the same expression, x/x^2. From this dual interpretation we state, by definition, that $x^{-m} = 1/x^m$.

The above definition then states that any quantity with a negative exponent may be written as the reciprocal of that quantity with the sign of the exponent changed to a positive value. (The *reciprocal* of any number is a number that when multiplied by the given number is equal to 1.) Thus any *factor* in the numerator of a fraction may be moved to the denominator of the fraction if the sign of the exponent is changed. Likewise, any *factor* in the denominator of a fraction may be moved to the numerator if the sign of the exponent is changed. This rule holds true only for *factors*. No *term* in the numerator or denominator of a fraction can be so interchanged.

Example 1. Simplify $x^3 \cdot x^{-2}$.

$$x^3 \cdot x^{-2} = x^{3+(-2)} = x^{3-2} = x$$

Example 2. Simplify $\dfrac{x^5}{x^{-2}}$.

$$\frac{x^5}{x^{-2}} = x^{5-(-2)} = x^{5+2} = x^7$$

This problem could, of course, be worked as follows:

$$\frac{x^5}{x^{-2}} = x^5 \cdot x^2 = x^7$$

Example 3. Simplify $\dfrac{x^{-2}}{x^{-2}}$.

$$\frac{x^{-2}}{x^{-2}} = x^{-2-(-2)} = x^{-2+2} = x^0 = 1$$

Example 4. Simplify $(x^{-2})^{-2}$.

$$(x^{-2})^{-2} = x^4$$

Example 5. Simplify $\left(\dfrac{x^{-2}y}{z^{-1}}\right)^{-3}$.

$$\left(\frac{x^{-2}y}{z^{-1}}\right)^{-3} = \frac{x^6 y^{-3}}{z^3} = \frac{x^6}{y^3 z^3}$$

Example 6. Simplify $\left(\dfrac{m^{-2}}{n^3}\right)^{-2}$.

$$\left(\frac{m^{-2}}{n^3}\right)^{-2} = \frac{m^4}{n^{-6}} = m^4 n^6$$

We introduced the radical symbol ($\sqrt{\ }$) in a previous discussion and roots of numbers in Section 29.

If a represents a number and n is any positive integer such that $a^n = b$, then a is known as the nth root of b. Thus if $a^n = b$, then $a = \sqrt[n]{b}$. Previously we stated that there were two square roots of a number. For example, $\sqrt{25}$ is either 5 or -5. For any positive number that has rational nth roots, we obtain *two* rational nth roots if n is an even number. Thus

$\sqrt[4]{16}$ has the two rational nth roots 2 and -2, and $\sqrt[6]{64}$ has the two rational nth roots 2 and -2.

If the radicand (the number under the radical) is positive and n is an odd number and there are any rational nth roots, there will be only *one* such rational nth root and it will be positive. Thus $\sqrt[3]{27} = 3$. If the radicand is a negative number and n is an odd number and there are any rational nth roots, there will be only *one* such rational nth root and it will be negative. Thus $\sqrt[3]{-27} = -3$.

The problem now arises as to how we shall define $x^{1/n}$ so that our laws of exponents will apply to fractional exponents. If $x^{1/2} \cdot x^{1/2} = x$ (x any positive number), then Law 2 for multiplication of like bases holds true. From our previous discussion we recall that one of two identical factors is the square root of the product of those factors. Thus $x^{1/2}$ is the square root of x, or $x^{1/2} = \sqrt{x}$. In a similar manner, $x^{1/3}$ is one of the three identical factors of $x^{1/3} \cdot x^{1/3} \cdot x^{1/3}$ and their product is x. Hence $x^{1/3} = \sqrt[3]{x}$.

In general, then, we define

$$x^{1/n} = \sqrt[n]{x}$$

This definition holds when x is positive and n is either even or odd and when x is negative and n is odd. In a later discussion we shall consider the case in which x is negative and n is even.

What meaning, then, should we give an expression such as $\sqrt[n]{x^2}$? Before continuing with this, let us consider a special case, $27^{2/3}$. If Law 5 is to hold true for this problem, then

$$
\begin{aligned}
27^{2/3} &= (27^2)^{1/3} \\
&= (729)^{1/3} \\
&= 9 \qquad \text{(from our table of powers} \\
& \text{and roots, p. 350)}
\end{aligned}
$$

A second approach to this problem provides an easier solution, one that will not require the use of a table of powers and roots. Thus

$$
\begin{aligned}
27^{2/3} &= (27^{1/3})^2 \\
&= (3)^2 \\
&= 9
\end{aligned}
$$

Then for x any real number and m/n a rational number ($n > 0$), we define

$$x^{m/n} = \sqrt[n]{x^m}$$

or

$$x^{m/n} = (\sqrt[n]{x})^m$$

This means, then, that when a fractional exponent is shown, the numerator of that fraction implies the power of the base (x in the above case) and the denominator indicates what root is to be found.

Example 7. Write the expression $x^{1/4}$ in radical form.

$$x^{1/4} = \sqrt[4]{x}$$

Example 8. Write the expression $m^{2/3}$ in radical form.

$$m^{2/3} = \sqrt[3]{m^2}$$

Example 9. Simplify $8^{1/3}$.

$$8^{1/3} = \sqrt[3]{8}$$
$$= 2$$

Example 10. Simplify $64^{2/3}$.

$$64^{2/3} = (64^{1/3})^2$$
$$= (4)^2$$
$$= 16$$

Example 11. Simplify $(z^{1/2}y^{1/3})^6$.

$$(z^{1/2}y^{1/3})^6 = z^{6/2}y^{6/3}$$
$$= z^3y^2$$

EXERCISE 57

A

Change all of the following expressions to ones that contain only positive exponents:

1. b^{-3}
2. $\dfrac{1}{m^{-4}}$
3. 2^{-3}
4. $\dfrac{a}{b^{-3}}$

5. $\dfrac{c^{-1}}{d}$
6. $\dfrac{r^2s^{-1}}{3}$
7. $\dfrac{xy^{-1}}{z}$
8. $\dfrac{m^{-1}}{n^{-2}}$

9. $\dfrac{3a^{-2}}{b}$
10. $\dfrac{(4b)^{-2}}{c}$
11. $\dfrac{x^{-1}y^{-2}}{z^{-1}}$
12. $\dfrac{ab^{-2}}{c^{-1}}$

13. $\dfrac{m^{-2}p^{-3}}{n^{-4}}$
14. $\dfrac{2b^{-4}}{c^{-2}}$
15. $\dfrac{2^{-2}r^2t^{-2}}{s}$

Simplify:

16. $d^{-2} \cdot d^5$
17. $2^{-3} \cdot 2^8$
18. $m^4 \cdot m^{-3}$
19. $\dfrac{y^4}{y^{-1}}$

20. $\dfrac{ab^{-2}}{a^{-1}b^{-5}}$ **21.** $\dfrac{2^{-3}r^{-1}}{2^{-4}r^3}$ **22.** $\dfrac{x^0y^{-2}}{x^{-3}}$ **23.** $\dfrac{2^0m^{-1}}{m^2}$

24. $\dfrac{4x^{-3}y^2}{2^2x^{-1}y^{-1}}$ **25.** $(a^{-2}b)^{-2}$ **26.** $x\left(\dfrac{y^{-1}}{3^{-1}}\right)^{-2}$ **27.** $\left(\dfrac{m^2n^{-1}}{a^{-2}}\right)^{-2}$

28. $(4^0b^2)^{-1}$ **29.** $(x^{-1}z^2)^3$ **30.** $(mn^{-1}p^{-3})^2$ **31.** $125^{2/3}$

32. $(-8)^{2/3}$ **33.** $32^{2/5}$ **34.** $81^{3/4}$ **35.** $(-8)^{4/3}$

B

Simplify:

1. $(y^{1/4})^4$ **2.** $(a^{1/2})^2$ **3.** $(d^{1/3})^6$ **4.** $(m^{2/3})^3$

5. $(r^{1/2})^6$ **6.** $(y^{2/3})^6$ **7.** $(t^{1/4})^8$ **8.** $(z^{1/3})^{12}$

9. $(w^{1/2}v^{1/3})^6$ **10.** $(a^{1/4}b^{1/2})^4$ **11.** $(c^{1/3}d^{2/3})^3$ **12.** $(x^{2/3}y^{1/2})^6$

13. $(m^2d^4)^{1/2}$ **14.** $(r^3s^9)^{1/3}$ **15.** $(x^8y^4)^{1/4}$ **16.** $(a^3b^6)^{2/3}$

Write the following with radicals:

17. $m^{3/4}$ **18.** $y^{3/2}$ **19.** $a^{2/3}$ **20.** $c^{1/4}$

21. $x^{1/2}y^{3/4}$ **22.** $m^{1/3}n^{2/3}$ **23.** $3a^{1/2}$ **24.** $2b^{2/3}$

Write each of the following in a form involving a fractional exponent (assume that all letters under the radical symbol are positive numbers):

25. $\sqrt{a}$ **26.** $\sqrt[3]{b}$ **27.** $\sqrt[4]{m}$ **28.** $\sqrt[3]{x^2}$

29. $\sqrt[3]{ab^2}$ **30.** $\sqrt{ab^2}$ **31.** $\sqrt{x^4y^2z^4}$ **32.** $\sqrt[3]{a^2bc^2}$

33. $\sqrt[4]{abc^2}$ **34.** $\sqrt[4]{a^4b^2c^8}$ **35.** $\sqrt[3]{8a^2}$ **36.** $\sqrt{16m^4}$

60. MULTIPLICATION OF RADICALS

From Law 6, Section 58, we found that $(xy)^m = x^my^m$. Hence any two or more factors raised to the same power may be multiplied together and their product raised to the same power. Then $3^{1/2} \cdot 6^{1/2} = (3 \cdot 6)^{1/2} = 18^{1/2}$. If we change $3^{1/2} \cdot 6^{1/2}$ to the form $\sqrt{3} \cdot \sqrt{6}$, then we get $\sqrt{18}$ and this can be simplified as follows:

$$\sqrt{3} \cdot \sqrt{6} = \sqrt{18}$$
$$= \sqrt{9 \cdot 2}$$
$$= 3\sqrt{2}$$

This procedure can be used only if the indices of the radicals involved are alike.

To multiply two or more radicals with like indices, use the following rule:

Rule 1. *To multiply two or more radicals with like indices, first multiply their coefficients to obtain the coefficient of the product. Then multiply the radicands to get the radicand of the product. Finally, simplify the radicand if possible. Both radicands must be positive numbers.*

Example 1. Multiply $\sqrt{18} \cdot \sqrt{2}$.

$$\sqrt{18} \cdot \sqrt{2} = \sqrt{36}$$
$$= 6$$

Example 2. Multiply $2\sqrt{32} \cdot 3\sqrt{2}$.

$$2\sqrt{32} \cdot 3\sqrt{2} = 6\sqrt{64}$$
$$= 6 \cdot 8$$
$$= 48$$

Example 3. Multiply $5\sqrt{2} \cdot 2\sqrt{6}$.

$$5\sqrt{2} \cdot 2\sqrt{6} = 10\sqrt{12}$$
$$= 10\sqrt{4 \cdot 3}$$
$$= 10 \cdot 2\sqrt{3}$$
$$= 20\sqrt{3}$$

Example 4. Multiply $3\sqrt{2} \cdot \sqrt{6} \cdot 2\sqrt{5}$.

$$3\sqrt{2} \cdot \sqrt{6} \cdot 2\sqrt{5} = 6\sqrt{60}$$
$$= 6\sqrt{4 \cdot 15}$$
$$= 6 \cdot 2\sqrt{15}$$
$$= 12\sqrt{15}$$

Example 5. Multiply $\sqrt[3]{2} \cdot 3\sqrt[3]{4}$.

$$\sqrt[3]{2} \cdot 3\sqrt[3]{4} = 3\sqrt[3]{8}$$
$$= 3 \cdot 2$$
$$= 6$$

Example 6. Multiply $3\sqrt[3]{3} \cdot \sqrt[3]{4} \cdot 2\sqrt[3]{6}$.

$$3\sqrt[3]{3} \cdot \sqrt[3]{4} \cdot 2\sqrt[3]{6} = 6\sqrt[3]{72}$$
$$= 6\sqrt[3]{8 \cdot 9}$$
$$= 6 \cdot 2\sqrt[3]{9}$$
$$= 12\sqrt[3]{9}$$

A

Simplify:

1. $\sqrt{50} \cdot \sqrt{2}$

2. $\sqrt{72} \cdot \sqrt{2}$

3. $\sqrt{27} \cdot \sqrt{3}$

4. $\sqrt{5} \cdot \sqrt{5}$

5. $3\sqrt{18} \cdot \sqrt{2}$

6. $2\sqrt{12} \cdot 4\sqrt{3}$

7. $\frac{1}{2}\sqrt{8} \cdot 4\sqrt{8}$

8. $\frac{2}{3}\sqrt{12} \cdot 6\sqrt{3}$

9. $\sqrt{10} \cdot \sqrt{5}$

10. $\sqrt{6} \cdot \sqrt{8}$

11. $2\sqrt{3} \cdot 3\sqrt{5}$

12. $4\sqrt{15} \cdot 3\sqrt{6}$

13. $4\sqrt{6} \cdot 2\sqrt{12}$

14. $7\sqrt{8} \cdot 3\sqrt{7}$

15. $a\sqrt{a} \cdot b\sqrt{a}$

16. $\sqrt{2} \cdot 3\sqrt{5} \cdot 2\sqrt{6}$

17. $\sqrt{3} \cdot 2\sqrt{6} \cdot 3\sqrt{8}$

18. $4\sqrt{10} \cdot 2\sqrt{2} \cdot 3\sqrt{5}$

B

Simplify:

1. $\sqrt{6} \cdot \sqrt{5} \cdot 3\sqrt{10}$

2. $5\sqrt{15} \cdot 2\sqrt{6} \cdot 4\sqrt{2}$

3. $\sqrt[3]{16} \cdot \sqrt[3]{4}$

4. $\sqrt[3]{4} \cdot \sqrt[3]{10}$

5. $2\sqrt[3]{6} \cdot \sqrt[3]{9}$

6. $3\sqrt[3]{3} \cdot 2\sqrt[3]{3} \cdot \sqrt[3]{9}$

7. $\sqrt[3]{25} \cdot \sqrt[3]{2} \cdot 3\sqrt[3]{5}$

61. SIMPLIFICATION OF RADICALS

A *radical* is the sign or symbol used to indicate the root of a number.

The *index* (*indices* if plural) of a root is the number with the symbol ($\sqrt[3]{8}$, $\sqrt[4]{16}$, $\sqrt[5]{32}$) to specify which root is to be taken. If no number is outside the radical, as the 3, 4, and 5 above, it is understood that square root is required. The 3 asks for cube root, the 4 for the fourth root, and the 5 for the fifth root of the number under the radical, called the *radicand*.

The radicand should be simplified if possible. An expression involving radicals is in simplest form if it meets the following four conditions:

a. There is no prime factor under the radical whose exponent is equal to or larger than the index.
b. The index is the smallest possible positive integer.
c. There are no fractions under the radical.
d. There are no radicals in the denominator.

To simplify a radical, factor the radicand, if possible, into two factors, one of which can be removed from under the radical. The part that is removed becomes a factor of the expression or may be considered the coefficient of the remaining radical. The following examples illustrate this process:

Example 1. Simplify $\sqrt{32}$.

We cannot get an integral square root of 32, but we can of 16. As 16 is a factor of 32, the following form is used:

$$\sqrt{32} = \sqrt{16 \cdot 2}$$
$$= \sqrt{16} \cdot \sqrt{2}$$
$$= 4\sqrt{2}$$

Example 2. Simplify $2\sqrt[3]{24}$.

$$2\sqrt[3]{24} = 2\sqrt[3]{8 \cdot 3}$$
$$= 2\sqrt[3]{8} \cdot \sqrt[3]{3}$$
$$= 2 \cdot 2 \cdot \sqrt[3]{3}$$
$$= 4\sqrt[3]{3}$$

Example 3. Simplify $\sqrt[4]{a^2}$.

If we wrote this using fractional exponents, we would have $a^{2/4}$. The fractional exponent can be reduced to $\frac{1}{2}$. Hence $a^{2/4} = a^{1/2}$. Then

$$\sqrt[4]{a^2} = a^{2/4}$$
$$= a^{1/2}$$
$$= \sqrt{a}$$

Example 4. Simplify $3\sqrt[6]{16}$.

$$3\sqrt[6]{16} = 3\sqrt[6]{4^2}$$
$$= 3 \cdot 4^{2/6}$$
$$= 3 \cdot 4^{1/3}$$
$$= 3\sqrt[3]{4}$$

Example 5. Simplify $\sqrt{\dfrac{5}{2}}$.

$$\sqrt{\frac{5}{2}} = \left(\frac{5}{2}\right)^{1/2}$$

$$= \frac{5^{1/2}}{2^{1/2}} \qquad \text{(Law 7)}$$

$$= \frac{\sqrt{5}}{\sqrt{2}}$$

The value of a fraction is unchanged if both the numerator and denominator are multiplied by the same value. Then

$$\frac{\sqrt{5}}{\sqrt{2}} = \frac{\sqrt{5}}{\sqrt{2}} \cdot \frac{\sqrt{2}}{\sqrt{2}}$$

$$= \frac{\sqrt{5 \cdot 2}}{\sqrt{2 \cdot 2}}$$

$$= \frac{\sqrt{10}}{\sqrt{4}}$$

$$= \frac{\sqrt{10}}{2}$$

Example 5 shows the method for eliminating a radical in the denominator, called *rationalizing* the denominator. Always select a number to multiply times both numerator and denominator to produce a value in the denominator that has an integral root specified by the index. This method is used only when there is one term in the denominator. The method used for removing binomials consisting of radicals is explained later in this chapter.

Example 6. Simplify $\sqrt{75}$.

$$\sqrt{75} = \sqrt{25 \cdot 3}$$
$$= 5\sqrt{3}$$

Example 7. Simplify $\sqrt{18x^3y^5}$.

$$\sqrt{18x^3y^5} = \sqrt{9x^2y^4 \cdot 2xy}$$
$$= 3xy^2\sqrt{2xy}$$

In Example 7 we do not know whether the letters under the radical represent positive or negative numbers when the exponents are even numbers. In this text we shall assume that they represent positive numbers. A subsequent course in algebra will extend the discussion of radicals to include such letters as representing negative numbers as well as positive numbers.

A

Simplify:

1. $\sqrt{50}$ 　　2. $\sqrt{48}$ 　　3. $\sqrt{27}$ 　　4. $\sqrt{72}$

5. $\sqrt{98}$ 　　6. $\sqrt{8}$ 　　7. $\sqrt{18}$ 　　8. $\sqrt{32}$

9. $\sqrt{128}$ 　　10. $\sqrt{200}$ 　　11. $\sqrt{12}$ 　　12. $\sqrt{75}$

13. $\sqrt{20}$ 　　14. $\sqrt{28}$ 　　15. $\sqrt[3]{16}$ 　　16. $\sqrt[3]{24}$

17. $\sqrt[3]{54}$ 　　18. $\sqrt[3]{72}$ 　　19. $\sqrt[3]{56}$ 　　20. $\sqrt[3]{80}$

21. $\sqrt[3]{128}$ 　　22. $\sqrt[4]{4}$ 　　23. $\sqrt[4]{9}$ 　　24. $\sqrt[3]{25}$

25. $\sqrt[6]{8}$ 　　26. $\sqrt[6]{16}$ 　　27. $\sqrt[6]{9}$ 　　28. $\sqrt[4]{49}$

29. $\sqrt[8]{81}$ 　　30. $\sqrt[6]{100}$ 　　31. $\sqrt[8]{64}$ 　　32. $\sqrt[8]{16}$

B

Simplify the following, assuming that all letters under the radical represent positive numbers:

1. $\sqrt[6]{144}$ 　　2. $\sqrt{\frac{3}{4}}$ 　　3. $\sqrt{\frac{3}{2}}$ 　　4. $\sqrt{\frac{5}{8}}$

5. $\sqrt{\frac{1}{3}}$ 　　6. $\sqrt{\frac{2}{3}}$ 　　7. $2\sqrt{\frac{2}{9}}$ 　　8. $2\sqrt{\frac{3}{2}}$

9. $\sqrt[3]{\frac{1}{2}}$ 　　10. $\sqrt[3]{\frac{2}{9}}$ 　　11. $\sqrt[3]{\frac{1}{4}}$ 　　12. $\sqrt[3]{\frac{5}{2}}$

13. $4\sqrt[3]{\frac{1}{2}}$ 　　14. $\sqrt{50x^2y^3}$ 　　15. $\sqrt{8m^5n^7}$ 　　16. $\sqrt{32c^4d^5}$

17. $\sqrt{48xy^5}$ 　　18. $\sqrt{98r^2st^2}$ 　　19. $\sqrt{72y^8z^3}$ 　　20. $\sqrt[3]{16x^3y^5}$

21. $\sqrt[3]{24m^2n^6}$ 　　22. $\sqrt[3]{54c^4d^4}$ 　　23. $2\sqrt[3]{32a^4b^7}$

62. ADDITION AND SUBTRACTION OF RADICALS

Only similar radicals can be combined by addition or subtraction. Radicals are similar if their indices and radicands are identical. Thus $\sqrt[3]{4}$, $3\sqrt[3]{4}$, and $5\sqrt[3]{4}$ are similar radicals.

The numerical factor preceding a radical is the coefficient of the radical. If no coefficient is indicated, it is assumed to be 1. Similar radicals may be added and subtracted by combining their coefficients as any similar terms may be combined. Thus $3\sqrt{2} + 5\sqrt{2} = 8\sqrt{2}$.

Example 1. Simplify $4\sqrt{2} - 3\sqrt{2}$.

$$4\sqrt{2} - 3\sqrt{2} = \sqrt{2}$$

Example 2. Simplify $\sqrt{5} + 6\sqrt{5} - 2\sqrt{5}$.

$$\sqrt{5} + 6\sqrt{5} - 2\sqrt{5} = 5\sqrt{5}$$

Example 3. Simplify $\sqrt[3]{2} - 5\sqrt[3]{2} + 3\sqrt[3]{2}$.

$$\sqrt[3]{2} - 5\sqrt[3]{2} + 3\sqrt[3]{2} = -\sqrt[3]{2}$$

Radicals that are not similar may sometimes be converted into similar radicals by the method developed in Section 61.

Example 4. Simplify $\sqrt{3} + \sqrt{12}$.

$$\begin{aligned}
\sqrt{3} + \sqrt{12} &= \sqrt{3} + \sqrt{4 \cdot 3} \\
&= \sqrt{3} + 2\sqrt{3} \\
&= 3\sqrt{3}
\end{aligned}$$

Example 5. Simplify $\sqrt{2} - \sqrt{8} + \sqrt{32}$.

$$\begin{aligned}
\sqrt{2} - \sqrt{8} + \sqrt{32} &= \sqrt{2} - \sqrt{4 \cdot 2} + \sqrt{16 \cdot 2} \\
&= \sqrt{2} - 2\sqrt{2} + 4\sqrt{2} \\
&= 3\sqrt{2}
\end{aligned}$$

EXERCISE 60

A

Simplify:

1. $\sqrt{12} + \sqrt{27}$ 2. $\sqrt{8} + \sqrt{72}$
3. $3\sqrt{2} + \sqrt{50}$ 4. $6\sqrt{12} - \sqrt{75}$
5. $\sqrt{20} + \sqrt{45}$ 6. $\sqrt{28} + \sqrt{63}$

7. $\sqrt{24} - \sqrt{54}$

8. $\sqrt{40} - \sqrt{10}$

9. $\sqrt[3]{3} + \sqrt[3]{24}$

10. $\sqrt[3]{2} + \sqrt[3]{16}$

11. $\sqrt[3]{32} - \sqrt[3]{108}$

12. $3\sqrt[3]{3} - \sqrt[3]{24}$

13. $\sqrt[3]{125} + 3\sqrt[3]{27}$

14. $7\sqrt[3]{54} - 2\sqrt[3]{16}$

B

Simplify:

1. $\sqrt{2} + \sqrt{32} - \sqrt{18}$

2. $\sqrt{12} + \sqrt{75} - \sqrt{48}$

3. $\sqrt{98} + \sqrt{72} - \sqrt{50}$

4. $\sqrt{200} - \sqrt{128} - \sqrt{32}$

5. $\sqrt{300} + \sqrt{27} - \sqrt{108}$

6. $\sqrt{20} + \sqrt{80} - \sqrt{45}$

7. $3\sqrt{24} - \sqrt{54} - \sqrt{150}$

8. $\sqrt{40} + 3\sqrt{160} - 4\sqrt{90}$

9. $\sqrt[3]{16} + \sqrt[3]{54} + \sqrt[3]{128}$

10. $3\sqrt[3]{24} - \sqrt[3]{81} + \sqrt[3]{375}$

11. $3\sqrt[3]{5} + \sqrt[3]{135} - \sqrt[3]{40}$

63. DIVISION OF RADICALS

Law 7, developed in Section 58, stated that $\left(\dfrac{x}{y}\right)^m = \dfrac{x^m}{y^m}.$ That law holds true for all exponents. Hence $\dfrac{x^{1/2}}{y^{1/2}} = \left(\dfrac{x}{y}\right)^{1/2}.$ If we substitute radicals for the fractional exponents, we get $\dfrac{\sqrt{x}}{\sqrt{y}}$ or $\sqrt{\dfrac{x}{y}}.$ Then the following rule applies to the division of radicals.

Rule 2. *The quotient of the roots of two numbers equals the indicated root of the quotient of the two numbers.*

Example 1. Simplify $\dfrac{\sqrt{18}}{\sqrt{2}}.$

$$\frac{\sqrt{18}}{\sqrt{2}} = \sqrt{\frac{18}{2}}$$
$$= \sqrt{9}$$
$$= 3$$

Example 2. Simplify $\dfrac{\sqrt{75}}{\sqrt{3}}$.

$$\frac{\sqrt{75}}{\sqrt{3}} = \sqrt{\frac{75}{3}}$$
$$= \sqrt{25}$$
$$= 5$$

Example 3. Simplify $\dfrac{6\sqrt{48}}{2\sqrt{3}}$.

$$\frac{6\sqrt{48}}{2\sqrt{3}} = \frac{6}{2}\sqrt{\frac{48}{3}}$$
$$= 3\sqrt{16}$$
$$= 3 \cdot 4$$
$$= 12$$

Example 4. Simplify $\dfrac{\sqrt[3]{24}}{\sqrt[3]{3}}$.

$$\frac{\sqrt[3]{24}}{\sqrt[3]{3}} = \sqrt[3]{\frac{24}{3}}$$
$$= \sqrt[3]{8}$$
$$= 2$$

Example 5. Simplify $\dfrac{12\sqrt[3]{36}}{3\sqrt[3]{3}}$.

$$\frac{12\sqrt[3]{36}}{3\sqrt[3]{3}} = \frac{12}{3}\sqrt[3]{\frac{36}{3}}$$
$$= 4\sqrt[3]{12}$$

When the radicand of the denominator is not an integral factor of the radicand of the numerator, the denominator is rationalized, as explained in Section 61.

Example 6. Simplify $\dfrac{4\sqrt{5}}{\sqrt{2}}$.

$$\frac{4\sqrt{5}}{\sqrt{2}} = \frac{4\sqrt{5}}{\sqrt{2}} \cdot \frac{\sqrt{2}}{\sqrt{2}}$$

$$= \frac{4\sqrt{10}}{\sqrt{4}}$$

$$= \frac{4\sqrt{10}}{2}$$

$$= 2\sqrt{10}$$

Example 7. Simplify $\dfrac{\sqrt[3]{9}}{\sqrt[3]{2}}$.

$$\frac{\sqrt[3]{9}}{\sqrt[3]{2}} = \frac{\sqrt[3]{9}}{\sqrt[3]{2}} \cdot \frac{\sqrt[3]{4}}{\sqrt[3]{4}}$$

$$= \frac{\sqrt[3]{36}}{\sqrt[3]{8}}$$

$$= \frac{\sqrt[3]{36}}{2}$$

$$= \tfrac{1}{2}\sqrt[3]{36}$$

Sometimes it is necessary to rationalize a binomial denominator. That binomial may be made up of a rational term and an irrational term or of two irrational terms. The irrational terms are called *surds* if the radicand is a rational expression. A *binomial surd* is an expression of two terms, one or both of which are surds. *Conjugate binomial surds* are two binomial surds of the second order (ones whose indices are 2 or ones indicating that the square root is to be found) that are exactly alike except that their second terms have opposite signs. The following are examples of conjugate binomial surds: $1 + \sqrt{2}$ and $1 - \sqrt{2}$, $\sqrt{a} - \sqrt{b}$ and $\sqrt{a} + \sqrt{b}$, $\sqrt{3} - 1$ and $\sqrt{3} + 1$.

The product of a pair of binomial surds is a rational number. Consider the following problem: $(1 - 3\sqrt{2})(1 + 3\sqrt{2})$.

$$
\begin{array}{r}
1 - 3\sqrt{2} \\
1 + 3\sqrt{2} \\
\hline
1 - 3\sqrt{2} \\
+ 3\sqrt{2} - 9\sqrt{4} \\
\hline
1 \qquad - 9\sqrt{4}
\end{array}
$$

$$1 - 9\sqrt{4} = 1 - (9 \cdot 2) = 1 - 18 = -17$$

To rationalize a denominator consisting of a binomial surd, multiply both the numerator and denominator of the fraction by the conjugate of the denominator.

Example 8. Simplify $\dfrac{1}{\sqrt{2}+1}$.

$$\frac{1}{\sqrt{2}+1} = \frac{1}{\sqrt{2}+1} \cdot \frac{\sqrt{2}-1}{\sqrt{2}-1}$$

$$= \frac{\sqrt{2}-1}{2-1}$$

$$= \frac{\sqrt{2}-1}{1}$$

$$= \sqrt{2}-1$$

Example 9. Simplify $\dfrac{4}{2-\sqrt{2}}$.

$$\frac{4}{2-\sqrt{2}} = \frac{4}{2-\sqrt{2}} \cdot \frac{2+\sqrt{2}}{2+\sqrt{2}}$$

$$= \frac{4(2+\sqrt{2})}{4-2}$$

$$= \frac{4(2+\sqrt{2})}{2}$$

$$= 2(2+\sqrt{2})$$
$$= 4 + 2\sqrt{2}$$

Example 10. Simplify $\dfrac{\sqrt{2}-1}{\sqrt{5}-\sqrt{2}}$.

$$\frac{\sqrt{2}-1}{\sqrt{5}-\sqrt{2}} = \frac{\sqrt{2}-1}{\sqrt{5}-\sqrt{2}} \cdot \frac{\sqrt{5}+\sqrt{2}}{\sqrt{5}+\sqrt{2}}$$

$$= \frac{\sqrt{10}+\sqrt{4}-\sqrt{5}-\sqrt{2}}{5-2}$$

$$= \frac{2+\sqrt{10}-\sqrt{5}-\sqrt{2}}{3}$$

A

Simplify:

1. $\dfrac{\sqrt{72}}{\sqrt{2}}$

2. $\dfrac{\sqrt{300}}{\sqrt{3}}$

3. $\dfrac{\sqrt[3]{16}}{\sqrt[3]{2}}$

4. $\dfrac{\sqrt[3]{81}}{\sqrt[3]{3}}$

5. $\dfrac{\sqrt[3]{375}}{\sqrt[3]{3}}$

6. $\dfrac{\sqrt{147}}{\sqrt{3}}$

7. $\dfrac{\sqrt{72}}{\sqrt{3}}$

8. $\dfrac{\sqrt{60}}{\sqrt{3}}$

9. $\dfrac{2\sqrt{80}}{\sqrt{5}}$

10. $\dfrac{3\sqrt{32}}{\sqrt{8}}$

11. $\dfrac{5\sqrt{56}}{\sqrt{7}}$

12. $\dfrac{15\sqrt{18}}{3\sqrt{6}}$

13. $\dfrac{4\sqrt{40}}{2\sqrt{5}}$

14. $\dfrac{3\sqrt{96}}{2\sqrt{3}}$

15. $\dfrac{\sqrt{84}}{3\sqrt{7}}$

B

Simplify:

1. $\dfrac{2\sqrt[3]{32}}{\sqrt[3]{4}}$

2. $\dfrac{3\sqrt[3]{56}}{\sqrt[3]{14}}$

3. $\dfrac{5\sqrt[3]{88}}{\sqrt[3]{11}}$

4. $\dfrac{4\sqrt[3]{128}}{\sqrt[3]{4}}$

5. $\dfrac{2\sqrt[3]{108}}{\sqrt[3]{4}}$

6. $\dfrac{5\sqrt[3]{81}}{3\sqrt[3]{3}}$

7. $\dfrac{\sqrt{7}}{\sqrt{3}}$

8. $\dfrac{\sqrt{15}}{\sqrt{6}}$

9. $\dfrac{\sqrt{32}}{\sqrt{3}}$

10. $\dfrac{\sqrt{11}}{\sqrt{2}}$

11. $\dfrac{\sqrt{27}}{\sqrt{2}}$

12. $\dfrac{\sqrt[3]{5}}{\sqrt[3]{2}}$

13. $\dfrac{\sqrt[3]{24}}{\sqrt[3]{9}}$

14. $\dfrac{\sqrt[3]{16}}{\sqrt[3]{25}}$

15. $\dfrac{1}{\sqrt{5}+2}$

16. $\dfrac{5}{\sqrt{10}+3}$

17. $\dfrac{12}{\sqrt{7}-\sqrt{3}}$

18. $\dfrac{\sqrt{3}}{3-\sqrt{5}}$

19. $\dfrac{\sqrt{2}+\sqrt{3}}{\sqrt{3}-\sqrt{2}}$

20. $\dfrac{4-\sqrt{5}}{\sqrt{2}+\sqrt{6}}$

EXERCISE 62

A

Perform any indicated operations and simplify.

1. $\dfrac{x^3 z^5}{x^2 z^2}$

2. $(mn^2)^2$

3. $(abc)^0$

4. $\left(\dfrac{a^3 b^2}{3}\right)^2$

5. $\left(\dfrac{c^4 d^5}{cd^3}\right)^2$

6. $\left(\dfrac{m^4 n^2}{m^2 n}\right)^3$

7. $m^4 \cdot m^{-2}$

8. $3x^5 \cdot 2x^{-3}$

9. $8x^2 \cdot (2x)^{-2}$

10. $\dfrac{3x^{-5} y^3}{xy^{-2}}$

11. $(m^0 n^5)^{-2}$

12. $\left(\dfrac{a^{-3} b^2 c^{-5}}{d^2}\right)^{-2}$

13. $(d^{1/3} c^{2/3})^6$

14. $(r^{1/2} s^2)^4$

15. $(a^{1/2} b^{1/4})^4$

16. $3\sqrt{72}$

17. $5\sqrt{48}$

18. $\sqrt{196}$

19. $4\sqrt{80}$

20. $5\sqrt{125}$

21. $4\sqrt{108}$

B

Perform any indicated operations and simplify.

1. $\sqrt{8} \cdot \sqrt{3}$

2. $\sqrt{12} \cdot \sqrt{5}$

3. $\sqrt{15} \cdot \sqrt{5}$

4. $\sqrt{21} \cdot \sqrt{3}$

5. $\sqrt{7} \cdot \sqrt{8}$

6. $\dfrac{\sqrt{96}}{\sqrt{6}}$

7. $\dfrac{\sqrt{45}}{\sqrt{18}}$

8. $\dfrac{\sqrt{60}}{\sqrt{20}}$

9. $\dfrac{\sqrt{24}}{\sqrt{3}}$

10. $5\sqrt{3} + \sqrt{12} - \sqrt{27}$

11. $2\sqrt{5} + 3\sqrt{45} - \sqrt{245}$

12. $2\sqrt{18} + 5\sqrt{72} - 3\sqrt{32}$

13. $\sqrt{8} \cdot \sqrt{12} \cdot \sqrt{3}$

14. $\sqrt{2} \cdot \sqrt{5} \cdot \sqrt{6}$

15. $\sqrt{6} \cdot 3\sqrt{2} \cdot 5\sqrt{3}$

16. $\dfrac{2}{\sqrt{5} + \sqrt{3}}$

17. $\dfrac{\sqrt{3}}{\sqrt{6} - \sqrt{2}}$

18. $\dfrac{\sqrt{7}}{\sqrt{2} + \sqrt{5}}$

19. $\dfrac{\sqrt{5} - \sqrt{3}}{\sqrt{3} + \sqrt{2}}$

20. $\dfrac{\sqrt{2} + \sqrt{3}}{\sqrt{10} - \sqrt{5}}$

On a sheet of paper write the numbers 1 through 20 to correspond to those in the left-hand column below. After each number place the letter that corresponds to the correct answer in the right-hand column. Do not use any letter more than once.

1. $a^2b^3 \cdot ab^2$		a. $2a^2b$	
2. $4^0a^2b \cdot 3a^3b^2$		b. $2a^4b^4$	
3. $(a^4b^2)^{1/2}$		c. $\dfrac{a^2}{b^4}$	
4. $\dfrac{4a^2b}{2a^2b}$			
5. $2ab \cdot (ab)^0$		d. $2ab^2$	
		e. $6a^2b$	
6. $\dfrac{a^5b^4}{a^3b}$		f. a^3b^5	
7. $2a^2b^3 \cdot a^2b$		g. $2a^2b^2$	
8. $(8a^6b^3)^{1/3}$		h. $4a^4b^4$	
9. $(a^6b^6)^{2/3}$		i. 2	
10. $\left(\dfrac{a}{b^2}\right)^2$		j. $6a^2b^2$	
		k. $8a^4b^4$	
11. $(36a^4b^6)^{1/2}$		l. $12a^5b^3$	
12. $(a^2b)^3$		m. a^6b^3	
13. $\dfrac{12ab}{2a^{-1}b^{-1}}$		n. $6a^6b^9$	
14. $(ab^3)^0$		o. $2ab$	
		p. 1	
15. $\left(\dfrac{2a^2b^3}{ab}\right)^2$		q. a^4b^4	
		r. 6	
16. $6a^4b^5 \cdot a^{-2}b^{-4}$		s. a^2b^3	
17. $(4a^8b^6)^{1/2}$		t. $4a^2b^4$	
18. $(2^3a^6b^6)^{2/3}$		u. $2a^4b^3$	
19. $(2a^{1/3}b^{1/3})^3$		v. a^2b	
20. $\left(\dfrac{a^2b}{a^5b^4}\right)^{-1}$		w. a^3b^3	
		x. $3a^5b^3$	
		y. $8ab$	
		z. $6a^2b^3$	

On a sheet of paper write the numbers 1 through 15 to correspond to those in the left-hand column below. After each number place the letter that corresponds to the correct answer in the right-hand column. Do not use any letter more than once.

1. $\sqrt{80}$ a. $5\sqrt[3]{2}$

2. $5\sqrt{3} - \sqrt{3}$ b. $2\sqrt[3]{8}$

3. $\sqrt{18} - \sqrt{8}$ c. $\sqrt{10}$

4. $\sqrt[3]{54} + \sqrt[3]{16}$ d. 3

5. $\sqrt[3]{64}$ e. $-4\sqrt{2} - 6$

6. $3\sqrt{2} + \sqrt{32}$ f. $\sqrt{2}$

7. $2\sqrt[3]{4} \cdot \sqrt[3]{4}$ g. $\sqrt{3}$

8. $\sqrt{20} \cdot \sqrt{2}$ h. $7\sqrt{2}$

9. $\sqrt{\frac{1}{3}}$ i. $4\sqrt[3]{2}$

10. $\dfrac{\sqrt{18}}{\sqrt{2}}$ j. $4\sqrt{5}$

k. $3 + 2\sqrt{2}$

11. $\dfrac{\sqrt{108}}{\sqrt{3}}$ l. 5

m. $2\sqrt{10}$

12. $\sqrt{160}$ n. $\dfrac{\sqrt{3}}{3}$

13. $\dfrac{1}{1 - \sqrt{2}}$ o. $4\sqrt{3}$

14. $\dfrac{2}{2\sqrt{2} - 3}$ p. $-1 - \sqrt{2}$

q. 1

15. $\dfrac{\sqrt{2} + 1}{\sqrt{2} - 1}$ r. 6

s. 4

t. $4\sqrt{10}$

12

Quadratic Equations

64. DEFINITIONS

A *quadratic equation* is an equation that, if written in its simplest form, involves the second power of the variable but no higher power.

The general quadratic equation is in the form

$$ax^2 + bx + c = 0 \qquad (a \neq 0)$$

in which case x is the variable and a, b, and c are constants. In the above form we say that the equation is a *complete quadratic equation*. Hence the complete quadratic equation contains three terms, one term with the variable raised to the second power, the second in which the variable is to the first power, and the third consisting of a constant. These three terms, of course, constitute the left member of the equation. An *incomplete quadratic equation* is one in which either the term containing the variable to the first power or the one containing the constant is missing. The following are incomplete quadratic equations: $x^2 - 36 = 0$, $x^2 = 25$, and $x^2 + 3x = 0$.

271

65. SQUARE ROOT

Frequently, in order to solve a quadratic equation it is necessary to obtain the square root of some number. In our previous discussion we defined the square root of a number as one of two identical factors that when multiplied together give the original number.

From the multiplication combinations, we are familiar with certain square roots. Six is the square root of 36 since 6 times 6 gives 36, and 9 is the square root of 81 since 9 times 9 gives 81. We demonstrated earlier in our discussion that every positive integer has two square roots, one a positive value and the other a negative value. Thus the square root of 49 is either 7 or −7.

The square roots of certain numbers are large and beyond our scope of recognition. Others are not integers and involve decimal notation. Consequently, we must know how to find the square root of such numbers. A standard method for finding the square root of a number will be shown in the following discussion.

When finding the square root of a number, we know, of course, that we must have a number that when multiplied by itself will give the original number or a close approximation of it. In order to develop this method, we shall first consider a simple problem. Assume that we wish to find the square root of 256. If we divide any number by a second number, the product of that second number (the divisor) and the quotient (the answer obtained) will give us the original number (the dividend).

Let us divide the 256 by 4 and we obtain

$$
\begin{array}{r}
64 \\
4\overline{)256} \\
\underline{24} \\
16 \\
\underline{16}
\end{array}
$$

If the divisor and quotient were equal, we would have the square root of 256. It is obvious that 4 and 64 are widely separated numbers. The required number is between the 4 and 64. If we take one-half the sum of 4 and 64, we will have some number between them, or the average of them. Thus

$$
\begin{aligned}
\tfrac{1}{2}(4 + 64) &= \tfrac{1}{2}(68) \\
&= 34
\end{aligned}
$$

Then we repeat the above process by dividing 256 by 34 and obtain

$$\begin{array}{r}
7.5 \\
34\overline{)256.0} \\
238 \\
\hline
18\ 0 \\
17\ 0 \\
\hline
\end{array}$$

We need not be concerned with the fact that this does not come out even. Again, we find the average of the divisor and quotient and get

$$\tfrac{1}{2}(34 + 7.5) = \tfrac{1}{2}(41.5)$$
$$= 20.75$$

Let us use only the 20 as a divisor and we obtain

$$\begin{array}{r}
12 \\
20\overline{)256} \\
20 \\
\hline
56 \\
40 \\
\hline
\end{array}$$

Then one-half the average of 20 and 12 gives

$$\tfrac{1}{2}(20 + 12) = \tfrac{1}{2}(32)$$
$$= 16$$

Repeating the process, using 16 as a divisor, we have

$$\begin{array}{r}
16 \\
16\overline{)256} \\
16 \\
\hline
96 \\
96 \\
\hline
\end{array}$$

and both our divisor and quotient are equal with no remainder. Thus 16 is the square root of 256.

Let us, by the same method, find the square root of 3249.

Before attempting the computation, let us observe that we may sometimes reduce the number of trials needed to find the solution if we estimate approximately what the answer is to be. We can readily establish that the square of 50 is 2500 and the square of 60 is 3600. Hence the required number is some number between 50 and 60. Let us start, then, by using 54 as a divisor.

$$\begin{array}{r}
60.16 \\
54\overline{)3249.00} \\
324 \\
\hline
9\ 0 \\
5\ 4 \\
\hline
3\ 60 \\
3\ 24 \\
\hline
\end{array}$$

Let us approximate the above quotient as 60.2 and find the average between that and the divisor, as was done in the previous example.

$$\tfrac{1}{2}(54 + 60.20) = \tfrac{1}{2}(114.20)$$
$$= 57.10$$

Let us round off this average to 57 and use that as our next divisor and we have

$$
\begin{array}{r}
57 \\
57\,\overline{\big)\,3249} \\
285 \\
\hline
399 \\
399 \\
\hline
\end{array}
$$

Then, since our divisor and quotient are identical with no remainder, we assume that 57 is the square root of 3249. We can readily check this by multiplication.

$$
\begin{array}{r}
57 \\
57 \\
\hline
399 \\
285 \\
\hline
3249 \\
\end{array}
$$

The above two problems were selected because they were relatively easy and the process used for obtaining the square root could be followed without interruption caused by the difficulty of the problem. Many such problems become somewhat tedious, especially when several decimal places are required and the result is only a close approximation of the required square root. Examples 1 and 2 that follow illustrate problems that may become somewhat detailed and tedious.

Example 1. Find the square root of 5 to three decimal places.

We know that the square root of 4 is 2 and of 9 is 3. Hence the square root of 5 lies some place between 2 and 3. Let us begin by dividing 5 by 2. Then

$$
\begin{array}{r}
2.5 \\
2\,\overline{\big)\,5.0} \\
4 \\
\hline
1\,0 \\
1\,0 \\
\hline
\end{array}
$$

Now we shall find the average between 2 and 2.5.

$$\tfrac{1}{2}(2 + 2.5) = \tfrac{1}{2}(4.5)$$
$$= 2.25$$

We proceed as before by dividing 5 by 2.25 to get

$$
\begin{array}{r}
2.222 \\
2.25\,\overline{\smash{)}\,5.000000} \\
\underline{4\ 50} \\
500 \\
\underline{450} \\
500 \\
\underline{450} \\
500 \\
\underline{450} \\
500 \\
\underline{450}
\end{array}
$$

The average between 2.25 and 2.222, then, is

$$\tfrac{1}{2}(2.25 + 2.222) = \tfrac{1}{2}(4.472)$$
$$= 2.236$$

To verify our answer, we multiply 2.236 by 2.236:

$$(2.236)(2.236) = 4.999696$$

which if rounded off to three decimal places gives us 5.000.

Example 2. Find, to four decimal places, the square root of 11.347.

We know that the square root of 9 is 3 and of 16 is 4. Then the square root of 11.347 will be more than 3 and less than 4. We begin by dividing 11.347 by 3.

$$
\begin{array}{r}
3.7 \\
3\,\overline{\smash{)}\,11.347} \\
\underline{9} \\
2\ 3 \\
\underline{2\ 1}
\end{array}
$$

The average between 3 and 3.7 is

$$\tfrac{1}{2}(3 + 3.7) = \tfrac{1}{2}(6.7)$$
$$= 3.35$$

We continue by dividing 11.347 by 3.35 and obtain

$$
\begin{array}{r}
3.38 \\
3.35\,\overline{\smash{)}\,11.3470} \\
\underline{10\ 05} \\
1\ 297 \\
\underline{1\ 005} \\
2920 \\
2680
\end{array}
$$

The average between 3.35 and 3.38 is

$$\tfrac{1}{2}(3.35 + 3.38) = \tfrac{1}{2}(6.73)$$
$$= 3.365$$

We proceed by dividing 11.347 by 3.365 and obtain

```
                3.372
    3.365 | 11.347 000
            10 095
             1 2520
             1 0095
               24250
               23555
```

Then the average between 3.365 and 3.372 is

$$\tfrac{1}{2}(3.365 + 3.372) = \tfrac{1}{2}(6.737)$$
$$= 3.3685$$

Finally, we divide 11.347 by 3.3685 and get

```
                   3.3685
    3.3685 | 11.3470000
             10 1055
              1 24150
              1 01055
                230950
                202110
                288400
                269480
                189200
                168425
```

Since our divisor and quotient are equal, to four decimal places, 3.3685, then, is the square root of 11.347. To verify our answer, we multiply 3.3685 by 3.3685.

$$(3.3685)(3.3685) = 11.34679255$$
$$= 11.347$$

rounded off to three decimal places.

EXERCISE 63

A

Find the square root of each of the following numbers (if the square root is not an integer, find its value to the nearest hundredth):

1. 729	2. 1444	3. 361	4. 10609
5. 54756	6. 789	7. 91	8. 30.8
9. 0.144	10. 1.793	11. 16.0753	12. 8.53
13. 132.1	14. 204.49	15. 49.07	

B

Find the square root of each of the following numbers to three decimal places:

1. 10.0362	2. 123.321	3. 36.036	4. 0.01277
5. 17.1807	6. 361.609	7. 4.00838	8. 0.9873
9. 0.06834	10. 0.000999		

66. SOLVING THE INCOMPLETE QUADRATIC EQUATION

When any quadratic equation has been correctly solved, two values are obtained. Those two values are roots of the quadratic equation and each will satisfy that equation.

The incomplete quadratic equation whose term to the first power is missing can be solved by extracting the square root of both members of the equation. In the previous section we found only the positive square root. When solving the following examples by extracting the square root of both members of the equation, it will be necessary to use both the positive and negative values in order to obtain the two roots of the quadratic equation.

Example 1. Solve the equation $x^2 = 36$.

Extract the square root of both members of the equation and we have

$$\pm x = \pm 6$$

Four cases are represented in this solution: $x = 6$, $x = -6$, $-x = -6$, and $-x = 6$. By multiplying both members of the equations in the last two cases ($-x = -6$ and $-x = 6$) by -1, we duplicate the first two cases. Consequently, it is not necessary to use the $\pm x$ in the left member of the above equation when solving. Hence the roots of the equation are 6 and -6.

Check:
$$x^2 = 36 \qquad x^2 = 36$$
$$(6)^2 = 36 \qquad (-6)^2 = 36$$
$$36 = 36 \qquad 36 = 36$$

Example 2. Solve the equation $4y^2 - 100 = 0$.

$$4y^2 - 100 = 0$$
$$4y^2 = 100$$
$$y^2 = 25$$
$$y = \pm 5$$

Check:
$$4y^2 - 100 = 0 \qquad 4y^2 - 100 = 0$$
$$4(5)^2 - 100 = 0 \qquad 4(-5)^2 - 100 = 0$$
$$4(25) - 100 = 0 \qquad 4(25) - 100 = 0$$
$$100 - 100 = 0 \qquad 100 - 100 = 0$$
$$0 = 0 \qquad 0 = 0$$

Example 3. Solve the equation $3x^2 - 81 = 0$.

$$3x^2 - 81 = 0$$
$$3x^2 = 81$$
$$x^2 = 27$$
$$x = \pm\sqrt{27} = \pm 3\sqrt{3} = \pm 5.196$$

If the value ± 5.196 is used to check the problem, there will be a slight difference due to the fact that ± 5.196 is only an approximate answer, correct to three decimal places. Answers are, more often than not, left in radical form.

Check:
$$3x^2 - 81 = 0 \qquad 3x^2 - 81 = 0$$
$$3(\sqrt{27})^2 - 81 = 0 \qquad 3(-\sqrt{27})^2 - 81 = 0$$
$$3(27) - 81 = 0 \qquad 3(27) - 81 = 0$$
$$81 - 81 = 0 \qquad 81 - 81 = 0$$
$$0 = 0 \qquad 0 = 0$$

Example 4. Solve the equation $x^2 - 40 = 0$.

$$x^2 - 40 = 0$$
$$x^2 = 40$$
$$x = \pm\sqrt{40}$$
$$x = \pm 2\sqrt{10}$$

The decimal equivalents of those roots are $\pm 2(3.162) = \pm 6.324$.

Check:

$x^2 - 40 = 0$	$x^2 - 40 = 0$
$(2\sqrt{10})^2 - 40 = 0$	$(-2\sqrt{10})^2 - 40 = 0$
$40 - 40 = 0$	$40 - 40 = 0$
$0 = 0$	$0 = 0$

The roots of the equation in Example 4, $2\sqrt{10}$ and $-2\sqrt{10}$, or their decimal approximations 6.324 and -6.324, are irrational numbers. They are a part of our real number system since their approximate location can be made on the number line.

To solve the incomplete quadratic equation whose constant term is missing, we use the factoring method. When two or more factors are multiplied together and the product is zero, at least one of these factors must be equal to zero. Hence if $x \cdot y = 0$, either $x = 0$ or $y = 0$ or both x and y may be equal to zero.

If the left member of a quadratic equation, whose right member is equal to zero, can be factored, each factor may be set equal to zero. Then, by methods previously learned, we may solve for the unknown quantity.

Example 5. Solve the equation $x^2 + 3x = 0$.

$$x^2 + 3x = 0$$
$$x(x + 3) = 0$$
$$x = 0 \quad \text{or} \quad x + 3 = 0$$
$$x = -3$$

Hence the roots of the equation are 0 and -3.

Check:

$x^2 + 3x = 0$	$x^2 + 3x = 0$
$0^2 + 3(0) = 0$	$(-3)^2 + 3(-3) = 0$
$0 + 0 = 0$	$9 + (-9) = 0$
$0 = 0$	$0 = 0$

Example 6. Solve the equation $x^2 - 6x = 0$.

$$x^2 - 6x = 0$$
$$x(x - 6) = 0$$
$$x = 0 \quad \text{or} \quad x - 6 = 0$$
$$x = 6$$

Hence the roots of the equation are 0 and 6.

Check:

$x^2 - 6x = 0$	$x^2 - 6x = 0$
$0^2 - 6(0) = 0$	$6^2 - 6(6) = 0$
$0 - 0 = 0$	$36 - 36 = 0$
$0 = 0$	$0 = 0$

Example 7. Solve the equation $3x^2 - 2x = 0$.

$$3x^2 - 2x = 0$$
$$x(3x - 2) = 0$$
$$x = 0 \quad \text{or} \quad 3x - 2 = 0$$
$$3x = 2$$
$$x = \tfrac{2}{3}$$

Hence the roots of the equation are 0 and $\tfrac{2}{3}$.

Check:

$$3x^2 - 2x = 0 \qquad\qquad 3x^2 - 2x = 0$$
$$3(0)^2 - 2(0) = 0 \qquad\qquad 3(\tfrac{2}{3})^2 - 2(\tfrac{2}{3}) = 0$$
$$0 - 0 = 0 \qquad\qquad 3(\tfrac{4}{9}) - \tfrac{4}{3} = 0$$
$$0 = 0 \qquad\qquad 3(\tfrac{1}{3} \cdot \tfrac{4}{3}) - \tfrac{4}{3} = 0$$
$$\tfrac{3}{3} \cdot \tfrac{4}{3} - \tfrac{4}{3} = 0$$
$$1 \cdot \tfrac{4}{3} - \tfrac{4}{3} = 0$$
$$\tfrac{4}{3} - \tfrac{4}{3} = 0$$
$$0 = 0$$

EXERCISE 64

A

Solve the following equations, leaving all answers in radical form if radicals are involved:

1. $x^2 = 121$
2. $x^2 - 64 = 0$
3. $2x^2 = 200$
4. $5x^2 = 405$
5. $3x^2 - 147 = 0$
6. $6x^2 - 216 = 0$
7. $x^2 - 5 = 0$
8. $x^2 - 18 = 0$
9. $4x^2 - 20 = 0$
10. $5x^2 - 125 = 0$
11. $x^2 + 7x = 0$
12. $x^2 - 5x = 0$
13. $x^2 = 3x$
14. $2x^2 = x$
15. $4x^2 = 2x$

B

Solve the following equations, leaving all answers in radical form if radicals are involved:

1. $x^2 = 45$
2. $x^2 = 72$
3. $x^2 - 120 = 0$
4. $3x^2 = 48$

5. $4x^2 - 144 = 0$ 6. $2x^2 = 96$

7. $3x^2 - 135 = 0$ 8. $x^2 - 360 = 0$

9. $2x^2 - 13 = x^2 + 12$ 10. $3x^2 + 4 = x^2 + 54$

11. $3x^2 + 2x = 0$ 12. $x^2 - \frac{1}{2}x = 0$

13. $\frac{1}{3}x^2 = x$ 14. $2x^2 = \frac{1}{3}x$

15. $\frac{2}{3}x^2 - \frac{1}{4}x = 0$

67. SOLVING COMPLETE QUADRATIC EQUATIONS BY FACTORING

The complete quadratic equation may be solved by factoring if all three members of the expression are in the left member of the equation and that trinomial is set equal to zero. We factor the trinomial and, again, set each factor equal to zero as was done with incomplete quadratic equations whose constant term was missing.

Example 1. Solve the equation $x^2 - 5x + 6 = 0$.

$$x^2 - 5x + 6 = 0$$
$$(x - 2)(x - 3) = 0$$
$$x - 2 = 0 \qquad x - 3 = 0$$
$$x = 2 \qquad x = 3$$

Hence the roots of the equation are 2 and 3 and no other values will satisfy the equation.

Check: $x^2 - 5x + 6 = 0$ $x^2 - 5x + 6 = 0$

         $(2)^2 - 5(2) + 6 = 0$ $(3)^2 - 5(3) + 6 = 0$

          $4 - 10 + 6 = 0$ $9 - 15 + 6 = 0$

               $0 = 0$ $0 = 0$

Example 2. Solve the equation $x^2 - x - 20 = 0$.

$$x^2 - x - 20 = 0$$
$$(x - 5)(x + 4) = 0$$
$$x - 5 = 0 \qquad x + 4 = \quad 0$$
$$x = 5 \qquad x = -4$$

Hence the roots of the equation are 5 and -4.

Check: $x^2 - x - 20 = 0$ $x^2 - x - 20 = 0$

       $(5)^2 - 5 - 20 = 0$ $(-4)^2 - (-4) - 20 = 0$

       $25 - 5 - 20 = 0$ $16 + 4 - 20 = 0$

           $0 = 0$ $0 = 0$

Example 3. Solve the equation $x^2 - 3x = 0$.

$$x^2 - 3x = 0$$
$$x(x - 3) = 0$$
$$x = 0 \qquad x - 3 = 0$$
$$x = 3$$

Hence the roots of the equation are 0 and 3.

Check:

$$x^2 - 3x = 0 \qquad\qquad x^2 - 3x = 0$$
$$(0)^2 - 3(0) = 0 \qquad (3)^2 - 3(3) = 0$$
$$0 - 0 = 0 \qquad\qquad 9 - 9 = 0$$
$$0 = 0 \qquad\qquad\qquad 0 = 0$$

Example 4. Solve the equation $12x^2 + 5x - 2 = 0$.

$$12x^2 + 5x - 2 = 0$$
$$(3x + 2)(4x - 1) = 0$$
$$3x + 2 = 0 \qquad\qquad 4x - 1 = 0$$
$$3x = -2 \qquad\qquad 4x = 1$$
$$x = -\tfrac{2}{3} \qquad\qquad x = \tfrac{1}{4}$$

Hence the roots of the equation are $-\tfrac{2}{3}$ and $\tfrac{1}{4}$.

Check:

$$12x^2 + 5x - 2 = 0 \qquad\qquad 12x^2 + 5x - 2 = 0$$
$$12(-\tfrac{2}{3})^2 + 5(-\tfrac{2}{3}) - 2 = 0 \qquad 12(\tfrac{1}{4})^2 + 5(\tfrac{1}{4}) - 2 = 0$$
$$12(\tfrac{4}{9}) - \tfrac{10}{3} - 2 = 0 \qquad\qquad 12(\tfrac{1}{16}) + \tfrac{5}{4} - 2 = 0$$
$$\tfrac{48}{9} - \tfrac{10}{3} - 2 = 0 \qquad\qquad \tfrac{12}{16} + \tfrac{5}{4} - 2 = 0$$
$$\tfrac{16}{3} - \tfrac{10}{3} - \tfrac{6}{3} = 0 \qquad\qquad \tfrac{3}{4} + \tfrac{5}{4} - \tfrac{8}{4} = 0$$
$$0 = 0 \qquad\qquad\qquad 0 = 0$$

EXERCISE 65

A

Solve the following equations by factoring:

1. $x^2 + 7x + 12 = 0$ 2. $x^2 + 8x + 12 = 0$

3. $x^2 - 4x + 4 = 0$ 4. $x^2 - 4x + 3 = 0$

5. $y^2 - 8y + 7 = 0$ 6. $y^2 - 11y + 18 = 0$

7. $z^2 + z - 12 = 0$ 8. $c^2 - 3c - 10 = 0$

9. $s^2 - s - 30 = 0$ 10. $p^2 + 8p + 16 = 0$

282   QUADRATIC EQUATIONS

Solve the following equations by factoring:

1. $d^2 + 5d - 24 = 0$

2. $b^2 - 14b + 24 = 0$

3. $x^2 - 4x - 12 = 0$

4. $y^2 - 3y - 28 = 0$

5. $s^2 - 3s - 40 = 0$

6. $2s^2 + 7s + 3 = 0$

7. $3r^2 - 8r - 3 = 0$

8. $6y^2 + 5y = 6$

9. $8y^2 = 3 - 2y$

10. $4x^2 + 16x = 9$

11. $15y^2 + 22y - 5 = 0$

12. $2b^2 + 7b + 5 = 0$

13. $2y^2 + 11y - 6 = 0$

14. $12d^2 + 7d - 12 = 0$

15. $3x^2 - 10x + 3 = 0$

68. SOLVING QUADRATIC EQUATIONS BY COMPLETING THE SQUARE

Some quadratic equations are quite difficult to factor. Therefore we must have other methods for solving such equations.

One such method is that known as solving by *completing the square*. In this process the constant is subtracted from both members of the equation, leaving the terms involving the unknown in the left member of the equation. Then to those terms in the left member of the equation we add a third term to form a perfect square trinomial, remembering to add the same value to the right member of the equation to maintain the equality. If the coefficient of the term involving the square of the unknown quantity is any value other than 1, we divide both members of the equation by that coefficient before completing the square.

To form a perfect square trinomial, we square one-half the coefficient of the term involving the first power of the unknown and add that value to both members of the equation.

Next we extract the square root of both members of the equation, prefixing the $\pm$ sign to the right member of the equation. Then we solve the resulting equations for the unknown quantity. The following examples illustrate solving by completing the square.

Example 1. Solve the equation $x^2 + 8x + 15 = 0$ by completing the square.

$$x^2 + 8x + 15 = 0$$
$$x^2 + 8x = -15$$
$$x^2 + 8x + 16 = -15 + 16$$
$$x^2 + 8x + 16 = 1$$

$$(x + 4)^2 = 1$$
$$x + 4 = \pm 1$$
$$x = -4 \pm 1$$

$x = -4 + 1$	$x = -4 - 1$
$x = -3$	$x = -5$

Hence the roots of the equation are -3 and -5.

Check:

$x^2 + 8x + 15 = 0$	$x^2 + 8x + 15 = 0$
$(-3)^2 + 8(-3) + 15 = 0$	$(-5)^2 + 8(-5) + 15 = 0$
$9 - 24 + 15 = 0$	$25 - 40 + 15 = 0$
$0 = 0$	$0 = 0$

Example 2. Solve the equation $4x^2 + 4x - 3 = 0$ by completing the square.

$$4x^2 + 4x - 3 = 0$$
$$4x^2 + 4x = 3$$
$$x^2 + x = \tfrac{3}{4}$$
$$x^2 + x + \tfrac{1}{4} = 1$$
$$(x + \tfrac{1}{2})^2 = 1$$
$$x + \tfrac{1}{2} = \pm 1$$
$$x = -\tfrac{1}{2} \pm 1$$

$x = -\tfrac{1}{2} + 1$	$x = -\tfrac{1}{2} - 1$
$x = \tfrac{1}{2}$	$x = -\tfrac{3}{2}$

Hence the roots of the equation are $\tfrac{1}{2}$ and $-\tfrac{3}{2}$.

Check:

$4x^2 + 4x - 3 = 0$	$4x^2 + 4x - 3 = 0$
$4(\tfrac{1}{2})^2 + 4(\tfrac{1}{2}) - 3 = 0$	$4(-\tfrac{3}{2})^2 + 4(-\tfrac{3}{2}) - 3 = 0$
$4(\tfrac{1}{4}) + \tfrac{4}{2} - 3 = 0$	$4(\tfrac{9}{4}) - \tfrac{12}{2} - 3 = 0$
$1 + 2 - 3 = 0$	$9 - 6 - 3 = 0$
$0 = 0$	$0 = 0$

Example 3. Solve the equation $x^2 + 2x - 4 = 0$ by completing the square.

$$x^2 + 2x - 4 = 0$$
$$x^2 + 2x = 4$$
$$x^2 + 2x + 1 = 5$$
$$(x + 1)^2 = 5$$
$$x + 1 = \pm \sqrt{5}$$
$$x = -1 \pm \sqrt{5}$$

$x = -1 + \sqrt{5}$	$x = -1 - \sqrt{5}$

Hence the roots of the equation are $-1 + \sqrt{5}$ and $-1 - \sqrt{5}$.

$\quad$ *Check:* $\qquad\qquad\qquad\qquad x^2 + 2x - 4 = 0$

$$(-1 + \sqrt{5})^2 + 2(-1 + \sqrt{5}) - 4 = 0$$
$$1 - 2\sqrt{5} + 5 - 2 + 2\sqrt{5} - 4 = 0$$
$$0 = 0$$

$$x^2 + 2x - 4 = 0$$
$$(-1 - \sqrt{5})^2 + 2(-1 - \sqrt{5}) - 4 = 0$$
$$1 + 2\sqrt{5} + 5 - 2 - 2\sqrt{5} - 4 = 0$$
$$0 = 0$$

EXERCISE 66

A

Solve the following equations by completing the square:

1. $x^2 - 6x + 5 = 0$ $\qquad\qquad$ 2. $x^2 - 10x + 24 = 0$
3. $x^2 + 4x - 12 = 0$ $\qquad\qquad$ 4. $x^2 - 6x - 27 = 0$
5. $x^2 + 6x + 5 = 0$ $\qquad\qquad$ 6. $y^2 + 2y - 48 = 0$
7. $b^2 - 4b - 21 = 0$ $\qquad\qquad$ 8. $d^2 + 3d - 4 = 0$
9. $y^2 + 5y - 24 = 0$ $\qquad\qquad$ 10. $2r^2 + r - 1 = 0$

B

Solve the following equations by completing the square:

1. $3t^2 - 14t + 8 = 0$ $\qquad\qquad$ 2. $s^2 - s - 6 = 0$
3. $b^2 + 4b + 1 = 0$ $\qquad\qquad$ 4. $x^2 - 6x + 7 = 0$
5. $2x^2 - x - 6 = 0$ $\qquad\qquad$ 6. $c^2 - 2c - 6 = 0$
7. $m^2 - 4m + 1 = 0$ $\qquad\qquad$ 8. $t^2 + 8t + 13 = 0$
9. $x^2 + 6x + 7 = 0$ $\qquad\qquad$ 10. $y^2 + 10y + 20 = 0$

69. SOLVING QUADRATIC EQUATIONS BY THE FORMULA

The equation

$$ax^2 + bx + c = 0$$

is called the *general quadratic equation*. The a, b, and c can represent any value, except a cannot equal zero. If a were equal to zero, the x^2 term would disappear and we would no longer have a quadratic equation. When the general quadratic equation is solved for x, then any quadratic equation can be solved by substituting in it the values of a, b, and c.

The following discussion illustrates the derivation of the quadratic formula by use of the principles involved in completing the square:

$$ax^2 + bx + c = 0$$

Subtract the constant c from both members of the equation.

$$ax^2 + bx = -c$$

Since a may be some value other than 1, divide both members of the equation by a.

$$x^2 + \frac{b}{a}x = -\frac{c}{a}$$

To complete the square, square one-half the coefficient of the x term and add that value to both members of the equation.

$$x^2 + \frac{b}{a}x + \frac{b^2}{4a^2} = \frac{b^2}{4a^2} - \frac{c}{a}$$

Obtain a common denominator in the right member of the equation and convert that part into a single fraction.

$$x^2 + \frac{b}{a}x + \frac{b^2}{4a^2} = \frac{b^2 - 4ac}{4a^2}$$

or

$$\left(x + \frac{b}{2a}\right)^2 = \frac{b^2 - 4ac}{4a^2}$$

Extract the square root of both members of the equation.

$$x + \frac{b}{2a} = \frac{\pm\sqrt{b^2 - 4ac}}{2a}$$

Subtract the $\frac{b}{2a}$ from both members of the equation.

$$x = -\frac{b}{2a} \pm \frac{\sqrt{b^2 - 4ac}}{2a}$$

$$= \frac{-b \pm \sqrt{b^2 - 4ac}}{2a}$$

This is called the *quadratic formula.* It can be observed that no letter except a, b, and c appears in the right member of the equation. Thus any quadratic equation can be solved by substituting into the formula the values of a, b, and c.

Example 1. Solve the equation $x^2 + 5x - 36 = 0$, using the quadratic formula.

We have $a = 1$, $b = 5$, and $c = -36$.

$$x = \frac{-b \pm \sqrt{b^2 - 4ac}}{2a}$$

$$x = \frac{-5 \pm \sqrt{25 - 4(1)(-36)}}{2}$$

$$x = \frac{-5 \pm \sqrt{25 + 144}}{2}$$

$$x = \frac{-5 \pm \sqrt{169}}{2}$$

$$x = \frac{-5 \pm 13}{2}$$

$$x = \frac{-5 + 13}{2} \qquad x = \frac{-5 - 13}{2}$$

$$x = \frac{8}{2} \qquad x = \frac{-18}{2}$$

$$x = 4 \qquad x = -9$$

Check:
$$x^2 + 5x - 36 = 0 \qquad\qquad x^2 + 5x - 36 = 0$$
$$(4)^2 + 5(4) - 36 = 0 \qquad\qquad (-9)^2 + 5(-9) - 36 = 0$$
$$16 + 20 - 36 = 0 \qquad\qquad 81 - 45 - 36 = 0$$
$$0 = 0 \qquad\qquad 0 = 0$$

Example 2. Solve the equation $2x^2 - 5x - 3 = 0$, using the quadratic formula.

We have $a = 2$, $b = -5$, and $c = -3$.

$$x = \frac{-b \pm \sqrt{b^2 - 4ac}}{2a}$$

$$x = \frac{-(-5) \pm \sqrt{25 - 4(2)(-3)}}{2(2)}$$

$$x = \frac{5 \pm \sqrt{25 + 24}}{4}$$

$$x = \frac{5 \pm \sqrt{49}}{4}$$

$$x = \frac{5 \pm 7}{4}$$

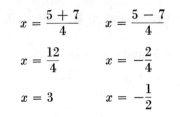

$$x = \frac{5 + 7}{4} \qquad x = \frac{5 - 7}{4}$$

$$x = \frac{12}{4} \qquad x = -\frac{2}{4}$$

$$x = 3 \qquad x = -\frac{1}{2}$$

Check:
$$\begin{array}{ll} 2x^2 - 5x - 3 = 0 & 2x^2 - 5x - 3 = 0 \\ 2(3)^2 - 5(3) - 3 = 0 & 2(-\tfrac{1}{2})^2 - 5(-\tfrac{1}{2}) - 3 = 0 \\ 2(9) - 15 - 3 = 0 & 2(\tfrac{1}{4}) + \tfrac{5}{2} - 3 = 0 \\ 18 - 15 - 3 = 0 & \tfrac{1}{2} + \tfrac{5}{2} - \tfrac{6}{2} = 0 \\ 0 = 0 & 0 = 0 \end{array}$$

Example 3. Solve the equation $3x^2 - 4x - 2 = 0$, using the quadratic formula.

We have $a = 3$, $b = -4$, and $c = -2$.

$$x = \frac{-b \pm \sqrt{b^2 - 4ac}}{2a}$$

$$x = \frac{-(-4) \pm \sqrt{16 - 4(3)(-2)}}{2(3)}$$

$$x = \frac{4 \pm \sqrt{16 + 24}}{6}$$

$$x = \frac{4 \pm \sqrt{40}}{6}$$

$$x = \frac{4 \pm 2\sqrt{10}}{6}$$

$$x = \frac{2 \pm \sqrt{10}}{3}$$

$$x = \frac{2 + \sqrt{10}}{3} \qquad x = \frac{2 - \sqrt{10}}{3}$$

Check:
$$3x^2 - 4x - 2 = 0$$

$$3\left(\frac{2 + \sqrt{10}}{3}\right)^2 - 4\left(\frac{2 + \sqrt{10}}{3}\right) - 2 = 0$$

$$3\left(\frac{4 + 4\sqrt{10} + 10}{9}\right) - \frac{8 + 4\sqrt{10}}{3} - 2 = 0$$

$$\frac{14 + 4\sqrt{10}}{3} - \frac{8 + 4\sqrt{10}}{3} - \frac{6}{3} = 0$$

$$14 + 4\sqrt{10} - 8 - 4\sqrt{10} - 6 = 0$$
$$0 = 0$$

$$3x^2 - 4x - 2 = 0$$
$$3\left(\frac{2 - \sqrt{10}}{3}\right)^2 - 4\left(\frac{2 - \sqrt{10}}{3}\right) - 2 = 0$$
$$3\left(\frac{4 - 4\sqrt{10} + 10}{9}\right) - \frac{8 - 4\sqrt{10}}{3} - 2 = 0$$
$$\frac{14 - 4\sqrt{10}}{3} - \frac{8 - 4\sqrt{10}}{3} - \frac{6}{3} = 0$$
$$14 - 4\sqrt{10} - 8 + 4\sqrt{10} - 6 = 0$$
$$0 = 0$$

Example 4. Solve the equation $\dfrac{x^2}{3} + x + \dfrac{1}{2} = 0$, using the quadratic formula.

Clear the equation of fractions and then solve.

$$2x^2 + 6x + 3 = 0$$

We have $a = 2$, $b = 6$, and $c = 3$.

$$x = \frac{-b \pm \sqrt{b^2 - 4ac}}{2a}$$

$$x = \frac{-6 \pm \sqrt{36 - 4(2)(3)}}{2(2)}$$

$$x = \frac{-6 \pm \sqrt{36 - 24}}{4}$$

$$x = \frac{-6 \pm \sqrt{12}}{4}$$

$$x = \frac{-6 \pm 2\sqrt{3}}{4}$$

$$x = \frac{-3 \pm \sqrt{3}}{2}$$

$$x = \frac{-3 + \sqrt{3}}{2} \qquad x = \frac{-3 - \sqrt{3}}{2}$$

Check:

$$\frac{x^2}{3} + x + \frac{1}{2} = 0$$

$$\frac{\left(\dfrac{-3 + \sqrt{3}}{2}\right)^2}{3} + \frac{-3 + \sqrt{3}}{2} + \frac{1}{2} = 0$$

$$\frac{\dfrac{9 - 6\sqrt{3} + 3}{4}}{3} + \frac{-3 + \sqrt{3}}{2} + \frac{1}{2} = 0$$

$$\frac{\dfrac{12 - 6\sqrt{3}}{4}}{3} + \frac{-3 + \sqrt{3}}{2} + \frac{1}{2} = 0$$

$$\frac{\dfrac{6 - 3\sqrt{3}}{2}}{3} + \frac{-3 + \sqrt{3}}{2} + \frac{1}{2} = 0$$

$$\frac{6 - 3\sqrt{3}}{6} + \frac{-3 + \sqrt{3}}{2} + \frac{1}{2} = 0$$

$$6 - 3\sqrt{3} - 9 + 3\sqrt{3} + 3 = 0$$
$$0 = 0$$

$$\frac{x^2}{3} + x + \frac{1}{2} = 0$$

$$\frac{\left(\dfrac{-3 - \sqrt{3}}{2}\right)^2}{3} + \frac{-3 - \sqrt{3}}{2} + \frac{1}{2} = 0$$

$$\frac{\dfrac{9 + 6\sqrt{3} + 3}{4}}{3} + \frac{-3 - \sqrt{3}}{2} + \frac{1}{2} = 0$$

$$\frac{12 + 6\sqrt{3}}{12} + \frac{-3 - \sqrt{3}}{2} + \frac{1}{2} = 0$$

$$12 + 6\sqrt{3} - 18 - 6\sqrt{3} + 6 = 0$$
$$0 = 0$$

It is quite evident from the previous examples that frequently the checking for the accuracy of the solution to quadratic equations is tedious and laborious. We shall present in the following discussion a method for checking that is somewhat simpler.

Consider for a moment the quadratic formula

$$x = \frac{-b \pm \sqrt{b^2 - 4ac}}{2a}$$

The two signs that precede the radical provide for the two roots of a quadratic equation. Let us designate the two roots by the symbols r_1 and r_2. Then we can make the following statements:

$$r_1 = \frac{-b + \sqrt{b^2 - 4ac}}{2a} \qquad \text{and} \qquad r_2 = \frac{-b - \sqrt{b^2 - 4ac}}{2a}$$

The sum of the two roots, then, may be written

$$r_1 + r_2 = \frac{-b + \sqrt{b^2 - 4ac}}{2a} + \frac{-b - \sqrt{b^2 - 4ac}}{2a}$$

Using techniques previously developed in this text, we can simplify this as follows:

$$r_1 + r_2 = \frac{-b + \sqrt{b^2 - 4ac} + (-b - \sqrt{b^2 - 4ac})}{2a}$$

$$= \frac{-b - b + \sqrt{b^2 - 4ac} - \sqrt{b^2 - 4ac}}{2a}$$

$$= \frac{-2b}{2a}$$

$$= -\frac{b}{a} \tag{1}$$

In a similar manner, the product of r_1 and r_2 may be derived as follows:

$$r_1 \cdot r_2 = \left(\frac{-b + \sqrt{b^2 - 4ac}}{2a}\right)\left(\frac{-b - \sqrt{b^2 - 4ac}}{2a}\right)$$

$$= \frac{(-b)^2 - (\sqrt{b^2 - 4ac})^2}{4a^2}$$

$$= \frac{b^2 - (b^2 - 4ac)}{4a^2}$$

$$= \frac{b^2 - b^2 + 4ac}{4a^2}$$

$$= \frac{4ac}{4a^2}$$

$$= \frac{c}{a} \tag{2}$$

We recall from the general quadratic equation, $ax^2 + bx + c = 0$, that a is the coefficient of the x^2 term, b the coefficient of the x term, and c the constant.

By use of these two formulas, $r_1 + r_2 = -b/a$ and $r_1r_2 = c/a$, let us check the roots we found in the four examples in this section.

Example 1 was given as $x^2 + 5x - 36 = 0$ and we found the roots to be 4 and -9. In this equation $a = 1$, $b = 5$, and $c = -36$. The sum of the two roots is -5 and their product is -36. The check for these roots is as follows:

$$r_1 + r_2 = -\frac{b}{a} \qquad r_1r_2 = \frac{c}{a}$$

$$= \frac{-5}{1} \qquad = \frac{-36}{1}$$

$$= -5 \qquad = -36$$

Hence both checks verify that the roots obtained are correct. It is well to use both formulas to rule out the possibility of an error in checking. If both formulas verify the accuracy of the roots obtained, the possibility of error is essentially nil.

The equation in Example 2 was given as $2x^2 - 5x - 3 = 0$ and the roots we found were 3 and $-\frac{1}{2}$. The check follows:

$$r_1 + r_2 = -\frac{b}{a} \qquad r_1r_2 = \frac{c}{a}$$

$$= -\frac{-5}{2} \qquad = \frac{-3}{2}$$

$$= \frac{5}{2} \qquad = -\frac{3}{2}$$

The sum of 3 and $-\frac{1}{2}$ is $2\frac{1}{2}$, or $\frac{5}{2}$, and the product of 3 and $-\frac{1}{2}$ is $-\frac{3}{2}$. Hence both checks verify the accuracy of the roots found.

The equation in Example 3 was given as $3x^2 - 4x - 2 = 0$ and the roots obtained were $\frac{2 + \sqrt{10}}{3}$ and $\frac{2 - \sqrt{10}}{3}$. The sum of these roots is $\frac{4}{3}$ and their product is $\frac{4 - 10}{9}$, which simplifies to $-\frac{2}{3}$. Checking by the formulas, we have

$$r_1 + r_2 = -\frac{b}{a} \qquad r_1r_2 = \frac{c}{a}$$

$$= -\frac{-4}{3} \qquad = \frac{-2}{3}$$

$$= \frac{4}{3} \qquad = -\frac{2}{3}$$

Hence the accuracy of the roots is verified.

The equation in Example 4 was given as $\frac{x^2}{3} + x + \frac{1}{2} = 0$, which simplifies to $2x^2 + 6x + 3 = 0$, and the roots found were $\frac{-3 + \sqrt{3}}{2}$ and $\frac{-3 - \sqrt{3}}{2}$. The sum of those roots is $\frac{-6}{2}$, which reduces to -3, and their product is $\dfrac{9-3}{4}$, or $\dfrac{6}{4}$, which reduces to $\dfrac{3}{2}$. The check by the formulas follows:

$$r_1 + r_2 = -\frac{b}{a} \qquad r_1 r_2 = \frac{c}{a}$$

$$= -\frac{6}{2} \qquad\qquad = \frac{3}{2}$$

$$= -3$$

Hence the roots obtained are verified in both formulas.

EXERCISE 67

A

Solve the following equations by use of the quadratic formula:

1. $x^2 - 9x + 20 = 0$ 2. $x^2 - 3x - 40 = 0$
3. $x^2 + 16x + 63 = 0$ 4. $x^2 + 8x + 15 = 0$
5. $x^2 - 7x + 12 = 0$ 6. $x^2 - 8x - 33 = 0$
7. $x^2 - 5 = 0$ 8. $x^2 + 5x = 0$
9. $x^2 - 8x = 0$ 10. $x^2 - 8 = 0$

B

Solve the following equations by use of the quadratic formula:

1. $2x^2 - 5x - 3 = 0$ 2. $6x^2 + 13x + 6 = 0$
3. $9x^2 + 3x - 2 = 0$ 4. $4x^2 + 15x - 4 = 0$
5. $2x^2 - 5x + 3 = 0$ 6. $18x^2 + 3x - 10 = 0$
7. $4x^2 + 5x - 6 = 0$ 8. $x^2 - \dfrac{3x}{2} - 1 = 0$
9. $\dfrac{x^2}{4} + \dfrac{x}{2} - 3 = 0$ 10. $\dfrac{2x^2}{3} + 2x + 1 = 0$

70. GRAPHICAL SOLUTION OF QUADRATIC EQUATIONS

In Chapter 9 we discussed extensively the concept of the *function of x* and designated it by the symbol "$f(x)$." The graph of

$$f(x) = ax^2 + bx + c \qquad\qquad (1)$$

can be used to find the solution of the equation

$$ax^2 + bx + c = 0 \qquad (2)$$

In Chapter 9 we found that in the coordinate plane

$$y = f(x) \qquad (3)$$

Then to graph a quadratic equation in the coordinate plane, we use the symbolism shown in equation (3) above.

For any value of x for which $f(x)$ or y equals zero, the graph will intersect the X-axis. Those points for which $f(x) = 0$ are known as the *zeros of the function*.

As we graphed linear functions, we found that the graphs consisted of straight lines. All quadratic functions, when graphed, produce smooth curved continuous lines if we use as our universal set all real numbers. When graphing quadratic functions, it is important to obtain a sufficient number of ordered pairs from the given relationship to ensure accuracy in the construction of the graph. An exact graph is difficult to construct in many cases, and so the resulting graph will probably be only a close approximation of the actual pictorial representation of the function under consideration. This is because many of the values of the ordered pairs associated with the quadratic functions are themselves only decimal or irrational values which are difficult to locate in the coordinate plane.

Example 1. Using the graphical method, estimate the zeros of the equation $x^2 - 4 = 0$.

Since we are looking for the zeros (or the roots of the equation), we let y equal the function and have

$$y = x^2 - 4$$

As in graphing linear equations, we assign any real value to x and determine the corresponding value of y to obtain several ordered pairs associated with the function.

If $x = 0$ 　　　　　If $x = \pm 1$ 　　　　　If $x = \pm 2$
$$\begin{aligned} y &= x^2 - 4 \\ &= 0 - 4 \\ &= -4 \end{aligned} \qquad \begin{aligned} y &= x^2 - 4 \\ &= 1 - 4 \\ &= -3 \end{aligned} \qquad \begin{aligned} y &= x^2 - 4 \\ &= 4 - 4 \\ &= 0 \end{aligned}$$

　　　　If $x = \pm 3$ 　　　　　If $x = \pm 4$
$$\begin{aligned} y &= x^2 - 4 \\ &= 9 - 4 \\ &= 5 \end{aligned} \qquad \begin{aligned} y &= x^2 - 4 \\ &= 16 - 4 \\ &= 12 \end{aligned}$$

x	-4	-3	-2	-1	0	1	2	3	4
y	12	5	0	-3	-4	-3	0	5	12

We locate the points, represented in the above table of ordered pairs, in the coordinate plane. It is obvious that an infinite number of values could be assigned to x that would fall between those chosen in the above table. To each of those there would be a corresponding value for y. This then would result in the smooth curved line. When a sufficient number of ordered pairs have been determined to give the general contour of the graph, we can complete it by joining those points by a gradually curving line, as shown in Figure 55. From the table of values shown at the bottom of page 294, it can be seen that the zeros of the function are 2 and -2.

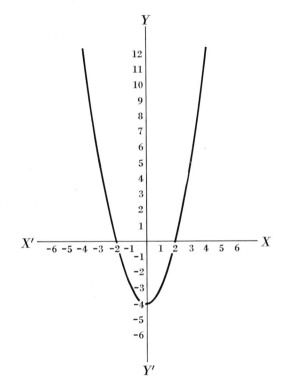

Figure 55

The algebraic solution will verify the graphical solution, as is shown in the following:

$$x^2 - 4 = 0$$
$$x^2 = 4$$
$$x = \pm 2$$

This solution could also be accomplished by using the factoring method, as shown on the following page:

$$x^2 - 4 = 0$$
$$(x + 2)(x - 2) = 0$$

$$x + 2 = 0 \qquad \text{and} \qquad x - 2 = 0$$
$$x = -2 \qquad\qquad\qquad x = 2$$

Example 2. By using graphical representation, estimate the zeros of the function $x^2 - 2x = 0$.

Again, in order to locate the graph in the coordinate plane, we use the functional form

$$y = x^2 - 2x$$

The following ordered pairs will be among those associated with the function:

If $x = -3$
$y = x^2 - 2x$
$\quad = (-3)^2 - 2(-3)$
$\quad = 9 + 6$
$\quad = 15$

If $x = -2$
$y = x^2 - 2x$
$\quad = (-2)^2 - 2(-2)$
$\quad = 4 + 4$
$\quad = 8$

If $x = -1$
$y = x^2 - 2x$
$\quad = (-1)^2 - 2(-1)$
$\quad = 1 + 2$
$\quad = 3$

If $x = 0$
$y = x^2 - 2x$
$\quad = 0^2 - 2(0)$
$\quad = 0$

If $x = 1$
$y = x^2 - 2x$
$\quad = (1)^2 - 2(1)$
$\quad = 1 - 2$
$\quad = -1$

If $x = 2$
$y = x^2 - 2x$
$\quad = (2)^2 - 2(2)$
$\quad = 4 - 4$
$\quad = 0$

If $x = 3$
$y = x^2 - 2x$
$\quad = (3)^2 - 2(3)$
$\quad = 9 - 6$
$\quad = 3$

If $x = 4$
$y = x^2 - 2x$
$\quad = (4)^2 - 2(4)$
$\quad = 16 - 8$
$\quad = 8$

If $x = 5$
$y = x^2 - 2x$
$\quad = (5)^2 - 2(5)$
$\quad = 25 - 10$
$\quad = 15$

x	-3	-2	-1	0	1	2	3	4	5
y	15	8	3	0	-1	0	3	8	15

The zeros of the function are 0 and 2 and the graph is shown in Figure 56.

Example 3. By using graphical methods, estimate the zeros of the function $x^2 - x - 12 = 0$.

$$y = x^2 - x - 12$$

If $x = -4$
$y = x^2 - x - 12$
$\quad = (-4)^2 - (-4) - 12$
$\quad = 16 + 4 - 12$
$\quad = 8$

If $x = -3$
$y = x^2 - x - 12$
$\quad = (-3)^2 - (-3) - 12$
$\quad = 9 + 3 - 12$
$\quad = 0$

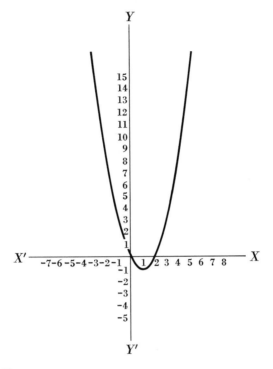

Figure 56

If $x = -2$
$$y = x^2 - x - 12$$
$$= (-2)^2 - (-2) - 12$$
$$= 4 + 2 - 12$$
$$= -6$$

If $x = -1$
$$y = x^2 - x - 12$$
$$= (-1)^2 - (-1) - 12$$
$$= 1 + 1 - 12$$
$$= -10$$

If $x = 0$
$$y = x^2 - x - 12$$
$$= 0^2 - 0 - 12$$
$$= 0 - 0 - 12$$
$$= -12$$

If $x = 1$
$$y = x^2 - x - 12$$
$$= (1)^2 - 1 - 12$$
$$= 1 - 1 - 12$$
$$= -12$$

If $x = 2$
$$y = x^2 - x - 12$$
$$= (2)^2 - 2 - 12$$
$$= 4 - 2 - 12$$
$$= -10$$

If $x = 3$
$$y = x^2 - x - 12$$
$$= (3)^2 - 3 - 12$$
$$= 9 - 3 - 12$$
$$= -6$$

If $x = 4$
$$y = x^2 - x - 12$$
$$= (4)^2 - 4 - 12$$
$$= 16 - 4 - 12$$
$$= 0$$

If $x = 5$
$$y = x^2 - x - 12$$
$$= (5)^2 - 5 - 12$$
$$= 25 - 5 - 12$$
$$= 8$$

x	-4	-3	-2	-1	0	1	2	3	4	5
y	8	0	-6	-10	-12	-12	-10	-6	0	8

It is evident that we have no lowest point. It can be observed that when $x = 0$ and $x = 1$, we have $y = -12$ for both values of x. At this stage we should use a value for x between 0 and 1.

If $x = \frac{1}{2}$
$$y = x^2 - x - 12$$
$$= (\tfrac{1}{2})^2 - \tfrac{1}{2} - 12$$
$$= \tfrac{1}{4} - \tfrac{1}{2} - 12$$
$$= -12\tfrac{1}{4}$$

The graph is shown in Figure 57.

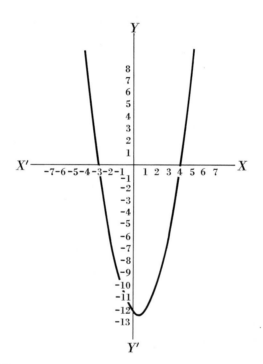

Figure 57

A

By use of graphical representation, estimate the zeros in the following functions:

1. $y = x^2 - 9$
2. $y = x^2 - 25$
3. $y = x^2 - 4x$
4. $y = x^2 - 6x$
5. $y = x^2 - x - 6$
6. $y = x$
7. $y = 4$
8. $y = x^2 + 3x - 1$

B

By use of graphical representation, estimate the zeros in the following functions:

1. $y = x^2 - 2$
2. $y = x^2 - 8$
3. $y = -1$
4. $y = x^2 - 4x + 3$
5. $y = x^2 - 4x - 7$

71. IMAGINARY NUMBERS

All the numbers we have studied thus far have been *real numbers*. All real numbers can be located on the number line, as explained in Chapter 1, and may be integers, common fractions, or decimal fractions. Real numbers are classified as *rational* or *irrational numbers*. A *rational number* we previously defined as any number that can be expressed as the ratio of two integers, either positive or negative. Such numbers as 5, $\frac{2}{3}$, 0.31, and $-\frac{1}{2}$ are rational numbers. *Irrational numbers* are those that are not rational.

A new type of number, known as an *imaginary number*, frequently is used in mathematics, the sciences, and engineering. Its practical use will be reserved until a more complete foundation in mathematics and elementary science has been established.

If we square a positive number, the product is a positive number. Likewise, if we square a negative number, the result is a positive number. Thus we can observe that the square of any real number always results in a positive value. Consequently, in our real number system we have no way to extract the square root of a negative number.

An *imaginary number* is the indicated square root of a negative number. We start our system of imaginary numbers with the $\sqrt{-1}$ and build the system from that symbol. Let us consider the equation $x^2 + 1 = 0$, assuming that it is our wish to determine what values of x will satisfy the equation, or in other words, what the roots of the equation are. If we use either 1 or -1, the square of either number is 1 and $1 + 1 \neq 0$. Thus we define

$$i = \sqrt{-1}$$

with the property that

$$i^2 = -1$$

The simplification of imaginary numbers is similar to that of radicals involving real numbers with certain exceptions that will be explained as we continue with our discussion.

Example 1. Simplify $\sqrt{-4}$.

$$\sqrt{-4} = \sqrt{(4)(-1)}$$
$$= 2\sqrt{-1}$$
$$= 2i$$

Example 2. Simplify $\sqrt{-4} + \sqrt{-9} - \sqrt{-1}$.

$$\sqrt{-4} + \sqrt{-9} + \sqrt{-1} = 2i + 3i - i$$
$$= 4i$$

Before proceeding with multiplication and division of imaginary numbers, certain cautions must be presented. In any calculation involving imaginary numbers in the form of $\sqrt{-1}$, we must always convert the expression into one involving the i before an attempt is made to carry out the implied computation.

Example 3. Simplify $(\sqrt{-16})(\sqrt{-25})$.

$$(\sqrt{-16})(\sqrt{-25}) = (4i)(5i)$$
$$= 20i^2$$

Then replace the i^2 with -1:

$$= 20(-1)$$
$$= -20$$

It will be recalled that earlier in our discussion we could multiply the radicands together, when we were multiplying radicals, if those radicals were of the same order.

In Chapter 11 when the number of rational roots associated with the various types of radicals was discussed, we purposefully omitted presenting the case when $a = \sqrt[n]{b}$, in which n is even and b is negative. This omission was made because such an expression does not represent a real number, and at that time we were interested only in real numbers. Likewise, the fact that earlier we multiplied together the radicands of similar radicals held true only for positive numbers. Again, before multiplying or dividing imaginary numbers in the form of $\sqrt{-1}$, we must always convert the expression to a form involving i, as shown in Examples 3 and 4.

Example 4. Simplify $\dfrac{\sqrt{-4}}{\sqrt{-27}}$.

$$\frac{\sqrt{-4}}{\sqrt{-27}} = \frac{\sqrt{(4)(-1)}}{\sqrt{(9)(-1)(3)}}$$

$$= \frac{2i}{3i\sqrt{3}}$$

$$= \frac{2}{3\sqrt{3}}$$

$$= \frac{2}{3\sqrt{3}} \cdot \frac{\sqrt{3}}{\sqrt{3}}$$

$$= \frac{2\sqrt{3}}{9}$$

EXERCISE 69

Simplify:

1. $\sqrt{-36}$
2. $\sqrt{-64}$
3. $3\sqrt{-6}$
4. $2\sqrt{-12}$
5. $5\sqrt{-24}$
6. $3\sqrt{-48}$
7. $4\sqrt{-20}$
8. $2\sqrt{-32}$
9. $3\sqrt{-45}$
10. $\sqrt{-1} + \sqrt{-4}$
11. $2\sqrt{-3} + \sqrt{-12} - \sqrt{-27}$
12. $5\sqrt{-16} - 2\sqrt{-49}$
13. $3\sqrt{-50} + \sqrt{-98} - \sqrt{-18}$
14. $\sqrt{-5} + \sqrt{-20} - \sqrt{-45}$
15. $(\sqrt{-36})(\sqrt{-4})$
16. $(2\sqrt{-1})(3\sqrt{-4})$

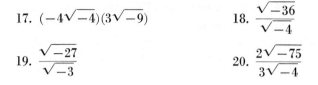

17. $(-4\sqrt{-4})(3\sqrt{-9})$

18. $\dfrac{\sqrt{-36}}{\sqrt{-4}}$

19. $\dfrac{\sqrt{-27}}{\sqrt{-3}}$

20. $\dfrac{2\sqrt{-75}}{3\sqrt{-4}}$

72. QUADRATIC EQUATIONS WITH IMAGINARY ROOTS

In quadratic equations with imaginary roots, if $b = 0$, the roots may be found by extracting the square root of both members of the equation. The following examples illustrate this method:

Example 1. Find the roots of the equation $x^2 + 3 = 0$.

$$x^2 + 3 = 0$$
$$x^2 = -3$$
$$x = \pm\sqrt{-3}$$
$$x = \pm i\sqrt{3}$$

Hence the roots of the equation are $i\sqrt{3}$ and $-i\sqrt{3}$.

$$\textit{Check:} \quad \begin{array}{cc} x^2 + 3 = 0 & x^2 + 3 = 0 \\ (i\sqrt{3})^2 + 3 = 0 & (-i\sqrt{3})^2 + 3 = 0 \\ 3i^2 + 3 = 0 & 3i^2 + 3 = 0 \\ -3 + 3 = 0 & -3 + 3 = 0 \\ 0 = 0 & 0 = 0 \end{array}$$

Example 2. Find the roots of the equation $x^2 = -18$.

$$x^2 = -18$$
$$x = \pm\sqrt{-18}$$
$$x = \pm\sqrt{(9)(-1)(2)}$$
$$x = \pm 3i\sqrt{2}$$

Hence the roots of the equation are $3i\sqrt{2}$ and $-3i\sqrt{2}$.

$$\textit{Check:} \quad \begin{array}{cc} x^2 = -18 & x^2 = -18 \\ (3i\sqrt{2})^2 = -18 & (-3i\sqrt{2})^2 = -18 \\ 9i^2 \cdot 2 = -18 & 9i^2 \cdot 2 = -18 \\ -18 = -18 & -18 = -18 \end{array}$$

It must be kept strictly in mind that i is imaginary and not a part of the *real* number system. Hence any root of an equation that contains the imaginary element i is not a real root of the equation in terms of our real number system.

In quadratic equations with imaginary roots, if $b \neq 0$, the roots may be found by use of the quadratic formula. The following examples illustrate the solution of such equations:

Example 3. Find the roots of the equation $x^2 - 2x + 6 = 0$.
We have $a = 1$, $b = -2$, and $c = 6$.

$$x = \frac{-b \pm \sqrt{b^2 - 4ac}}{2a}$$

$$x = \frac{-(-2) \pm \sqrt{4 - 4(1)(6)}}{2(1)}$$

$$x = \frac{2 \pm \sqrt{4 - 24}}{2}$$

$$x = \frac{2 \pm \sqrt{-20}}{2}$$

$$x = \frac{2 \pm 2i\sqrt{5}}{2}$$

$$x = 1 \pm i\sqrt{5}$$

Hence the roots of the equation are $1 + i\sqrt{5}$ and $1 - i\sqrt{5}$.

Check:

$$r_1 + r_2 = 1 + i\sqrt{5} + 1 - i\sqrt{5}$$
$$= 2$$
$$r_1 r_2 = (1 + i\sqrt{5})(1 - i\sqrt{5})$$
$$= 1^2 - (i\sqrt{5})^2$$
$$= 1 - 5i^2$$
$$= 1 - 5(-1)$$
$$= 1 + 5$$
$$= 6$$

$$r_1 + r_2 = -\frac{b}{a} \qquad r_1 r_2 = \frac{c}{a}$$

$$= -\frac{-2}{1} \qquad = \frac{6}{1}$$

$$= 2 \qquad = 6$$

Hence the formulas verify the accuracy of the roots found.

Example 4. Find the roots of the equation $2x^2 + 8x + 9 = 0$.

We have $a = 2$, $b = 8$, and $c = 9$.

$$x = \frac{-b \pm \sqrt{b^2 - 4ac}}{2a}$$

$$x = \frac{-8 \pm \sqrt{64 - 4(2)(9)}}{2(2)}$$

$$x = \frac{-8 \pm \sqrt{64 - 72}}{4}$$

$$x = \frac{-8 \pm \sqrt{-8}}{4}$$

$$x = \frac{-8 \pm 2i\sqrt{2}}{4}$$

$$x = \frac{-4 \pm i\sqrt{2}}{2}$$

Hence the roots of the equation are $\dfrac{-4 + i\sqrt{2}}{2}$ and $\dfrac{-4 - i\sqrt{2}}{2}$.

Check:

$$r_1 + r_2 = \frac{-4 + i\sqrt{2}}{2} + \frac{-4 - i\sqrt{2}}{2}$$

$$= \frac{-4 + i\sqrt{2} - 4 - i\sqrt{2}}{2}$$

$$= \frac{-8}{2}$$

$$= -4$$

$$r_1 r_2 = \left(\frac{-4 + i\sqrt{2}}{2}\right)\left(\frac{-4 - i\sqrt{2}}{2}\right)$$

$$= \frac{(-4)^2 - (i\sqrt{2})^2}{4}$$

$$= \frac{16 - 2i^2}{4}$$

$$= \frac{16 - 2(-1)}{4}$$

$$= \frac{16 + 2}{4}$$

$$= \frac{18}{4}$$

$$= \frac{9}{2}$$

$$r_1 + r_2 = \frac{-b}{a} \qquad r_1 r_2 = \frac{c}{a}$$

$$= \frac{-8}{2} \qquad\qquad = \frac{9}{2}$$

$$= -4$$

Hence the roots obtained check in the formulas.

Find the roots of the following equations:

1. $x^2 + 1 = 0$ 2. $x^2 + 49 = 0$
3. $x^2 = -121$ 4. $x^2 = -81$
5. $x^2 + 80 = 0$ 6. $x^2 + 54 = 0$
7. $x^2 + x + 5 = 0$ 8. $x^2 + 4x + 7 = 0$
9. $x^2 - 3x + 8 = 0$ 10. $x^2 + 5x + 8 = 0$
11. $2x^2 + 5x + 4 = 0$ 12. $4x^2 - x + 3 = 0$
13. $3x^2 + 8x + 9 = 0$ 14. $2x^2 - 7x + 8 = 0$
15. $3x^2 - 2x + 1 = 0$

73. STATED PROBLEMS

The given data in a great many stated problems lead to a quadratic equation. The following examples illustrate the solution of such problems:

Example 1. The difference between two positive numbers is 9. If their product is 52, what are the numbers?

Let x be the smaller number and $x + 9$ the larger number. Then

$$x(x + 9) = 52$$
$$x^2 + 9x - 52 = 0$$
$$(x - 4)(x + 13) = 0$$
$$x - 4 = 0 \qquad x + 13 = 0$$
$$x = 4 \qquad\qquad x = -13$$

The -13 is discarded since the problem states that we are seeking positive numbers. Then, if $x = 4$,

$$x + 9 = 13$$

Hence the numbers are 4 and 13.

Check: $13 - 4 = 9 \qquad 4(13) = 52$

Example 2.   If the length of a rectangle is 4 inches more than the width and the area is 192 square inches, what are the dimensions of the rectangle?

Let x be the number of inches in the width and $x + 4$ the number of inches in the length. Then

$$x(x + 4) = 192$$
$$x^2 + 4x = 192$$
$$x^2 + 4x - 192 = 0$$
$$(x + 16)(x - 12) = 0$$

$$x + 16 = 0 \qquad\qquad x - 12 = 0$$
$$x = -16 \text{ inches} \qquad\qquad x = 12 \text{ inches}$$

The width of a rectangle cannot be a negative number. Thus we shall discard the -16. Then, if $x = 12$ inches,

$$x + 4 = 16 \text{ inches}$$

Check:

$$16 - 12 = 4 \text{ inches} \qquad 12(16) = 192 \text{ square inches}$$

EXERCISE 71

A

1. The sum of two positive numbers is 21 and their product is 108. What are the numbers?
2. The product of two consecutive positive even numbers is 288. What are the numbers?
3. Two positive consecutive even numbers are selected. If the smaller one is doubled and the larger one is increased by 1, the product will be 360. What are the original numbers?
4. The difference between two negative numbers is 5. If their product is 104, what are the numbers?
5. The length of a rectangle is twice the width. If the area is 128 square inches, what are the dimensions of the rectangle?
6. The length of a rectangle is 7 inches more than the width. If the area is 198 square inches, what are the dimensions of the rectangle?

7. The length of a rectangle is 4 inches more than the width. If the width is doubled and 3 inches is added to the length, the area is increased by 75 square inches. What are the dimensions of the original rectangle?

8. The length of a rectangle is 6 inches more than the width. If the width is tripled and the length is increased by 3 inches, the area is increased by 155 square inches. What are the dimensions of the new rectangle?

9. A square flower bed has a 3-foot walk surrounding it. If the walk were removed and that space added to the flower bed, the area of the flower bed would be four times as large as the original area. What is the length of one side of the original flower bed?

10. The difference between two positive numbers is 4. The sum of their squares is 208 greater than the product of the two numbers. What are the numbers?

B

1. A motorist, maintaining a constant speed, made a trip of 300 miles. If his rate had been 10 miles per hour slower, it would have taken him one hour longer. What was his rate?

2. A rectangular piece of tin was used to make a box by cutting squares out of each corner, turning up the sides, and welding together the corners. If the piece of tin was 18 inches by 10 inches and the finished box held 168 cubic inches, by trial and error and using long division, determine the length of each side of the squares cut out of each corner.

3. A man drove at a constant speed from his home to a city 180 miles distant. On the return trip he increased his constant speed by 5 miles per hour and made the return trip in 24 minutes less time than was required to drive to the city. What was his speed from home to the city?

4. A motorboat maintained a constant speed downstream for 200 miles in a current whose rate is 5 miles per hour. On the return trip the motorboat maintained the same constant speed as on its trip downstream. There was no stopping and no delay and the round trip was made in 9 hours. How fast would the motorboat have been traveling had it been in still water? (The constant speeds mentioned are those recorded on the boat's speedometer.)

5. A trucker, maintaining a constant speed with his empty truck, traveled 480 miles. The return trip was made with a loaded truck which reduced his constant speed by 20 miles per hour. The return trip took 4 hours longer than the first trip. What was his speed with the loaded truck?

EXERCISE 72

A

Find the roots of the following quadratic equations by any method learned:

1. $x^2 - 169 = 0$
2. $2x^2 - 288 = 0$
3. $5x^2 - 80 = 0$
4. $6x^2 = 216$
5. $x^2 - x - 56 = 0$
6. $x^2 - 3x - 108 = 0$
7. $3x^2 - 12x = 135$
8. $x^2 - 3x = 0$
9. $2x^2 = 8x$
10. $x^2 = 6x - 9$
11. $x^2 - 7x = 8$
12. $x^2 + 12x + 32 = 0$
13. $x^2 - 11x + 24 = 0$
14. $x^2 + 14x + 40 = 0$
15. $2x^2 - 5x - 3 = 0$
16. $3x^2 + 5x - 2 = 0$
17. $9x^2 - 8x + 2 = 0$
18. $4x^2 - 1 = 0$
19. $x^2 + 2x + 3 = 0$
20. $x^2 - 8x + 20 = 0$

B

Find the roots of the following quadratic equations by any method learned:

1. $\dfrac{x^2}{3} - 12 = 0$
2. $\dfrac{x^2}{2} - \dfrac{x}{3} + 1 = 0$
3. $\dfrac{x^2 + 1}{2} + \dfrac{x - 3}{3} - 4 = 0$
4. $\dfrac{x^2}{5} - \dfrac{2x}{3} + 2 = 0$
5. $\dfrac{x^2 - 1}{4} - \dfrac{x + 2}{3} - \dfrac{1}{2} = 0$

REVIEW TEST 25

The roots of the equations in the left-hand column below will be found in the right-hand column. On a sheet of paper write the numbers 1 through 15 to correspond to the numbered equations in the left-hand column. After each number place the letter that corresponds to the correct answer in the right-hand column. Do not use any letter more than once.

1. $x^2 + 5x - 24 = 0$ a. $-3, -8$
2. $x^2 - 2x - 24 = 0$ b. $6, 4$

3. $x^2 + 16 = 0$ c. 12, 2
4. $x^2 - 5x - 24 = 0$ d. 3, −8
5. $4x^2 - 1 = 0$ e. 4, −4
6. $x^2 + 14x + 24 = 0$ f. $\frac{1}{2}i, -\frac{1}{2}i$
7. $x^2 + 8x + 16 = 0$ g. 6, −4
8. $12x^2 - 25x + 12 = 0$ h. −6, 4
9. $x^2 + 2x - 24 = 0$ i. −4, −4
10. $12x^2 - 7x - 12 = 0$ j. $\frac{3}{4}, \frac{4}{3}$
11. $x^2 - 11x + 24 = 0$ k. −3, 8
12. $x^2 + \frac{1}{4} = 0$ l. $-\frac{3}{4}, -\frac{3}{4}$
13. $x^2 - 10x + 24 = 0$ m. 12, 1
14. $12x^2 + 7x - 12 = 0$ n. −6, −4
15. $x^2 + 11x + 24 = 0$ o. $-\frac{4}{3}, \frac{3}{4}$

     p. 3, 8
     q. $-\frac{1}{2}, \frac{1}{2}$
     r. −12, −2
     s. $-\frac{3}{4}, \frac{4}{3}$
     t. $-4i, 4i$

REVIEW TEST 26

On a sheet of paper write the numbers 1 through 20 to correspond to the numbered equations below. After each number write the word *real* or the word *imaginary* to indicate whether the roots of the equations are real or imaginary.

1. $x^2 + 4x + 3 = 0$ 2. $x^2 - 5x - 84 = 0$
3. $x^2 + 5x = 0$ 4. $x^2 + 2 = 0$
5. $x^2 = 9x$ 6. $x^2 + x + 5 = 0$
7. $x^2 = -3$ 8. $x^2 + 3x = 2$
9. $3x^2 - 7x - 1 = 0$ 10. $2x^2 + x + 3 = 0$
11. $4x^2 = -x - 3$ 12. $5x^2 - 3x + 1 = 0$
13. $2x^2 - 7x + 3 = 0$ 14. $x^2 + 3 = 2x$
15. $x^2 + x + 1 = 0$ 16. $x^2 - x - 1 = 0$
17. $x^2 + 8x + 3 = 0$ 18. $x = 8 - x^2$
19. $3 = x^2 - 4x$ 20. $12 = 7x - 3x^2$

13

Ratio, Proportion, and Variation

74. RATIO

The *ratio* of two numbers is the quotient obtained by dividing the first number by the second number. By expressing the ratio of two numbers, we get a comparison of those two numbers. Thus the ratio of $1 to $10 is $\frac{1}{10}$, and of $10 to $1 is $\frac{10}{1}$. Before a ratio can be determined, the two numbers must be expressed in the same unit of measure. Thus the ratio of a nickel to a quarter is $\frac{5}{25}$, or $\frac{1}{5}$. The ratio is read "1 to 5" and is often written in the form 1:5.

When a quantity is measured, we have found a ratio. If a distance is measured and found to be 15 feet, the ratio is $\frac{15}{1}$. This means that the distance contains 15 units of our unit of measure, which is one foot. If a gasoline barrel has a capacity of 50 gallons and into it is placed 40 gallons, we say it is filled to $\frac{40}{50}$, or $\frac{4}{5}$, capacity.

When a ratio has been changed to lowest terms and the denominator of the fraction is 1, that denominator is omitted. Thus the ratio of 30 : 6 is $\frac{30}{6}$, or $\frac{5}{1}$, or 5.

A

Express the following ratios as fractions and simplify:

1. $4 : 6$ 2. $10 : 15$

3. $20 : 5$ 4. $45 : 9$

5. $15 : 75$ 6. $4 : 20$

7. $90 : 60$ 8. $80 : 16$

9. $18 : 72$ 10. $24 : 64$

11. $x : x^2$ 12. $x^2 : x$

13. $4x : x^3$ 14. $x^3 : 3x$

15. $(x + y) : (x^2 - y^2)$ 16. $(x^2 - y^2) : (x - y)$

17. $3x : (2x - xy)$ 18. $(x^2 - x) : x$

19. $(x^2 - 5x + 6) : (x - 3)$ 20. $(x - 4) : (x^2 - x - 12)$

B

Express the following ratios as fractions and simplify:

1. The ratio of 1 day to 1 week.

2. The ratio of 1 week to 2 days.

3. The ratio of 1 dime to a half dollar.

4. The ratio of 1 foot to 1 yard.

5. The ratio of 1 inch to 1 yard.

6. The ratio of 15 inches to 1 yard.

7. The ratio of 25 minutes to 1 hour.

8. The ratio of 30 seconds to 1 hour.

9. The ratio of 12 ounces to 2 pounds.

10. The ratio of 1 square foot to 1 square yard.

11. The ratio of 1 foot 3 inches to 4 feet.

12. The ratio of 5 feet to 2 feet 6 inches.

13. The ratio of 2 gallons to 6 quarts.

14. The ratio of 6 pints to 2 gallons.

15. The ratio of 2 yards to 1 mile.

75. PROPORTION

A *proportion* is a statement that two ratios are equal, and may be written in either of the two forms shown below:

$$\frac{a}{b} = \frac{c}{d} \qquad \text{or} \qquad a : b = c : d$$

In either case the above proportion is read "*a* is to *b* as *c* is to *d*."

When a proportion consists of four different quantities, the fourth quantity is called the *fourth proportional* to the other three quantities, taken in the order that they appear. Thus in the above proportion *d* is the fourth proportional to *a*, *b*, and *c*.

In any proportion the first and last terms are known as the *extremes* and the second and third terms are called the *means*. Consider the proportion

$$\frac{a}{b} = \frac{c}{d}$$

If we obtain a common denominator and clear of fractions, we have

$$\frac{ad}{bd} = \frac{bc}{bd} \qquad \text{or} \qquad ad = bc$$

From the above computation, it can be observed that *the product of the extremes equals the product of the means.* This holds true for any proportion and provides the principle for determining the value of any unknown term in the proportion when the other three terms are given.

If the second and third terms are identical in a proportion, as in $a : b = b : c$, the *b* is called the *mean proportional* between *a* and *c*. In this type of proportion the last term, *c*, is referred to as the *third proportional* to *a* and *b*.

Example 1.   Find the unknown quantity in the proportion $3 : x = 4 : 12$.

By using the principle which states that the product of the extremes equals the product of the means, we have

$$4x = 36$$
$$x = 9$$

Check:

$$3 : x = 4 : 12$$
$$3 : 9 = 4 : 12$$
$$36 = 36$$

Example 2.   Find the value of *x* in the proportion $4 : x = x : 9$.

$$4 : x = x : 9$$
$$x^2 = 36$$
$$x = \pm 6$$

Check:
$$4 : x = x : 9 \qquad\qquad 4 : x = x : 9$$
$$4 : 6 = 6 : 9 \qquad\qquad 4 : (-6) = (-6) : 9$$
$$36 = 36 \qquad\qquad\qquad 36 = 36$$

Many times, in such a problem, the negative value is an unreasonable answer and will be discarded. This will be shown in the solution of stated problems later in the discussion.

Example 3. Find the value of x in the proportion $3 : 2x = \dfrac{x}{2} : 3$.

$$3 : 2x = \frac{x}{2} : 3$$
$$\frac{2x^2}{2} = 9$$
$$x^2 = 9$$
$$x = \pm 3$$

Check:
$$3 : 2x = \frac{x}{2} : 3 \qquad\qquad 3 : 2x = \frac{x}{2} : 3$$
$$3 : 2(3) = \frac{3}{2} : 3 \qquad\qquad 3 : 2(-3) = \frac{-3}{2} : 3$$
$$3 : 6 = \frac{3}{2} : 3 \qquad\qquad 3 : (-6) = \left(\frac{-3}{2}\right) : 3$$
$$9 = 9 \qquad\qquad\qquad 9 = 9$$

Example 4. Find the value of x in the proportion $4 : (x + 5) = 1 : 2$.
$$4 : (x + 5) = 1 : 2$$
$$x + 5 = 8$$
$$x = 3$$
Check:
$$4 : (x + 5) = 1 : 2$$
$$4 : (3 + 5) = 1 : 2$$
$$4 : 8 = 1 : 2$$
$$8 = 8$$

EXERCISE 74

A

Solve for the unknown in each of the following proportions:

1. $x : 3 = 5 : 15$　　　　　　　2. $2 : x = 4 : 20$

3. $3 : 2 = x : 10$　　　　　　　4. $4 : 3 = 8 : x$

5. $4 : 7 = x : 2$

6. $2 : 5 = 3 : x$

7. $8 : x = x : 2$

8. $5 : x = x : 20$

9. $3 : x = x : 8$

10. $4 : x = x : 5$

11. $6 : 3x = 2x : 5$

12. $8 : 2x = 2x : 4$

13. $\dfrac{3}{x} = \dfrac{2}{5}$

14. $\dfrac{x}{2} = \dfrac{5}{10}$

15. $\dfrac{3}{2} = \dfrac{x}{14}$

16. $\dfrac{6}{5} = \dfrac{3}{x}$

17. $\dfrac{2x}{3} = \dfrac{4}{3}$

18. $\dfrac{2}{3x} = \dfrac{3}{9}$

19. $\dfrac{2}{x} = \dfrac{2x}{16}$

20. $\dfrac{3}{2x} = \dfrac{2x}{12}$

21. $\dfrac{5}{x} = \dfrac{x}{4}$

22. $\dfrac{3}{5x} = \dfrac{x}{10}$

23. $\dfrac{1}{4x} = \dfrac{x}{12}$

24. $\dfrac{2}{3x} = \dfrac{2x}{3}$

25. $(x + 1) : 3 = 8 : 4$

26. $2 : (x - 2) = 4 : 12$

27. $1 : 5 = (x - 3) : 10$

28. $2 : 3 = 3 : (x + 1)$

29. $\dfrac{1}{x - 2} = \dfrac{3}{4}$

30. $\dfrac{4}{3} = \dfrac{x + 3}{5}$

B

Solve for the unknown in each of the following proportions:

1. $\dfrac{x + 1}{x^2 - 1} = \dfrac{1}{2}$ (*Hint:* Factor and simplify the fraction.)

2. $\dfrac{x^2 + x}{x + 1} = \dfrac{4}{5}$

3. $\dfrac{x + 1}{x} = \dfrac{2}{3}$

4. $(x^2 - 4) : (x + 2) = 3 : 1$

5. $x : (x + 1) = x : 4$

6. Find the fourth proportional to 2, 3, and 4.

7. Find the third proportional to 4 and 6.

8. Find the mean proportional between 8 and 18.

9. Find the mean proportional between 6 and 30.

10. Find the fourth proportional to $(a + b)$, $(a - b)$, and $(a + b)$.

There are times when one wishes to divide a given quantity into certain parts. The following example illustrates this type of problem:

Example 1. A man has a rope 180 feet long that he wishes to cut into three parts in the ratio of 2 : 3 : 4. How long will each piece of the rope be?

Let x be a unit of the rope. Then

$$2x = \text{the first part}$$
$$3x = \text{the second part}$$
$$4x = \text{the third part}$$
$$9x = \text{the sum of the parts}$$
$$9x = 180 \text{ feet}$$
$$x = 20$$
$$2x = 40 \text{ feet}$$
$$3x = 60 \text{ feet}$$
$$4x = 80 \text{ feet}$$

Thus the three lengths of rope will be 40, 60, and 80 feet respectively.

Check: $\quad\quad\quad\quad 40 + 60 + 80 = 180$

Two similar triangles are triangles that have the same shape but may be different in size. It is proved in plane geometry that the sides of two similar triangles are proportional. By that is meant that the ratio of any two corresponding sides is the same as the ratio of any other pair of corresponding sides.

Example 2. The three sides of one triangle are 4 inches, 6 inches, and 9 inches. If the shortest side of a similar triangle is 6 inches, what are the lengths of the two remaining sides of the second triangle?

Let x be the second side of the second triangle. Then

$$4 : 6 = 6 : x$$
$$4x = 36$$
$$x = 9 \text{ inches}$$

Let y be the third side of the second triangle. Then

$$4 : 6 = 9 : y$$
$$4y = 54$$
$$y = 13\tfrac{1}{2} \text{ inches}$$

It is shown in the study of chemistry that if a gas is heated, it will expand and thereby occupy a greater volume. Likewise, if the gas is cooled, it will contract and occupy a smaller volume. This principle is set up as a proportion as shown below:

$$\frac{V_1}{V_2} = \frac{T_1}{T_2}$$

Example 3. A certain gas occupies a volume of 300 cubic centimeters when the temperature of the gas is 250°. If the temperature is increased to 300°, what is the volume of the gas?

$$\frac{V_1}{V_2} = \frac{T_1}{T_2}$$

$$\frac{300}{V_2} = \frac{250}{300}$$

$$250\,V^2 = 90,000$$

$$V^2 = 360 \text{ cubic centimeters}$$

EXERCISE 75

1. A man has a board 12 feet long. He wishes to cut it into two parts in the ratio of 2 : 6. How long will each part be?
2. A telephone cable 160 feet long must be cut into four parts in a ratio of 2 : 3 : 5 : 6. How long will each part be?
3. A man left a will in which his estate, valued at $24,000, was to be divided among his widow, his son, and his daughter in a ratio of 4 : 3 : 1 respectively. How much did each receive from the estate?
4. Find four numbers whose sum is 225 and whose ratio is 2 : 3 : 4 : 6.
5. The three sides of a triangle are 3 feet, 4 feet, and 6 feet. The shortest side of a similar triangle is 5 feet. What is the length of the longest side of the second triangle?
6. A flagpole, located beside a fence post, casts a shadow 12 feet long. The shadow of the fence post is 3 feet long. If the fence post is 7 feet high, how high is the flagpole? (*Hint:* Construct similar triangles by drawing lines from the top of the flagpole and the top of the fence post to the points at which their shadows end)
7. The three sides of a triangle are 6 feet, 8 feet, and 10 feet. The longest side of a similar triangle is 24 feet. What is the perimeter of the second triangle?
8. At a temperature of 200° a certain gas occupies a volume of 400 cubic

centimeters. If the temperature is increased to 225°, what will be the volume of the gas?

9. If a certain gas occupies 300 cubic centimeters when the temperature is 250°, what will the temperature be if the volume is reduced to 250 cubic centimeters?

10. If a certain gas occupies 300 cubic centimeters when the temperature is 270°, how much will the temperature have to be increased to raise the volume to 400 cubic centimeters?

77. VARIATION

If y varies directly as x, we say

$$y = kx$$

The constant k is known as the *constant of variation*. This type of variation is referred to as *direct variation* and means that as one quantity increases, the other quantity increases. Another way of stating this relationship between the two quantities is to say that y is *directly proportional* to x.

The formula for finding the circumference of a circle, $C = \pi d$, is an example of direct variation. The constant π is the constant of variation and C increases as d increases.

Example 1. If y varies as x, and $y = 8$ when $x = 4$, what is the value of y when $x = 6$?

$$y = kx$$
$$8 = k(4)$$
$$4k = 8$$
$$k = 2$$

Then

$$y = kx$$
$$y = 2x$$
$$y = 2(6)$$
$$y = 12$$

Example 2. If y varies as x^2, and $y = 12$ when $x = 2$, find the value of y when $x = 5$.

$$y = kx^2$$
$$12 = k(2)^2$$
$$12 = 4k$$
$$4k = 12$$
$$k = 3$$

Then

$$y = kx^2$$
$$y = 3x^2$$
$$y = 3(5)^2$$
$$y = 3(25)$$
$$y = 75$$

When two quantities are so related that as one increases the other one decreases, we have what is known as *inverse variation*.

If y varies inversely as x, our equation reads

$$y = \frac{k}{x}$$

and, again, k is the constant of variation.

This type of variation is associated with Boyle's Law, used in the physical sciences, which states that the volume of a gas varies inversely as the pressure exerted on that gas. This principle makes use of the formula

$$V = \frac{k}{P}$$

Example 3. If y varies inversely as x, and $y = 5$ when $x = 2$, find the value of y when $x = 1$.

$$y = \frac{k}{x}$$

$$5 = \frac{k}{2}$$

$$k = 10$$

Substituting this value in the original equation, we have

$$y = \frac{10}{x}$$

Then

$$y = \frac{10}{1}$$

$$y = 10$$

Example 4. If y varies inversely as the square of x, and $y = 24$ when $x = 2$, find the value of y when $x = 4$.

$$y = \frac{k}{x^2}$$

$$24 = \frac{k}{4}$$

$$k = 96$$

Substituting this value in the original equation, we have

$$y = \frac{96}{4^2}$$

$$y = \frac{96}{16}$$

$$y = 6$$

If y varies directly as x and z, we state that relationship as

$$y = kxz$$

This type of variation is referred to as *joint variation*. The k, again, is the constant of variation. The formula for finding the area of a triangle, $A = \frac{1}{2}bh$, is an illustration of joint variation. The $\frac{1}{2}$ is the constant of variation and the area is dependent upon the two variables, the base and the altitude of the triangle.

Example 5. If y varies as x and z, and $y = 32$ when $x = 2$ and $z = 4$, find y when $x = 3$ and $z = 5$.

$$y = kxz$$
$$32 = k(2)(4)$$
$$8k = 32$$
$$k = 4$$

Substituting this value in the original equation, we have

$$y = 4xz$$

Then

$$y = 4(3)(5)$$
$$y = 60$$

Example 6. If y varies as x^2 and z^3, and $y = 6$ when $x = 3$ and $z = 2$, find the value of y when $x = 2$ and $z = 3$.

$$y = kx^2z^3$$
$$6 = k(3)^2(2)^3$$
$$6 = k(9)(8)$$
$$72k = 6$$
$$k = \tfrac{1}{12}$$

Substituting this value in the original equation, we have

$$y = \tfrac{1}{12}x^2z^3$$

Then

$$y = \tfrac{1}{12}(2)^2(3)^3$$
$$y = \tfrac{1}{12}(4)(27)$$
$$y = \tfrac{108}{12}$$
$$y = 9$$

Sometimes a problem involves a combination of two or more of the types of variation that we have used in the foregoing discussion.

Example 7. If y varies directly as x and inversely as z, and $y = 8$ when $x = 4$ and $z = 2$, find the value of y when $x = 2$ and $z = 3$.

$$y = \frac{kx}{z}$$

$$8 = \frac{k(4)}{2}$$

$$4k = 16$$
$$k = 4$$

Substituting this value in the original equation, we have

$$y = \frac{4x}{z}$$

Then

$$y = \frac{4(2)}{3}$$

$$y = \frac{8}{3}$$

$$y = 2\tfrac{2}{3}$$

Example 8. If y varies jointly as x and z and inversely as the square of t, and $y = 3$ when $x = 2$, $z = 1$, and $t = 2$, find the value of y when $x = 1$, $z = 3$, and $t = 3$.

$$y = \frac{kxz}{t^2}$$

$$3 = \frac{k(2)(1)}{4}$$

$$2k = 12$$
$$k = 6$$

Substituting this value in the original equation, we have

$$y = \frac{6xz}{t^2}$$

Then

$$y = \frac{6(1)(3)}{9}$$

$$y = \frac{18}{9}$$

$$y = 2$$

A

1. If y varies directly as x, and $y = 20$ when $x = 4$, find the value of y when $x = 7$.
2. If y varies as x^2, and $y = 36$ when $x = 3$, find the value of y when $x = 5$.
3. If y varies inversely as x, and $y = 3$ when $x = 2$, find the value of y when $x = 12$.
4. If y varies inversely as the square of x, and $y = 6$ when $x = 4$, find the value of y when $x = 8$.
5. If y varies as the cube of x, and $y = 24$ when $x = 2$, find the value of y when $x = 3$.
6. If y varies inversely as the cube of x, and $y = 1$ when $x = 2$, find the value of y when $x = 3$.
7. If y varies jointly as x and z, and $y = 4$ when $x = 2$ and $z = \frac{1}{2}$, find the value of y when $x = 3$ and $z = 2$.
8. If y varies jointly as x and the square of z, and $y = 54$ when $x = 2$ and $z = 3$, find the value of y when $x = \frac{1}{3}$ and $z = 4$.
9. If y varies jointly as the square of x and the cube of z, and $y = 36$ when $x = 2$ and $z = 2$, find the value of y when $x = 2$ and $z = 3$.
10. If y varies jointly as x and the square of z and inversely as a, and $y = 18$ when $x = 6$, $z = \frac{1}{2}$, and $a = 3$, find the value of y when $x = 4$, $z = 2$, and $a = \frac{1}{2}$.

B

1. It has been proved in physics that an object falling from rest (having been given no initial force) varies directly as the square of the time. If an object falls 64 feet in 2 seconds, how far will it fall in 5 seconds?
2. If an object is dropped from the top of a building and takes 3 seconds to reach the ground, how high is the building?
3. The volume of a pyramid, whose base is a square, varies directly as the area of the base and the altitude of the pyramid. If the volume of a pyramid whose base is 64 square feet and whose altitude is 9 feet is 192 cubic feet, what is the volume of a pyramid whose base is 10 feet on a side and whose altitude is 12 feet?
4. A certain gas has a volume of 450 cubic centimeters when the tem-

perature is 300°. If the temperature is reduced to 250°, by how much has the volume been reduced?

5. A certain gas occupies 500 cubic centimeters under a pressure of 40. By how much will the pressure be reduced if the volume is increased to 600 cubic centimeters?

REVIEW TEST 27

On a sheet of paper write the numbers 1 through 10 to correspond to the numbered problems below. After each number place the letter that corresponds to the correct answer in the right-hand column. Do not use any letter more than once.

1. If y varies directly as x, and $y = 6$ when $x = 2$, what is the value of y when $x = 1$?

2. If y varies inversely as x, and $y = 2$ when $x = 1$, what will be the value of y when $x = 3$?

3. If y varies jointly as x and z, and $y = 8$ when $x = 1$ and $z = 1$, what will be the value of y when $x = 1$ and $z = 4$?

4. If y varies directly as x^3, and $y = 32$ when $x = 2$, what will be the value of y when $x = \frac{1}{2}$?

5. If y varies inversely as x^2, and $y = 20$ when $x = \frac{1}{2}$, what will be the value of y when $x = 1$?

6. If y varies as the square of x and inversely as z, and $y = 25$ when $x = 5$ and $z = 2$, what will be the value of y when $x = 2$ and $z = 3$?

7. If y varies inversely as the square of x, and $y = 18$ when $x = \frac{1}{3}$, what will be the value of y when $x = 4$?

8. If y varies jointly as x and z and inversely as m, and $y = 24$ when $x = 3$, $z = 4$, and $m = 2$, what will be the value of y when $x = 1$, $z = 3$, and $m = 3$?

9. If y varies directly as the cube of x and inversely as the square of z, and $y = 9$ when $x = 2$ and $z = \frac{1}{3}$, what will be the value of y when $x = 2$ and $z = 2$?

10. If y varies as the cube of x, and $y = \frac{1}{4}$ when $x = \frac{1}{2}$, what will be the value of y when $x = 1$?

a. 5
b. $\frac{1}{4}$
c. $\frac{1}{3}$
d. $\frac{1}{8}$
e. $1\frac{2}{3}$
f. 32
g. 4
h. 16
i. $\frac{2}{3}$
j. $\frac{1}{16}$
k. $2\frac{2}{3}$
l. $1\frac{1}{3}$
m. 3
n. 2
o. $\frac{1}{2}$

Answers to
Odd-Numbered Problems

EXERCISE 1, page 8

A

1. $\{13, 14, 15, \ldots, 19\}$ 3. $\{1, 3, 5, 7, 9\}$
5. $\{9, 18, 27, 36, 45\}$ 7. $\varnothing$ 9. $\{2, 4, 6, \ldots\}$

11. The set of natural numbers greater than 12 and less than 20 that have no exact integral divisors except themselves and 1.   13. The set of all natural numbers less than 10 that are perfect squares.   15. The set of all natural numbers less than 40 whose units digit is 6.   17. The set of all natural numbers less than 30 that are divisible by 7.   19. The set of all odd natural numbers.

B

1. $\{1, 2, 3, 4\}$ 3. $\varnothing$ 5. $\{2, 4, 6, 8, 10, 12, 14\}$
7. $\{4, 5, 6, 7, 8\}$ 9. $\{7, 8, 9, 10, 11\}$
11. $\varnothing$, $\{0, 1, 2\}$, $\{0\}$, $\{1\}$, $\{2\}$, $\{0, 1\}$, $\{0, 2\}$, $\{1, 2\}$
13. $A \cap B = \varnothing$, $A \cup B = \{0, 1, 2, 3, 4, 5, 6\}$

323

EXERCISE 2, page 16

A

1. The commutative law for addition. 3. The distributive law of multiplication with respect to addition. 5. The law of closure for addition. 7. The associative law for multiplication. 9. If equals are divided by equals, the quotients are equal.

B

1. The additive identity and if equals are multiplied by equals, the products are equal. 3. The commutative law for multiplication and the distributive law. 5. If equals are multiplied by equals and the symmetric relationship.

EXERCISE 3, page 19

A

1. $\{3, 4\}$ 3. $\varnothing$ 5. $\{5, 6\}$ 7. $\varnothing$ 9. $\varnothing$

B

1. $\{0\}$ 3. $\varnothing$ 5. $\varnothing$ 7. $\{-2, -1, 0, 1\}$ 9. $\{-1, 0, 1, 2\}$

EXERCISE 4, page 22

A

1. The number represented by n is added to the number represented by m. 3. The number represented by c is subtracted from the sum of the numbers represented by a and b. 5. The number represented by a is added to three times the number represented by b. 7. The number represented by x is squared. 9. One is subtracted from the square of the number represented by x. 11. The number represented by y is subtracted from the number represented by x and their difference is divided by 3.

13. $4a + 5$ 15. $m - x$ 17. $3(x + y)$

19. πd 21. $\frac{1}{2}(x + y + z)$ 23. $\frac{1}{4}(3xy)$ or $\dfrac{3xy}{4}$

25. $2a - 3x$

B

1. The square of the number represented by x is multiplied by 3.   3. The square of the number represented by y is added to the square of the number represented by x.   5. Three is added to the cube of the number represented by x and their sum is divided by 2.   7. The sum of the numbers represented by x and y is multiplied by 3 and that result is divided by 4.

9. $\dfrac{4d}{5}$ 11. $\dfrac{x^3}{2}$ 13. $6 - x^3$ 15. $\frac{2}{3}ab$

EXERCISE 5, page 24

A

1. 3	3. 6	5. 0	7. 3
9. 5	11. 1	13. 2	15. 1
17. 6	19. 14	21. 3	23. 9
25. 5	27. 3	29. 1	

B

1. 1	3. 1	5. 1	7. $2\frac{1}{2}$	9. 1

EXERCISE 6, page 24

A

1. The set of natural numbers that are exactly divisible by 3.   3. The set of one-digit prime numbers.   5. The set of perfect squares greater than 24 and less than 50.   7. $\{3\}$.   9. $\{1, 2, 3, 5, 6, 7\}$.   11. The number represented by m is subtracted from 4.   13. Two-thirds of the square of the number represented by x. 15. The sum of the number represented by m and three times the number represented by n, all divided by 2.   17. 7.   19. 2.

B

1. $\varnothing$ 3. $\{-3, -2, -1, 0, 1, 2, 3, 4, 5\}$ 5. $\{3, 4, 5\}$
7. 4   9. 1

EXERCISE 7, page 36

A

1. 3
3. -6
5. 1
7. -5
9. $-19s$
11. $4x^2 + 3y$
13. $4c^2 + d$
15. $-4x^2 + 3z^2$
17. $2b^2 + 2d$
19. $4a^2b^2c - 3de + 6ab^2$
21. 2
23. -3
25. $3xy$
27. $a + 2b$
29. $2c - 2b$

B

1. $7x^2y - xy^2$
3. $7a^2 - 4b + c^2 + 2d^2$
5. $9c^2d + d^2c + 6x + 5y$
7. $-6x^2y$
9. $25x^2a$
11. $-4d^2 - 7e + 11f$
13. $d - 2e + 7f$
15. $6m - n + 6p$
17. $-2a^2b^2 + 6c - 5d$
19. $4a^2 + 5b^2 + 3c^2$
21. $3r - 10s - 4t$

EXERCISE 8, page 40

A

1. $3m - 3n + 1$
3. $2x - 3y$
5. $x + 3y + 3$
7. $3p - 4q + 8$
9. $-8y$
11. $3x$
13. $3w + 1$
15. $x - 7y - 2z$
17. $2x + 2y$
19. $2p$

B

1. $4x - 6$
3. $6d - c + 12$
5. $r + s$
7. $5b - 4a$
9. $2m - 2n$

EXERCISE 9, page 41

1. $c + d$
3. $6(w - v)$
5. $-3(x + 3)$
7. $5(x + y + z)$
9. $-4(m + n - p)$
11. $3(3 - 7y + z)$
13. $-7(x - y)$
15. $(m + n - p)$
17. $3(x - y)$
19. $3(3 - a)$
21. $7(d + b)$
23. $-2(a + b - 2)$
25. $5(x - 3y)$
27. $-6(x - y - z)$
29. $9(a + b - c)$
31. 0
33. $-2(a + b + c + d)$
35. $9(h + a + x + 3)$

1. 3	3. -2	5. 3	7. -11	9. 5
11. 0	13. 23	15. 0	17. -11	19. 8
21. 30	23. -8	25. 1	27. -24	29. 32

1. $-2a - 3$	3. $-5m^2 + 1$	5. $2b$
7. $4x^2 - y^2 - 3z^2$	9. $5m + 7n$	11. $7a^2$
13. $y - 11z$	15. $4z^2 - 6y^2$	17. $-3m^2 - n^2$
19. $2a + 4b - 9c$	21. $13 - t + 3s$	23. $2x^2 - 5y^2 - 2z^2$
25. $-14a - 4b + 7c$	27. $-2ab + c - 1$	29. $2(a - b)$
31. $2(m - n + p)$	33. $3a$	35. $3m - 4n$
37. 10	39. -6	41. 25
43. 20	45. 4	47. -65
49. 20		

1. 21	3. 30	5. -36	7. -56
9. 56	11. -99	13. 92	15. 114
17. 135	19. -105	21. -2	23. 6
25. 2	27. 4	29. -7	31. -13
33. -4	35. -3	37. -4	39. -16

A

1. x^5	3. a^7	5. d^9	7. r^7
9. 3^5	11. 4^5	13. b^3	15. w^5
17. $-x^3$	19. $5m^2$	21. $8b^2$	23. $-6a^5$
25. x^3y^3	27. $6wr^2$	29. a^3b^4	31. y^3
33. r^3	35. s^2	37. $4b$	39. $-2x^2y$

41. $-2z^3$ 43. $-2st$ 45. $-5r^2s^2t^2$ 47. $3cd$

49. $-3a^3b^4c$ 51. $\dfrac{4}{a}$ 53. $-\dfrac{3s^2}{r^3}$ 55. $-\dfrac{3b^3}{a}$

57. $-\dfrac{3z}{m}$ 59. $-\dfrac{5n^4}{m}$

B

1. $r^3s^2t^2$ 3. $15x^3$ 5. $-40m^3n^6$ 7. $18x^4$
9. $10c^4d^7$ 11. $24xz^2$ 13. $-x^3y^2z^4$ 15. $-21m^2np^3$
17. $8a^3b^2d^4$ 19. $-x^4y^4$ 21. $3mnp$ 23. $9w^2z$

25. $3x^4y^5$ 27. $3a^3b$ 29. $4b^2y^2$ 31. $\dfrac{s^4}{3r}$

33. $\dfrac{4x^3y^3}{z}$ 35. $-\dfrac{w^2}{4x^3}$

EXERCISE 14, page 60

A

1. $x^4 - x^3 - 3x^2 + 7x - 3$ 3. $m^4 - 2m^3 - 4m^2 + 3$
5. $a^2 + 3ab - b^2$ 7. $b^3 + 3b^2x + 3bx^2 + x^3$
9. $x^5 - 5x^4y + 10x^3y^2 - 10x^2y^3 + 5xy^4 - y^5$ 11. $a^2 - 2ab + b^2$
13. $s^2 + 4st + 4t^2$ 15. $a^2 + a - 6$
17. $t^2 - s^2$ 19. $21u^2 + 25u - 4$
21. $-15n^2 + 41n - 14$ 23. $-8s^2 + 6sw - w^2$
25. $t^3 - t^2 + 3t - 3$ 27. $t^4 - t^3 + 5t - 5$
29. $2z^3 - 2z^2y + zy - y^2$ 31. $cd - 3d^2 + de^2 - ce + 3de - e^3$
33. $6a^3 - 9a^2b + 2ab^2 + 2ac^2 - 3b^3 - 3bc^2$
35. $x^3y^2 + x^2y + xz + 3x^2y^3 + 3xy^2 + 3yz$
37. $a^2 + 2ab + ac + ad + b^2 + bc + bd$
39. $a^2b + abc - acd - 2a + ab^2 + b^2c - bcd - 2b$

B

1. $2m^4 + 3m^3 - 17m^2 + 14m - 3$
3. $r^4 + r^3s - 5r^2s^2 + 5rs^3 - 2s^4$
5. $3b^3 + 2b^2x + 3b^2y + 10b^2z + 6bxz + 9byz + 3bz^2$
7. $x^4 + 4x^3 + 6x^2 + 4x + 1$
9. $m^3 - 3m^2n + 3mn^2 - n^3 - 2m^2 + 4mn - 2n^2$
11. $3s^5 + 5s^4 + 8s^3 + s^2 - 2s$
13. $x^4 + 8x^3 + 23x^2 + 28x + 12$
15. $x^3y^3 + 3x^2y^2z + 3xyz^2 + z^3$

EXERCISE 15, page 64

A

1. $-6b - 3$
3. $23c + 5d$
5. $5y + z$
7. $3a^2 - a + 2b$
9. $y - x^2$
11. $11a - 14b$
13. $3x^2 - 9x + 12$
15. $9a^2 - 2ab$
17. -15
19. -1
21. 1
23. 9
25. 34
27. $(y - 2x) - (n - m)$
29. $(x^2 - 2xy + y^2) - (m^2 + 2m - n^2)$
31. $(2x^2 - y^2) - (m^2 - 7n)$
33. $(x - y) - (m + mn - n)$
35. $(y - 3x) - (m - 3n)$
37. $(x^2 - xy + 12y^2) - (m^2 + 4mn - 21n^2)$

B

1. $c^2 - (a + b^2)$
3. $(r + 3s) - (3p + q)$
5. $(4z - 3y) - (2b + 5d)$
7. $180° - (2x° + y°)$
9. $\$20 - [2x + 3y]$

EXERCISE 16, page 68

A

1. $x + 6$
3. $y + 3$
5. $b + 9$
7. $x + 8$
9. $r - 4$
11. $2m - 1$
13. $4s - 5$
15. $3t + 2$
17. $4a - 5$
19. $5a - b$
21. $3r - 2s$
23. $4x + 3$, rem. 20
25. $4m - 1$, rem. -1
27. $4a^2 - 2a + 1$
29. $16y^2 - 8yb + 4b^2$

B

1. $x^2 + 3x - 1$
3. $2x^2 - x - 3$
5. $2r^2 + r + 1$
7. $5c^2d^2 - 3cd + 2$
9. $x^2 + x + 1$

EXERCISE 17, page 69

1. $14x^3 - 33x^2 - 7x + 5$
3. $x^3y^3 - 9x^2y^2 + 9xy + 35$
5. $18s^3 - 18s^2 - 23s + 5$
7. $8z^4 - 42z^3 - 3z^2 - 11z - 6$

9. $3x - 2$

11. $x^2 - 4$

13. $x^2 - 7$

15. $a^2b^2 - 3c^2d^2$

17. $x^2 + x - y + 2y^2$

19. $9x + 5y - 9$

21. $8y - 3x$

23. $x^2 - 9x - 8$

25. $4p + q + 3$

27. $(n - m^2) - (2x + 3y^2)$

29. $(-m^2n^2 - p^2) - (z^2 - x^2y^2)$

31. -4 33. -3 35. 3

EXERCISE 18, page 83

A

1. 6   3. 6   5. 14   7. 9

9. 20   11. 5   13. 24   15. 0

17. 4   19. 6   21. 3   23. 5

25. -4

B

1. 24   3. -10 5. -3 7. 2

9. 1   11. 12   13. 10   15. 6

17. 18   19. -6 21. 6   23. 7

25. 2   27. -4 29. -18

EXERCISE 19, page 85

A

1. 2   3. 1   5. 2   7. 2

9. 6   11. 6   13. 6   15. 4

B

1. 2   3. 3   5. 1   7. 1

9. -29

A

1. 37, 41   3. 58, 53   5. 12   7. 8 ft.
9. 12 ft.   11. 6 ft.   13. 21 ft.   15. 8 in., 10 in., and 11 in.
17. 5 in., 9 in.   19. 4 in. by 9 in.   21. Trailer, $800; automobile, $2400
23. $1100   25. 4 yrs.; 12 yrs.

B

1. 7   3. 210 miles   5. 120 student; 135 adult
7. 90 pounds   9. $3,000, $1,500, $3,500, $2,000

EXERCISE 22, page 108

A

1. $x > 6$ 3. $x > -5$ 5. $x < 6$ 7. $x < 0$ 9. $5 > x > 3$

B

1. $x > -10$ and $x < 14$ 3. $x > -3$ and $x < \dfrac{5}{3}$
5. $x > 9$ or $x < -3$

EXERCISE 23, page 112

1. $(3)(5)$ 3. $(2)(3)(3)$ 5. $(2)(2)(7)$ 7. $(5)(7)$
9. $(2)(2)(2)(3)(3)$ 11. $(2)(2)(2)(2)(7)$
13. $(2)(2)(2)(2)(2)(7)$ 15. $(2)(3)(5)(5)(5)$
17. $(2)(2)(2)(2)(2)(2)(5)(5)$ 19. $(2)(2)(3)(3)(3)(3)(3)(5)$

A

1. $p^2 - q^2$ 3. $4a^2 - 1$ 5. $16z^2 - 9y^2$ 7. $m^2n^2 - p^2$
9. $4a^2b^2 - c^2$ 11. $x^2y^2z^2 - 4$ 13. $9c^2 - m^2n^2$ 15. $b^2d^2 - 49c^2$
17. $(x + 3y)(x - 3y)$
19. $(4m + 7n)(4m - 7n)$
21. $(6y + 5w)(6y - 5w)$
23. $(pq + 1)(pq - 1)$
25. $(2cd + 7)(2cd - 7)$
27. $(n + 10)(n - 10)$
29. $(1 + 7m)(1 - 7m)$
31. $(ab + cd)(ab - cd)$
33. $(5rs + 1)(5rs - 1)$
35. $(mnp + 1)(mnp - 1)$

B

1. $(d^2 + c^2)(d + c)(d - c)$
3. $(9x^2 + 4y^2)(3x + 2y)(3x - 2y)$
5. $(4 + p^2)(2 + p)(2 - p)$
7. $(a^4 + b^4)(a^2 + b^2)(a + b)(a - b)$
9. $(4a^2 - b^2 + x^2 - y^2)(4a^2 - b^2 - x^2 + y^2)$

A

1. $y^2 - 3y + 2$ 3. $m^2 + 9m + 14$ 5. $z^2 + 6z + 9$
7. $b^2 - 10b + 16$ 9. $n^2 - 11n + 28$ 11. $y^2 + 2y - 24$
13. $6s^2 + 11st + 3t^2$ 15. $2a^2 + ab - 15b^2$ 17. $5x^2 - 13xy - 6y^2$
19. $1 + 2a + a^2$ 21. $x^2 + 4xy + 4y^2$ 23. $y^2 - 6yz + 9z^2$
25. $z^2 - 10z + 25$ 27. $(y + 3)(y + 5)$ 29. $(a + 6)(a + 8)$
31. $(t - 3)(t - 1)$ 33. $(a - 3)(a - 5)$ 35. $(y - 9)(y - 4)$
37. $(c + 6)(c - 4)$ 39. $(b - 5)(b + 2)$ 41. $(b + 4)(b + 7)$
43. $(c - 3)(c - 3)$ 45. $(y - 1)(y - 1)$ 47. $(3y - 2)(3y - 2)$
49. $(p - 9)(p - 9)$

B

1. $(2x - 3y)(2x - 3y)$ 3. $(7t - 1)(7t - 1)$
5. $(q - 12)(q - 12)$ 7. $(y + 9)(y - 7)$
9. $(d - 9)(d + 3)$ 11. $(4c - 3)(3c + 4)$
13. $3(4z - 1)(2z + 3)$ 15. $(x + y + 3)(x + y + 2)$
17. $(4c - 4d + 3)(c - d - 2)$ 19. $(m - n - 9)(m - n + 7)$

1. $(m - d)(m^2 + md + d^2)$
5. $(3 - w)(9 + 3w + w^2)$
9. $(rs + xy)(r^2s^2 - rsxy + x^2y^2)$

3. $(r + s)(r^2 - rs + s^2)$
7. $(4 + m)(16 - 4m + m^2)$

A

1. $a(3 - b)$
7. $2(2b + c)$
13. $d(c - m)$
19. $pq^2(pq - 1)$
23. $4mp(p - 4)(p + 1)$
27. $cd(x + y)(x - y)$
31. $2b(2y + 3z)(2y - 3z)$
35. $3(2mn + 3p)(2mn - 3p)$
39. $3(3d + 5c)(3d - 5c)$
43. $3(x^2 + z^2)(x + z)(x - z)$

3. $2(m + n + p)$
9. $m^2(x - y)$
15. $3m(5m - 6)$

5. $2s(t - r)$
11. $3(4a - 3b)$
17. $10z^2(3y^2 + 2)$
21. $-3ab(ab + 2a^2b^2 + 3)$
25. $7rt(4r - 5t - 9r^2t^2)$
29. $4a(r + 3s)(r - 3s)$
33. $2ax(b + 5c)(b - 5c)$
37. $mnp(1 + d)(1 - d)$
41. $(m^2 + n^2)(m + n)(m - n)$
45. $2mn(n^2 + m^2)(n + m)(n - m)$

B

1. $3m(2y - 1)(6y + 5)$
5. $2(3b + 1)(b + 2)$
9. $2(2x + y)(4x^2 - 2xy + y^2)$
13. $(y - x)(x + 4y)$

3. $3(4z - 1)(2z + 3)$
7. $3m(b - c)(b^2 + bc + c^2)$
11. $2a^2(c - 2d)(c^2 + 2cd + 4d^2)$

A

1. $(x + y)(z + a)$
5. $(a + 1)(b + c)$
9. $(3x - 2y)(z + 1)$
13. $2(a + 2c)(b + d)$
17. $(3b - c)(a - 2d)$

3. $(m - n)(p + q)$
7. $(m - n)(p - q)$
11. $(u + v)(w - 5)$
15. $(3b - a)(2c + 3d)$
19. $2a(4m - x)(3n - 2y)$

B

1. $(r + s - 1)(r + s + 1)$ 3. $(m - 2n - p)(m - 2n + p)$
5. $(c - 3d - a + 6b)(c - 3d + a - 6b)$ 7. $(a + b)(1 + a + b)$
9. $(c + d)(c + d + 2)$

EXERCISE 29, page 131

1. 391	3. 1575	5 2419	7. 7569	9. 9216
11. 819	13. 8464	15. 3375	17. 5929	19. 4836
21. 11,881	23. 9775	25. 9375		

EXERCISE 30, page 132

A

1. $m(b + c + d)$
3. $3m(4cd + c + 6d)$
5. $(x - 2z)(x + 2z)$
7. $(mn - p)(mn + p)$
9. $(xz + ac)(xz - ac)$
11. $3(m + 3n)(m - 3n)$
13. $3a(2p + 5q)(2p - 5q)$
15. $(11s + 12t)(11s - 12t)$
17. $2m(4b + 5c)(4b - 5c)$
19. $axy(y + 1)(y - 1)$
21. $(t - 2)(t - 2)$
23. $(3 - s)(3 - s)$
25. $(p - 3)(p + 6)$
27. $b(c + 4)(c + 2)$
29. $(t - 1)(t - 10)$
31. $(2w - 1)(w - 8)$
33. $(6c - 5)(4c + 3)$
35. $m(8d + 1)(3d - 4)$
37. $3m(m^2 + 4m + 6)$
39. $4c(x - 3y)(x + y)$
41. $(6t + 5)(2t + 7)$
43. $ab(ab + 1)(ab - 1)$
45. $t(t + 4)(t - 4)$
47. $5a(3m + 1)(2m - 3)$
49. $(12a - 5)(3a + 1)$

B

1. $(3c - 1)(4c + 9)$
3. $(4r - 3)(3r - 4)$
5. $(x + 3y)(2x - y)$
7. $(3m - n)(2m + 15n)$
9. $(cd - x)(4cd - 5x)$
11. $(m - n)(m^2 + mn + n^2)$
13. $a(d - 1)(d^2 + d + 1)$
15. $(x - y - z)(x + y + z)$
17. $(x - a - 2)(x + a + 2)$
19. $2(3 - 2p)(9 + 6p + 4p^2)$
21. $(5q - 1)(25q^2 + 5q + 1)$
23. $2(x + y - 2z)(x + y + 2z)$

25. $4a(3b - 5c + 2d - 7m + n)$

27. $(4mnp - 3)(3mnp + 2)$

29. $(p - 3)(m - q)$

31. 37

33. 32

35. 108

EXERCISE 31, page 144

A

1. $\dfrac{3}{5}$

3. $\dfrac{4}{7}$

5. $\dfrac{2}{15}$

7. $\dfrac{z}{4a}$

9. $\dfrac{4r^2t^2}{5s}$

11. $\dfrac{5t^2}{a}$

13. $\dfrac{b + x}{m - n}$

15. $\dfrac{y - 2}{2x - 1}$

17. Will not simplify

19. $\dfrac{1}{s - r}$

21. $\dfrac{z + 2}{z - 2}$

23. $\dfrac{1 + c}{1 - c}$

25. $\dfrac{a + b + c}{m - n}$

27. $\dfrac{y + b}{3}$

29. $\dfrac{a + 2}{a - 2}$

B

1. $\dfrac{y - 4}{y + 4}$

3. $\dfrac{3b + 1}{2b + 3}$

5. Will not simplify

7. $\dfrac{4y + 5}{y + 2}$

9. $\dfrac{m - 2n}{m + 2n}$

11. Will not simplify

13. $\dfrac{3 + x}{2 - x}$

15. $\dfrac{a^2 + 9}{3}$

EXERCISE 32, page 150

A

1. $\dfrac{ax}{by}$

3. $\dfrac{mb}{n}$

5. st

7. $\dfrac{3b}{8y^2}$

9. $\dfrac{2x^2y}{3z}$

11. $x + y$

13. $3b - 3$

15. d^2

17. $\dfrac{4a}{c}$

19. $\dfrac{4cx}{d}$

21. $2bd^2$

23. $\dfrac{3s}{mn}$

25. 2 27. x^2 29. $\dfrac{3}{m}$ 31. $\dfrac{3x}{2}$

33. $\dfrac{9}{8}$ 35. $\dfrac{2xy^2}{3}$ 37. $2x^2$ 39. $\dfrac{6}{m-5}$

B

1. $\dfrac{q+3}{q}$ 3. $\dfrac{w-13}{3}$ 5. $\dfrac{2m-n}{m-2n}$ 7. $\dfrac{2x}{x-3}$

9. $\dfrac{b^2}{3}$ 11. $\dfrac{2+b}{4}$ 13. $y(4x-1)$ 15. $\dfrac{r+2}{r+5}$

17. $\dfrac{ab}{b+3}$ 19. $\dfrac{3}{c}$ 21. $x(x+y)$

23. $-(c+3)(d+3)$ 25. $\dfrac{x-3}{x-4}$

EXERCISE 33, page 154

1. 30 3. 24 5. 180 7. 72
9. $x^3y^3z^2$ 11. $48mn^2p$ 13. $36p^3q^2$ 15. $21b^2mn^2$
17. $t(t+1)(t-1)$ 19. $y(y+1)(y+1)(y-1)$
21. $(d-2)(d-2)(d-3)(d-3)$ 23. $(y+2)(y-2)(y-4)(y+6)$
25. $6(x-1)(x-1)(x+1)(x-4)$

EXERCISE 34, page 160

A

1. $\dfrac{15x+4y}{10}$ 3. $\dfrac{5b-3a}{ab}$ 5. $\dfrac{23t}{15}$

7. $\dfrac{bc+ac+ab}{abc}$ 9. $\dfrac{3a^2+2ab+5b^2}{(a+b)(a-b)}$ 11. $\dfrac{5n-m}{6}$

13. $\dfrac{3z^2+z-2}{6}$ 15. $\dfrac{3a^2+18a-9}{(a-3)(a+3)}$ 17. $\dfrac{-b-4c}{(2b-c)(b-c)}$

B

1. $\dfrac{x}{x-3}$

3. $\dfrac{4x^2 + 16xy}{(x+y)(x+y)(x-y)(x-y)}$

5. $\dfrac{1}{m+n}$

7. $-\dfrac{2x^2 - 3x + 2}{x+2}$

9. $\dfrac{x-1}{(x-4)(x+1)(x-3)}$

EXERCISE 35, page 162

A

1. $\frac{3}{5}$ 3. $\frac{1}{2}$ 5. $2\frac{2}{5}$ 7. 4   9. 1

11. $\frac{5}{3}$ 13. -1 15. $-\frac{3}{2}$ 17. $-\frac{1}{6}$ 19. 6

21. $\frac{5}{4}$ 23. 3   25. 1

B

1. 9   3. $1\frac{3}{12}$ 5. 4   7. $\frac{1}{2}$ 9. 16

EXERCISE 36, page 167

A

1. $\dfrac{c}{b}$ 3. $\dfrac{x}{y}$ 5. $\dfrac{t^3}{y^2}$ 7. $6wx$ 9. $\dfrac{abc}{2}$

11. $\dfrac{4c-1}{2c}$ 13. $\dfrac{m}{n+m}$ 15. $\dfrac{3}{ab}$

B

1. $\dfrac{2}{d+1}$ 3. $\dfrac{m^2-1}{m^2+1}$ 5. $-\dfrac{1}{z}$ 7. x 9. $y-x$

EXERCISE 37, page 170

A

1. 1   3. $\frac{1}{4}$ 5. $\frac{5}{12}$ 7. $\frac{5}{2}$ 9. 24

11. 15   13. $\frac{1}{2}$ 15. 36   17. 3   19. $\frac{1}{5}$

B

1. 6   3. -8 5. 1   7. $\frac{7}{8}$ 9. 1

11. 1

EXERCISE 38, page 171

1. $\dfrac{x+1}{x-3}$ 3. $\dfrac{a-1}{a-2}$ 5. $\dfrac{b-5}{b-4}$ 7. $\dfrac{p+1}{p-4}$

9. $\dfrac{x-3}{x+3}$ 11. 1   13. $\dfrac{2x-3}{x+1}$ 15. $\dfrac{x-2y}{x+y}$

17. $\dfrac{9x-13}{4}$ 19. $\dfrac{25t-53}{12}$ 21. $\dfrac{49a-64b}{18}$

23. $\dfrac{2m-11n+3}{8}$ 25. $\dfrac{x+2y}{9}$

EXERCISE 39, page 174

A

1. 33 feet by 22 feet   3. 30 feet   5. $13,000 and $8,000

7. Trailer, $1600; automobile, $2400   9. 84

B

1. 48 feet by 66 feet   3. 168 student; 126 adult; 28 under 12

5. 4

A

1. $P = \dfrac{I}{rt}$

3. $b = y - mx$

5. $r = \dfrac{C}{2\pi}$

7. $t = \dfrac{I}{Pr}$

9. $h = \dfrac{V}{\pi r^2}$

11. $r = \dfrac{I}{Pt}$

13. $x = \dfrac{y - b}{m}$

15. $l = \dfrac{A}{w}$

17. $r^2 = \dfrac{3V}{\pi h}$

19. $h = \dfrac{3V}{\pi r^2}$

21. $R = \dfrac{E}{I}$

23. $r = \sqrt{\dfrac{3V}{\pi h}}$

25. $h = \dfrac{3V}{B}$

27. $b^2 = c^2 - a^2$

29. $c = \sqrt{a^2 + b^2}$

31. $b = \sqrt{c^2 - a^2}$

33. $t^2 = \dfrac{S}{16}$

35. $y = x^2 - c$

B

1. $h = \dfrac{2A}{b + b'}$

3. $F = \dfrac{9}{5}C + 32°$

5. $p = \sqrt{m + c}$

7. $a = l - (n - 1)d$

9. $a = \dfrac{2s - ln}{n}$

11. $g = \dfrac{mv^2}{2K}$

13. $n = \dfrac{l + d - a}{d}$

A

1. $15\frac{1}{2}$ in.   3. $2\frac{1}{2}$ yrs.   5. 4 in.   7. 7 in.
9. 3 seconds   11. 5 in.   13. $13\frac{1}{2}$ in.   15. 95°
17. $13\frac{1}{2}$ ft.   19. 81 sq. ft.

B

1. 12 in.   3. 12 ft.   5. $1570   7. 7%
9. $38\frac{1}{2}$ sq. in.   11. $5\frac{1}{2}$ ohms   13. 3 sq. ft.   15. $339\frac{3}{7}$ sq. ft.

EXERCISE 43, page 197

1. $10; 5; 0; -5; -10$
3. $7; 5; 3; 1; -1$
5. $4; 1; 0; 1; 4$
7. $6; 0; -4; -6; -6$
9. $0; 1; 0; -3; -8$
11. Domain: all real numbers; range: all real numbers
13. Domain: all real numbers; range: all nonnegative real numbers
15. Domain: all real numbers; range: all real numbers ≤ 2.
17. Domain: all real numbers except 0; range: all real numbers except 0
19. Domain: all real numbers; range: all real numbers

EXERCISE 47, page 213

A

1. Domain: $\{-2, -1, 0, 1, 2\}$; range: $\{-2, -1, 0, 1\}$
3. $f(0) = 1; f(-1) = 5$

B

1. Domain: all real numbers except -2 and 2; range: all real numbers

EXERCISE 48, page 216

A

1. $\{7\}$ 3. $\{-1, 7\}$ 5. $\{17\}$ 7. $\{9, 10\}$ 9. $\varnothing$

B

1. $A \cap B = \{(x, y) \mid 2x + y = 5 \text{ and } x - y = 1\}$
3. $A \cap B = \{(x, y) \mid x + y = 3 \text{ and } x - y = -3\}$
5. $A \cap B = \{(x, y) \mid x + y = 0 \text{ and } x - y = 2\}$
7. $A \cap B = \{(x, y) \mid x + 2y = 4 \text{ and } x - 2y = -8\}$
9. $A \cap B = \{(x, y) \mid x + y = 4 \text{ and } x - y = 0\}$

EXERCISE 49, page 221

A

1. $\{(1, 4)\}$ 3. $\{(2, 5)\}$ 5. $\{(4, 4)\}$ 7. $\{(-3, -1)\}$
9. $\{(1, 0)\}$ 11. $\{(-2, 3)$ 13. $\{(1, 2)\}$ 15. $\{(-2, -3)\}$
17. $\{(8, -2)\}$ 19. $\{(0, -4)\}$

B

1. $\{(\frac{1}{2}, 3)\}$ 3. $\{(\frac{1}{2}, 0)\}$ 5. $\{(10, 2)\}$ 7. $\{(4, 6)\}$
9. $\{(15, \frac{1}{2})\}$

EXERCISE 50, page 226

A

1. $\{(4, 1)\}$ 3. $\{(-2, 7)\}$ 5. $\{(5, 0)\}$ 7. $\{(\frac{1}{2}, 4)\}$
9. $\{(1, \frac{1}{3})\}$ 11. $\{(-3, -1)\}$ 13. $\{(-4, 6)\}$ 15. $\{(\frac{1}{3}, \frac{2}{3})\}$
17 $\{(4, 0)\}$ 19. $\{(1, -5)\}$

B

1. $\{(10, 3)\}$ 3. $\{(\frac{1}{2}, 6)\}$ 5. $\{(4, \frac{1}{4})\}$ 7. $\{(8, -3)\}$
9. $\{(10, 20)\}$

EXERCISE 51, page 229

A

1. $x = 3, y = 1$ 3. $x = 4, y = -3$ 5. $x = 4, y = 6$
7. $x = \frac{1}{3}, y = 5$ 9. $x = 8, y = 9$

B

1. $x = 2, y = 2$ 3. $x = -3, y = -1$ 5. $x = -2, y = 1$

A

1. 26 and 18	3. 13 and 39
5. 16 ft. by 10 ft.	7. 32 ft. by 8 ft.
9. 3 quarters and 10 nickels	11. 9 at $35 and 14 at $45
13. $9,500 and $12,500	15. $1\frac{2}{15}$

B

1. 60 ft. wide; 120 ft. deep	3. $66\frac{2}{3}$ lbs. walnuts; $33\frac{1}{3}$ lbs. peanuts
5. 22 and -16	7. Shirts, $4; slacks, $18
9. 24	

A

1. $\{(3, 3)\}$ 3. $\{(0, 6)\}$ 5. $\{(1, -1)\}$ 7. $\{(8, 4)\}$
9. $\{(-3, 8)\}$ 11. $\{(5\frac{1}{2}, -\frac{1}{2})\}$

B

1. $\{(10, 4)\}$ 3. $\{(-3, -5)\}$ 5. $\{(15, 10)\}$ 7. $\{(8, 8)\}$

A

1. a^5 3. b^4 5. 4^4 7. y^6 9. 2^9
11. x^2 13. ab^2 15. m^3n 17. 3   19. a^6
21. m^2n^2 23. $8x^6y^6$ 24. $\dfrac{b^4}{c^2}$ 27. $\dfrac{4m^2}{n^4}$

B

1. 3   3. 1   5. c^6d^{12} 7. $\dfrac{9a^4}{b^6}$ 9. $\dfrac{c^8d^4}{a^{12}}$ 11. $\dfrac{8a^3b^6}{c^6d^3}$

EXERCISE 57, page 255

A

1. $\dfrac{1}{b^3}$ 3. $\dfrac{1}{2^3}$ or $\dfrac{1}{8}$ 5. $\dfrac{1}{cd}$ 7. $\dfrac{x}{yz}$ 9. $\dfrac{3}{a^2b}$

11. $\dfrac{z}{xy^2}$ 13. $\dfrac{n^4}{m^2p^3}$ 15. $\dfrac{r^2}{4st^2}$ 17. 2^5 or 32 19. y^5

21. $\dfrac{2}{r^4}$ 23. $\dfrac{1}{m^3}$ 25. $\dfrac{a^4}{b^2}$ 27. $\dfrac{n^2}{a^4m^4}$ 29. $\dfrac{z^6}{x^3}$

31. 25 33. 4 35. 16

B

1. y 3. d^2 5. r^3 7. t^2 9. w^3v^2

11. cd^2 13. md^2 15. x^2y 17. $\sqrt[4]{m^3}$ 19. $\sqrt[3]{a^2}$

21. $\sqrt[4]{x^2y^3}$ 23. $3\sqrt{a}$ 25. $a^{1/2}$ 27. $m^{1/4}$ 29. $a^{1/3}b^{2/3}$

31. x^2yz^2 33. $a^{1/4}b^{1/4}c^{1/2}$ 35. $8^{1/3}a^{2/3}$

EXERCISE 58, page 258

A

1. 10 3. 9 5. 18 7. 16 9. $5\sqrt{2}$

11. $6\sqrt{15}$ 13. $48\sqrt{2}$ 15. a^2b 17. 72

B

1. $30\sqrt{3}$ 3. 4 5. $6\sqrt[3]{2}$ 7. $15\sqrt[3]{2}$

EXERCISE 59, page 261

A

1. $5\sqrt{2}$ 3. $3\sqrt{3}$ 5. $7\sqrt{2}$ 7. $3\sqrt{2}$

9. $8\sqrt{2}$ 11. $2\sqrt{3}$ 13. $2\sqrt{5}$ 15. $2\sqrt[3]{2}$

17. $3\sqrt[3]{2}$

19. $2\sqrt[3]{7}$

21. $4\sqrt[3]{2}$

23. $\sqrt{3}$

25. $\sqrt{2}$

27. $\sqrt[3]{3}$

29. 3

31. $\sqrt[4]{8}$

B

1. $\sqrt[3]{12}$

3. $\frac{1}{2}\sqrt{6}$

5. $\frac{1}{3}\sqrt{3}$

7. $\frac{2}{3}\sqrt{2}$

9. $\frac{1}{2}\sqrt[3]{4}$

11. $\frac{1}{2}\sqrt[3]{2}$

13. $2\sqrt[3]{4}$

15. $2m^2n^3\sqrt{2mn}$

17. $4y^2\sqrt{3xy}$

19. $6y^4z\sqrt{2z}$

21. $2n^2\sqrt[3]{3m^2}$

23. $4ab^2\sqrt[3]{4ab}$

EXERCISE 60, page 262

A

1. $5\sqrt{3}$

3. $8\sqrt{2}$

5. $5\sqrt{5}$

7. $-\sqrt{6}$

9. $3\sqrt[3]{3}$

11. $-\sqrt[3]{4}$

13. 14

B

1. $2\sqrt{2}$

3. $8\sqrt{2}$

5. $7\sqrt{3}$

7. $-2\sqrt{6}$

9. $9\sqrt[3]{2}$

11. $4\sqrt[3]{5}$

EXERCISE 61, page 267

A

1. 6

3. 2

5. 5

7. $2\sqrt{6}$

9. 8

11. $10\sqrt{2}$

13. $4\sqrt{2}$

15. $\frac{2}{3}\sqrt{3}$

B

1. 4

3. 10

5. 6

7. $\frac{1}{3}\sqrt{21}$

9. $\frac{4\sqrt{6}}{3}$

11. $\frac{3\sqrt{6}}{2}$

13. $\frac{2}{3}\sqrt[3]{9}$

15. $\sqrt{5}-2$

17. $3\sqrt{7}+3\sqrt{3}$

19. $5+2\sqrt{6}$

EXERCISE 62, page 268

A

1. xz^3
3. 1
5. c^6d^4
7. m^2
9. 2
11. $\dfrac{1}{n^{10}}$
13. d^2c^4
15. a^2b
17. $20\sqrt{3}$
19. $16\sqrt{5}$
21. $24\sqrt{3}$

B

1. $2\sqrt{6}$
3. $5\sqrt{3}$
5. $2\sqrt{14}$
7. $\frac{1}{2}\sqrt{10}$
9. $2\sqrt{2}$
11. $4\sqrt{5}$
13. $12\sqrt{2}$
15. 90
17. $\dfrac{3\sqrt{2}+\sqrt{6}}{4}$
19. $\sqrt{15}-\sqrt{10}-3+\sqrt{6}$

EXERCISE 63, page 277

A

1. 27
3. 19
5. 234
7. 9.54
9. 0.38
11. 4.01
13. 11.49
15. 7.00

B

1. 3.168
3. 6.001
5. 4.144
7. 2.002
9. 0.261

EXERCISE 64, page 280

A

1. $x = \pm 11$
3. $x = \pm 10$
5. $x = \pm 7$
7. $x = \pm\sqrt{5}$
9. $x = \pm\sqrt{5}$
11. $0, -7$
13. $0, 3$
15. $0, \frac{1}{2}$

B

1. $x = \pm 3\sqrt{5}$
3. $x = \pm 2\sqrt{30}$
5. $x = \pm 6$
7. $x = \pm 3\sqrt{5}$
9. $x = \pm 5$
11. $0, -\frac{2}{3}$
13. $0, 3$
15. $0, \frac{3}{8}$

EXERCISE 65, page 282

A

1. $-3, -4$
3. $2, 2$
5. $7, 1$
7. $-4, 3$
9. $6, -5$

B

1. $3, -8$
3. $-2, 6$
5. $-5, 8$
7. $-\frac{1}{3}, 3$
9. $-\frac{3}{4}, \frac{1}{2}$
11. $\frac{1}{5}, -\frac{5}{3}$
13. $-6, \frac{1}{2}$
15. $3, \frac{1}{3}$

EXERCISE 66, page 285

A

1. $1, 5$
3. $2, -6$
5. $-1, -5$
7. $-3, 7$
9. $3, -8$

B

1. $\frac{2}{3}, 4$
3. $-2 \pm \sqrt{3}$
5. $2, -\frac{3}{2}$
7. $2 \pm \sqrt{3}$
9. $-3 \pm \sqrt{2}$

EXERCISE 67, page 293

A

1. $4, 5$
3. $-9, -7$
5. $4, 3$
7. $\pm\sqrt{5}$
9. $8, 0$

B

1. $-\frac{1}{2}, 3$ 3. $\frac{1}{3}, -\frac{2}{3}$ 5. $1, \frac{3}{2}$ 7. $-2, \frac{3}{4}$
9. $-1 \pm \sqrt{13}$

EXERCISE 69, page 301

1. $6i$ 3. $3i\sqrt{6}$ 5. $10i\sqrt{6}$ 7. $8i\sqrt{5}$
9. $9i\sqrt{5}$ 11. $i\sqrt{3}$ 13. $19i\sqrt{2}$ 15. -12
17. 72 19. 3

EXERCISE 70, page 305

1. $\pm i$ 3. $\pm 11i$ 5. $\pm 4i\sqrt{5}$

7. $\dfrac{-1 \pm i\sqrt{19}}{2}$ 9. $\dfrac{3 \pm i\sqrt{23}}{2}$ 11. $\dfrac{-5 \pm i\sqrt{7}}{4}$

13. $\dfrac{-4 \pm i\sqrt{11}}{3}$ 15. $\dfrac{1 \pm i\sqrt{2}}{3}$

EXERCISE 71, page 306

A

1. $9, 12$ 3. $12, 14$ 5. 8 in., 16 in.
7. 5 in., 9 in. 9. 6 ft.

B

1. 60 mph.   3. 45 mph.   5. 40 mph.

EXERCISE 72, page 308

A

1. ± 13

3. ± 4

5. $8, -7$

7. $9, -5$

9. $4, 0$

11. $8, -1$

13. $3, 8$

15. $-\frac{1}{2}, 3$

17. $\dfrac{4 \pm i\sqrt{2}}{9}$

19. $-1 \pm i\sqrt{2}$

B

1. ± 6

3. $\dfrac{-1 \pm \sqrt{82}}{3}$

5. $\dfrac{2 \pm \sqrt{55}}{3}$

EXERCISE 73, page 311

A

1. $\frac{2}{3}$

3. 4

5. $\frac{1}{5}$

7. $\frac{3}{2}$

9. $\frac{1}{4}$

11. $\dfrac{1}{x}$

13. $\dfrac{4}{x^2}$

15. $\dfrac{1}{x - y}$

17. $\dfrac{3}{2 - y}$

19. $x - 2$

B

1. $\frac{1}{7}$

3. $\frac{1}{5}$

5. $\frac{1}{36}$

7. $\frac{5}{12}$

9. $\frac{3}{8}$

11. $\frac{5}{16}$

13. $\frac{4}{3}$

15. $\frac{1}{880}$

EXERCISE 74, page 313

A

1. 1

3. 15

5. $\frac{8}{7}$

7. ± 4

9. $\pm 2\sqrt{6}$

11. $\pm\sqrt{5}$

13. $7\frac{1}{2}$

15. 21

17. 2   19. ±4   21. ±2√5   23. ±√3
25. 5   27. 5   29. $3\frac{1}{3}$

B

1. 3   3. −3   5. 0, 3   7. 9
9. ±6√5

EXERCISE 75, page 316

1. 3 ft., 9 ft.   3. $12,000, widow; $9,000, son; $3,000, daughter
5. 10 ft.   7. 57.6 ft.   9. $208\frac{1}{3}°$

EXERCISE 76, page 321

A

1. 35   3. $\frac{1}{2}$ 5. 81   7. 24   9. $121\frac{1}{2}$

B

1. 400 ft.   3. 400 cu. ft.   5. $6\frac{2}{3}$

Appendix

TABLE OF POWERS AND ROOTS

No.	Squares	Cubes	Square Root	Cube Root	No.	Squares	Cubes	Square Root	Cube Root
1	1	1	1.000	1.000	51	2,601	132,651	7.141	3.708
2	4	8	1.414	1.260	52	2,704	140,608	7.211	3.732
3	9	27	1.732	1.442	53	2,809	148,877	7.280	3.756
4	16	64	2.000	1.587	54	2,916	157,464	7.348	3.780
5	25	125	2.236	1.710	55	3,025	166,375	7.416	3.803
6	36	216	2.449	1.817	56	3,136	175,616	7.483	3.826
7	49	343	2.646	1.913	57	3,249	185,193	7.550	3.848
8	64	512	2.828	2.000	58	3,364	195,112	7.616	3.871
9	81	729	3.000	2.080	59	3,481	205,379	7.681	3.893
10	100	1,000	3.162	2.154	60	3,600	216,000	7.746	3.915
11	121	1,331	3.317	2.224	61	3,721	226,981	7.810	3.936
12	144	1,728	3.464	2.289	62	3,844	238,328	7.874	3.958
13	169	2,197	3.606	2.351	63	3,969	250,047	7.937	3.979
14	196	2,744	3.742	2.410	64	4,096	262,144	8.000	4.000
15	225	3,375	3.873	2.466	65	4,225	274,625	8.062	4.021
16	256	4,096	4.000	2.520	66	4,356	287,496	8.124	4.041
17	289	4,913	4.123	2.571	67	4,489	300,763	8.185	4.062
18	324	5,832	4.243	2.621	68	4,624	314,432	8.246	4.082
19	361	6,859	4.359	2.668	69	4,761	328,509	8.307	4.102
20	400	8,000	4.472	2.714	70	4,900	343,000	8.367	4.121
21	441	9,261	4.583	2.759	71	5,041	357,911	8.426	4.141
22	484	10,648	4.690	2.802	72	5,184	373,248	8.485	4.160
23	529	12,167	4.796	2.844	73	5,329	389,017	8.544	4.179
24	576	13,824	4.899	2.884	74	5,476	405,224	8.602	4.198
25	625	15,625	5.000	2.924	75	5,625	421,875	8.660	4.217
26	676	17,576	5.099	2.962	76	5,776	438,976	8.718	4.236
27	729	19,683	5.196	3.000	77	5,929	456,533	8.775	4.254
28	784	21,952	5.292	3.037	78	6,084	474,552	8.832	4.273
29	841	24,389	5.385	3.072	79	6,241	493,039	8.888	4.291
30	900	27,000	5.477	3.107	80	6,400	512,000	8.944	4.309
31	961	29,791	5.568	3.141	81	6,561	531,441	9.000	4.327
32	1,024	32,768	5.657	3.175	82	6,724	551,368	9.055	4.344
33	1,089	35,937	5.745	3.208	83	6,889	571,787	9.110	4.362
34	1,156	39,304	5.831	3.240	84	7,056	592,704	9.165	4.380
35	1,225	42,875	5.916	3.271	85	7,225	614,125	9.220	4.397
36	1,296	46,656	6.000	3.302	86	7,396	636,056	9.274	4.414
37	1,369	50,653	6.083	3.332	87	7,569	658,503	9.327	4.431
38	1,444	54,872	5.164	3.362	88	7,744	681,472	9.381	4.448
39	1,521	59,319	6.245	3.391	89	7,921	704,969	9.434	4.465
40	1,600	64,000	6.325	3.420	90	8,100	729,000	9.487	4.481
41	1,681	68,921	6.403	3.448	91	8,281	753,571	9.539	4.498
42	1,764	74,088	6.481	3.476	92	8,464	778,688	9.592	4.514
43	1,849	79,507	6.557	3.503	93	8,649	804,357	9.643	4.531
44	1,936	85,184	6.633	3.530	94	8,836	830,584	9.695	4.547
45	2,025	91,125	6.708	3.557	95	9,025	857,375	9.747	4.563
46	2,116	97,336	6.782	3.583	96	9,216	884,736	9.798	4.579
47	2,209	103,823	6.856	3.609	97	9,409	912,673	9.849	4.595
48	2,304	110,592	6.928	3.634	98	9,604	941,192	9.899	4.610
49	2,401	117,649	7.000	3.659	99	9,801	970,299	9.950	4.626
50	2,500	125,000	7.071	3.684	100	10,000	1,000,000	10.000	4.642

FORMULAS

The following list of formulas are commonly used in mathematical computations. The student will find them useful as a reference source, especially when setting up stated problems.

1. $P = 4s$ (The perimeter of a square where P represents the perimeter and s a side)

2. $P = 2l + 2w$ (The perimeter of a rectangle where P represents the perimeter, l the length, and w the width of the rectangle)

3. $A = s^2$ (The area of a square where A represents the area and s a side of the square)

4. $A = lw$ (The area of a rectangle where A represents the area, l the length, and w the width of the rectangle)

5. $A = \pi r^2$ (The area of a circle, where A represents the area, r the radius of the circle, and π approximately $\frac{22}{7}$)

6. $C = 2\pi r$ (The circumference of a circle where C represents the circumference and r the radius of the circle)

7. $V = s^3$ (The volume of a cube where V represents the volume and s an edge of the cube)

8. $V = lwh$ (The volume of a rectangular solid where V represents the volume, l the length, w the width, and h the height of the solid)

9. $V = \pi r^2 h$ (The volume of a cylinder where V represents the volume, r the radius of the base, and h the height of the cylinder)

10. $V = \frac{1}{3}\pi r^2 h$ (The volume of a cone where V represents the volume, r the radius of the base, and h the altitude of the cone)

11. $F = \frac{9}{5}C + 32°$ (The reading on a Fahrenheit thermometer where F represents that reading on the Fahrenheit thermometer and C the reading on a Centigrade thermometer)

12. $C = \frac{5}{9}(F - 32°)$ (The reading on a Centigrade thermometer when the Fahrenheit reading is given)

13. $I = \dfrac{E}{R}$ (Ohm's Law—where I represents the intensity of the current in amperes, E the electromotive force in volts, and R the resistance in Ohms)

14. $d = rt$ (The distance formula where d represents the distance traveled in miles, r the rate in miles per hour, and t the time in hours)

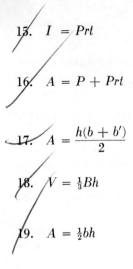

15. $I = Prt$ (The amount of interest paid where I represents the interest, P the principal, r the rate of interest per year, and t the time in years)

16. $A = P + Prt$ (The amount to be repaid on a loan where A represents the amount, P the principal, r the rate per year, and t the time in years)

17. $A = \dfrac{h(b + b')}{2}$ (The area of a trapezoid where A represents the area, h the altitude, and b and b' the two bases of the trapezoid)

18. $V = \frac{1}{3}Bh$ (The volume of a pyramid where V represents the volume, B the area of the base, and h the altitude of the pyramid)

19. $A = \frac{1}{2}bh$ (The area of a triangle where A represents the area, b the length of the base, and h the altitude of the triangle)

Index